SUBCELLULAR PARTICLES

Sponsored by

THE SOCIETY OF GENERAL PHYSIOLOGISTS

Published for

THE AMERICAN PHYSIOLOGICAL SOCIETY

SUBCELLULAR PARTICLES

A SYMPOSIUM HELD DURING THE MEETING OF THE SOCIETY OF GENERAL PHYSIOLOGISTS AT THE MARINE BIOLOGICAL LABORATORY, WOODS HOLE, MASSACHUSETTS, JUNE 9–11, 1958

Edited by

Teru Hayashi

THE RONALD PRESS COMPANY • NEW YORK

LIBRARY OF CONGRESS
CATALOGUE CARD NUMBER
59-11056

PRINTED IN THE UNITED STATES OF AMERICA

Contents

Preface

The subject of this year's Symposium of the Society of General Physiologists, 'Subcellular Particles,' was selected by the Council of the Society. In the organization of this symposium, the aim was two-fold: first, to bring to the attention of the variegated membership of the Society the most recent work of the foremost investigators studying subcellular particles; and second, to emphasize the structural aspects of subcellular particles as related to their function, especially with regard to the properties of the heterogeneous system created by the very presence of the particulate material within the cell. It would be presumptuous to say that these aims were achieved with any degree of success, especially in the case of the second part of the over-all aim, where a large area of ignorance faces the experimenter.

The post-war years will, I believe, be considered a 'Golden Era' in the biological sciences and certainly in the study of cell inclusions. Tremendous advances have been made in elucidating the various activities of subcellular structures, due primarily to advances in technology and the inspiration of new concepts and new information from allied fields, as microbiology. Thus improvements in, and the coordination of, techniques in ultracentrifugation, electron microscopy and microchemical analysis have made possible a more definitive correlation between the particles or the parts thereof and their activities within the cell. Likewise, new information about important biochemical substances, as the nucleic acids, have influenced the trend of thought as to the function of intracellular structures. Yet, essentially, this type of progress of knowledge in this field does not shed light on such questions as 1) why are structural units necessary at all, and 2) what effect does structure have on chemical or biochemical conditions and/or reactions within the cell?

However, certain consistent generalities can be observed as the result of the sharp attention paid to intracellular structures. For example, structures seem to be involved in those situations where the cell requires protection from disrupting agents which, nonetheless, the cell must include as a part of its over-all organization in order to maintain a specialized function. Thus enzymes which, if allowed loose in the cell, would cause autolysis would be included in this category. Several papers in this volume point to this aspect of cellular structure and function.

Structure also seems to be necessary in the general situation where synthesis of substances is taking place. Here, however, in spite of the speculations concerning 'templates' the situation is not so simple nor so clear that the conclusion can be stated with any finality. A third and what seems to be a most important requirement for structure within the cell is found in the case of cellular activities resulting in the transformation of energy. Thus the chloroplast structure plays a prominent part in the transformation of radiant energy into the potential energy of oxidation-reduction reactions or the chemical energy of 'high energy' phosphate bonds (photosynthetic phosphorylation).

It is to be expected that reactions so intrinsically a part of the cell's being would have their characteristics determined by the fact that the components of the reactions appear to be part of a highly-organized and definite structure, and not freely in solution subject to classical kinetics. Here again surprisingly little information is available. Yet an awareness of the effect of a heterogeneous milieu is of paramount importance if we wish to appreciate in full the activities and potentialities of the cell.

It is gratifying to note that while these problems are as yet far from being understood, many of the papers in this symposium are directly concerned with them, and through ingenious experiments a great deal of new knowledge has been brought forth bearing on these questions. To this extent it is hoped that this volume will be of benefit to all those who consider themselves students of the cell.

The Society of General Physiologists gratefully acknowledges the support in the form of a grant from the National Institutes of Health. I should like to express my appreciation to Dr. William D. McElroy, Dr. Eric G. Ball, and Dr. Van R. Potter for having served as chairmen in the three sessions of the symposium, which they did with skill and discretion. My appreciation is also extended to the administration and staff of the Marine Biological Laboratory for their unfailing cooperation and efforts to make the meeting a success. Finally, my thanks go to Mr. Robert Kirchen and Miss Lillian Blaschke for serving as volunteer messengers during the symposium, and to Mrs. Sally Hayashi and the staff of the American Physiological Society, who deserve the major credit for the editing and assembling of this volume.

TERU HAYASHI
February, 1959

Approaches to the In Vivo Function of Subcellular Particles[1]

ALEX B. NOVIKOFF

Albert Einstein College of Medicine
New York City

THANKS TO BRACHET (3) we have available a popular term which includes the subject matter of this conference, *Biochemical Cytology*—or, if biochemists prefer, *Cytologic Biochemistry.*

Perhaps it is a sign of maturity of the field that one notes a growing tolerance by specialists in one area of the vast domain of biochemical cytology for the pursuits of those in other areas. There are fewer 'gloomy critics,' as I like to call those people with essentially destructive comments on a technique which they do not themselves employ.

We can all recall the categorical assertion that hope for significant information concerning the *in vivo* function of subcellular particles was lost the moment the cell was disrupted or homogenized. Or, that the use of aqueous media like sucrose could yield only misleading particles, especially worthless nuclei. Or, that oxidative phosphorylation could never be retained once the organized structure of the complete mitochondrion was broken. Or, that electron microscopy was one huge blunder, based as it was on osmium artifacts. Or, that quantitative microspectrophotometry of stained tissue sections was deprived of meaning by the marked structural heterogeneity of the subcellular particles. Or, that enzyme destruction by fixative, and diffusion of reaction product during incubation, made staining methods worthless for demonstrating the intracellular *in situ* localization of enzymes, particularly important ones.

It might be asserted by some that the 'gloomy critics' have helped focus on the pitfalls of biochemical cytology techniques. Others may consider this debatable and contend that it is data rather than critics which move investigators to refine their methods. As the field of biochemical cytology has developed, not only have technical refinements been introduced, but increasingly within the same, or nearby, laboratories integrated studies are pursued, with two or more techniques applied to the same problem.

[1] Work from our laboratory has been supported by grants from the American Cancer Society, Inc.; Public Health Service, U.S. Dept. of Health, Education and Welfare; and the National Science Foundation.

PHASE CONTRAST MICROSCOPY APPLIED TO LIVING AND SURVIVING CELLS

Our survey of techniques of biochemical cytology naturally begins with the living cell. The tissue culture cells virtually speak for themselves in the excellent motion pictures taken with the phase-contrast microscope or interference microscope. Among the films we have seen are those of Dr. Gey, showing remarkable mitochondrial movement, cell membrane activity and pinocytosis (14); Dr. Biesele, showing the speeding of mitochondrial movement by coenzyme A addition and the accentuation of the tendency of mitochondria in the mouse fibroblasts to join end to end (55);[2] Drs. Frederic and Chèvremont, showing the dramatic changes in mitochondria induced by a variety of drugs (6); Dr. Rose, showing the remarkable transformations of pinocytosis vacuoles in a variant of the HeLa cell (45);[2] and Drs. Bloom and Zirkle, showing mitosis in amphibian fibroblasts, with chromosomes and kinetochore evident as well as the extensive surface bubbling at late anaphase and telophase.[2]

Even tissue culture has a limitation we encounter with other techniques: it reveals the *capacities* of the cultured cells, but perhaps not the *actualities* of these cells in the organized structure of the multicellular organism. The specialized milieu in which they are grown is quite different from that encountered naturally by cells embedded in tissue mucopolysaccharide or wedged in tightly among neighboring cells, as in epithelium—cells always under the controlling neural, hormonal and neurohumoral influences of the organism. Thus, the chromosomal changes which many cells in culture undergo so readily may occur very rarely within the tissue. The very extensive pinocytosis or the surface bubbling at late mitotic anaphase and telophase may be exaggerations of surface changes which cells display in the organism.

This in no way minimizes the importance of such films in emphasizing the dynamic nature of the cell. They are balancing forces needed when we reflect upon the static electron micrographs of mitochondria or of plasma membranes in cells, or when we consider the biochemist's descriptions of the multi-enzyme machinery of mitochondria, such as Dr. Green's brilliant description in this volume (17) of the shuttling of small molecules within the lipoprotein matrix. The description of the cell's constant dynamism in biochemical terms is the great challenge for future biochemical cytologists.

Phase-contrast micrography can be of great value to biochemists and others without cinemaphotography equipment and even without truly living cells. I have in mind examination of fractions isolated by differential centrifugation, or of surviving (or dying) cells, as in homogenates.

In figures 1 and 2 are phase contrast photographs of cells in homogenates. It is evident that in liver cells the mitochondria are large and numerous, while in cells

[2] A short sequence from this film was shown at the Conference. I am grateful to the authors for permission to show the film.

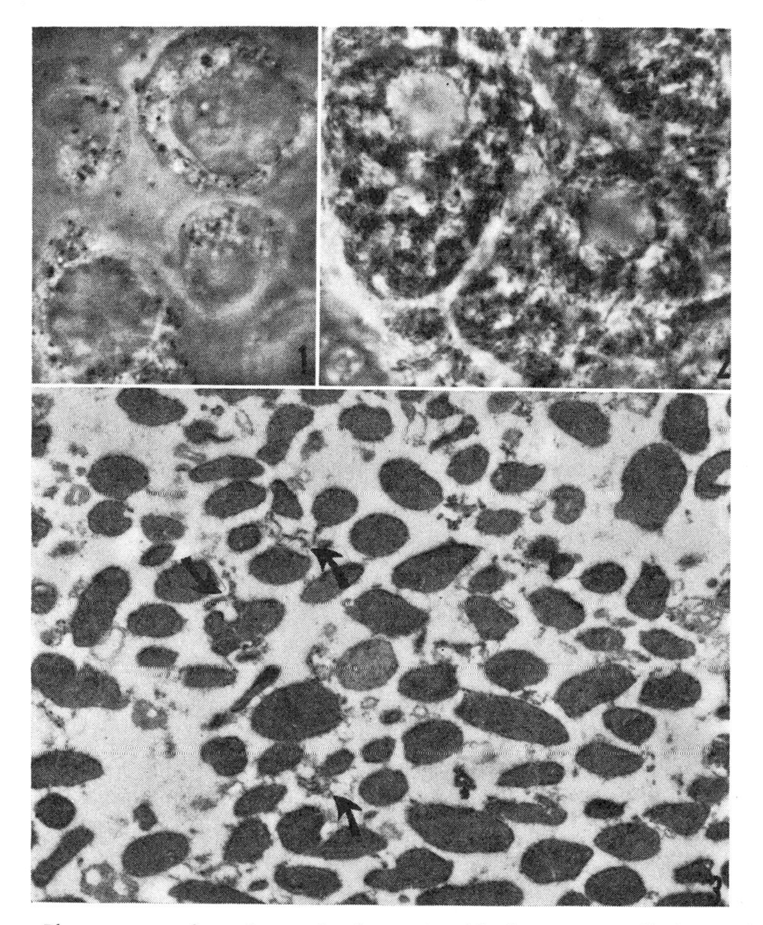

FIG. 1. Phase-contrast photomicrograph of transplantable liver tumor cells in a polyvinyl-pyrollidone-sucrose homogenate. [From (29).] The cells, somewhat flattened, show large clear nuclei, small elongate mitochondria, and spherical lipid droplets. Objects in focus appear dark or gray, those out of focus are bright. × 950.

FIG. 2. Phase-contrast photomicrograph of parenchymatous cells of rat liver in a polyvinyl-pyrollidone-sucrose homogenate. [From (29).] The cytoplasm contains many large elongate mitochondria. × 925.

FIG. 3. Electron micrograph of section of mitochondrial fraction. This is an unwashed fraction obtained from a 0.88 M sucrose homogenate of rat liver. The mitochondria are well preserved; their cristae appear as lighter areas. Microsomal contamination is shown by arrows. × 12,500.

of the transplantable liver tumor (fig. 1), they are smaller and less numerous. The striking difference in nucleus to cytoplasm ratio is evident, as is the large number of lipid droplets in the tumor cell. In favorable material, phase contrast microscopy can reveal the presence of structures at times considered artifacts by some. Thus, the Golgi apparatus can readily be seen in these transplantable liver tumor cells (29) and the endoplasmic reticulum was seen by Fawcett and Ito (11) in guinea pig spermatocytes.

Naturally, such purely morphological observations, together with the resolution limitation of light microscopy, leave much room for speculation. The observations do not tell us what really happens when the mitochondria move up to the nuclear membrane, or what the nature and fate of the pinocytosis vacuoles are.

ELECTRON MICROSCOPY

The limitation of resolution may be overcome, to a great degree, by electron microscopy.

Elsewhere in this volume (38) we see new examples of the power of electron microscopy from Dr. Palade, the man to whom not only biochemistry but all of biology and medicine owes so great a debt. I am confident that he, Dr. Keith Porter and other electron microscopists will promptly agree that our dependence upon osmium fixation leaves some important questions unanswered for the moment; for example, that not too much chemical meaning can yet be attached to detailed appearance and precise measurements of membranes in electron micrographs. From the work of Fernández-Morán and Finean (12), of Birbeck and Mercer (4), of Peachey (41), and of Ito and Fawcett (18), it is apparent that the double membranes seen in osmium-fixed sections may result from films of very different biochemical substances.

Yet electron microscopy of thin sections has helped answer many questions of biochemical cytology. Perhaps more important, it has raised many other questions which could not even be phrased without this new look into the near-molecular level within the cell.

To cite a few examples, it is now possible to assert categorically that organelles like the mitochondria of liver survive homogenization and centrifugation quite handsomely, and to indicate the kinds of changes which occur in other subcellular particles.

Figure 3 is chosen because it is sometimes said that mitochondria isolated from liver homogenates in unfortified sucrose solutions do not show good preservation of fine structure. Sections like this show that such is not the case. Mitochondrial fine structure is excellently preserved in this pellet obtained from a 0.88 M sucrose homogenate. The figure also demonstrates how readily contamination by microsomes may be identified. Since microsomes arise largely through fragmentation of ergastoplasm, the ribonucleoprotein granules of Palade (37) and endoplasmic reticulum of Porter and Palade (42) may be used as identifying markers (27, 28).

Figure 4 is a section through a microsome fraction from the same homogenate. The manner in which the ergastoplasm is fragmented is not yet understood. Generally, the fragments are quite short, as in this figure. Sometimes, as in the so-called 'fluffy layer,' they may be surprisingly long (fig. 5).

That the microsome fraction, even in liver, contains other cytological entities is well recognized. In our laboratory, we are trying to determine the extent to which the so-called 'smooth membranes' seen in the microsome fraction are derived from the microvilli on the surface of the liver cell. These microvilli may be of considerable enzymatic importance, as we shall see later, and they are extremely numerous.

Figure 6 is a section of liver demonstrating the microvilli on the cell surface exposed to the blood sinusoid (space of Disse). The area thus exposed to the blood (plasma?) is very large, and it is covered by literally millions of these tiny extensions of the plasma membrane. We do not know how many microvilli survive homogenization and how many are centrifuged into the microsome fraction.

Figure 6 also shows numerous structures near the sinusoidal surfaces which resemble pinocytosis vacuoles. Such vacuoles are seen in electron micrographs of other tissues and appear most numerous in capillary endothelium (25).

Microvilli are also present over other areas of the hepatic cell, those exposed to the bile canaliculi (fig. 7). As we suggest later, the enzymatic nature of these microvilli may differ from that of Disse space microvilli. Some of the canalicular microvilli sediment into the nuclear fraction, as part of the bile canaliculus fragments (33, 34). It would not surprise us if others end in the microsome fraction.

The section shown in figure 7 passes through a structure with a long, stormy history, the Golgi apparatus. The reality of this organelle can no longer reasonably be questioned, thanks to electron microscopy. Elsewhere in this volume, Dr. Kuff (21) discusses some chemical properties of the Golgi apparatus isolated from epididymis. An excellent review of the Golgi apparatus, by Dr. Palay, has just appeared (39).

From electron micrographs it is difficult to sense what is readily apparent in the thicker sections used for light microscopy, namely that in liver parenchymatous cells the Golgi apparatus is a multiple structure, arranged on either side of the bile canaliculi along their entire length (fig. 9; also (34)).

Figure 7 also shows the peribiliary 'dense bodies,' structures of current interest because they *may* be the lysosomes postulated by de Duve and colleagues. Dr. de Duve refers to the 'dense bodies' when he discusses this important concept of lysosomes later in this volume (8).

Because electron microscopists frequently try to reconstruct processes from static photographs, and because everything is yet so novel, there is a great tempta-

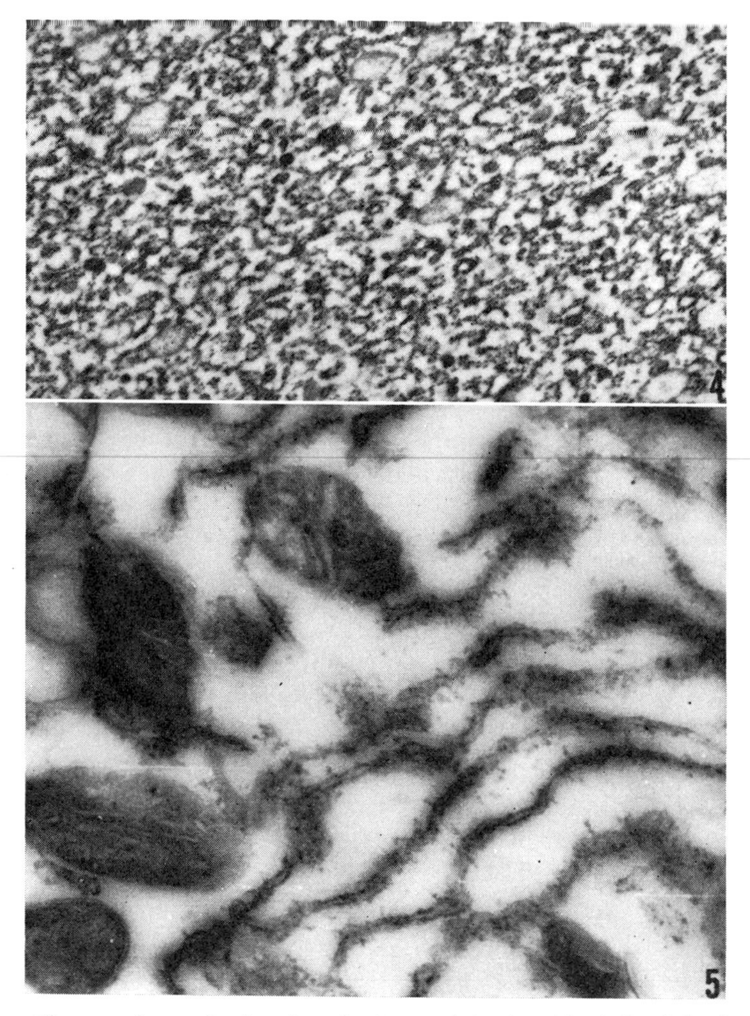

FIG. 4. Electron micrograph of section of microsomal fraction. The bulk of the fraction is made of fragments of ergastoplasm. The ribonucleoprotein granules are readily identified. × 12,800.

FIG. 5. Electron micrograph of section of purified 'fluffy layer' (28). Note long lengths of ergastoplasm, in which both endoplasmic reticulum membranes and ribonucleoprotein granules are readily identified. Mitochondria are fairly well preserved. × 34,250.

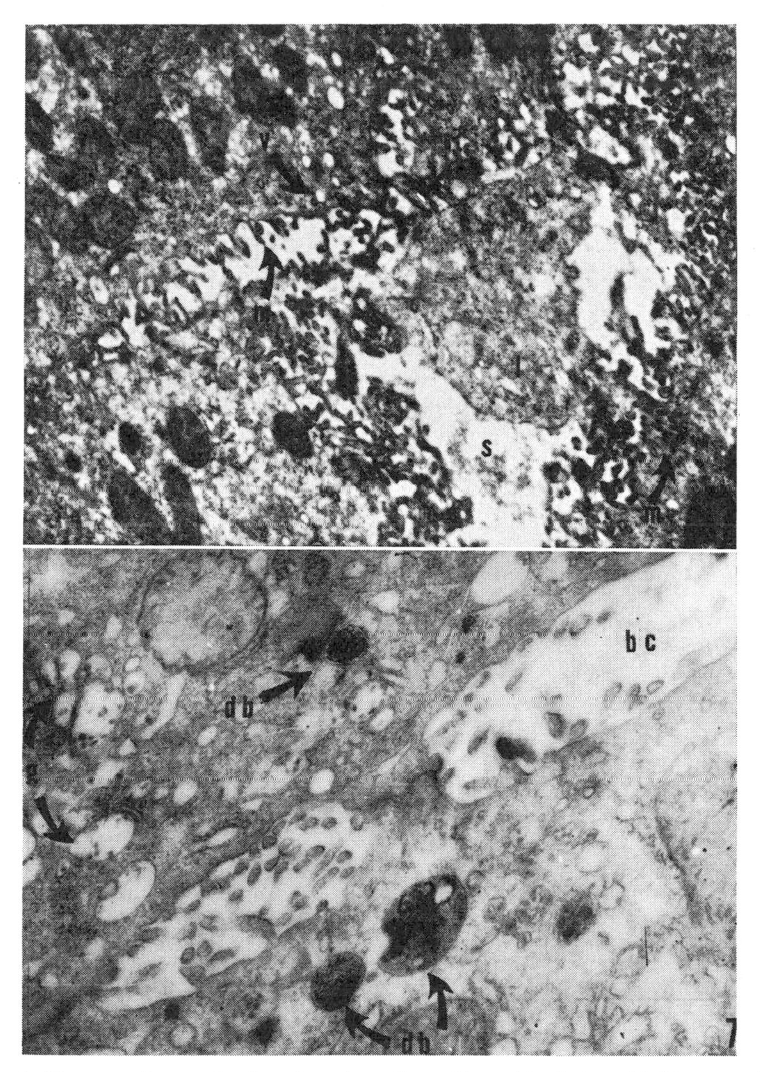

FIG. 6. Electron micrograph of section of rat liver. Shows blood sinusoid (*s*); a portion of a lining cell (*l*), probably a Kupffer cell; and numerous extensions of the parenchymatous cells into microvilli exposed to the sinusoid (space of Disse). Some of the microvilli (*m*) show linearly-arranged granules, producing an apparent cross-striation. Within the parenchymatous cells, note the vacuoles (*v*), dark mitochondria, and the ribonucleoprotein granules of the ergastoplasm. × 10,500.

FIG. 7. Electron micrograph of rat liver. [From (32).] Shows microvilli extending into bile canaliculus (*bc*), peribiliary 'dense bodies' (*db*), and Golgi apparatus (*g*). × 14,400.

tion for speculation; so much so that Sjöstrand, in a recent review, pleads that electron microscopists guard against making the field a 'science of guesses' (48).

However one may feel about such speculation, it is apparent that at best electron microscopy alone remains purely descriptive and essentially morphological. It needs to be supplemented by techniques providing biochemical information.

RADIOAUTOGRAPHY

The most direct approach to *in vivo* biochemical events within particulates is that of radioautography. Dr. Taylor, in this volume, shows the impressive cytological resolution now possible with this technique (54). I will refer to only two reports in the literature.

The first is that of the now classic experiments of Goldstein and Plaut (15). These combine radioautography with the microdissection of living cells possible with *Ameba* and other large cells.

By feeding *Ameba* microorganisms reared on P^{32}-orthophosphate, its nucleus is made to incorporate P^{32} into its ribonucleic acid (RNA). The fate of this radioactive nuclear RNA can then be followed when transplanted into an enucleated half of a nonradioactive *Ameba*. After some 62 hours, considerable radioactivity has moved into the cytoplasm. That this is not a random loss from the nucleus is shown by transplanting a radioactive ('hot') nucleus into a whole nonradioactive ('cold') *Ameba*. While much radioactivity moves into the cytoplasm of the 'cold' *Ameba,* none goes into the 'cold' nucleus.

From indirect evidence, such as effects of ribonuclease digestion, the conclusion is drawn that the material moving from nucleus to cytoplasm is RNA or a material much like it.

Radioautography has another important aspect. It lends itself to fairly good quantitation, as may be illustrated by the work of McMaster-Kaye and Taylor (24). From the time curves of the number of reduced grains appearing over cytological structures, the authors concluded that P^{32} is incorporated into nucleolar RNA considerably earlier than into cytoplasmic RNA.

Even radioautography, however, is not free of difficulties. Aside from dependence upon indirect methods for the identification of the substance in which the radioactivity is incorporated, there are the difficulties that soluble radioactive substances are lost in the methods of tissue preparation currently employed, that ignorance of the nature and magnitude of precursor pools may make interpretation difficult, and that incorporation sites need not necessarily be the sites of function.

ISOLATION OF SUBCELLULAR PARTICLES BY CENTRIFUGATION

Despite all its uncertainties and limitations, the isolation of subcellular fractions by centrifugation of homogenates has provided the main foundation of biochemical cytology (35). The chief characteristic of the newer cytology is the vast body of biochemical data upon which it is based. The last decade has witnessed an ever-accelerating expansion in our knowledge of metabolic pathways. As new reactions are uncovered their distributions among isolated subcellular fractions are plotted, thus providing an important step towards grasping the interrelationships among these biochemical events. It is fitting that the technique of differential centrifugation was introduced by two cytologists, R. R. Bensley and N. H. Hoerr, and then pursued most vigorously by biochemists, A. Claude, W. C. Schneider and G. Hogeboom, C. de Duve and J. Berthet, O. Lindberg and L. Ernster, and many others. The beautiful work described in subsequent chapters of this volume illustrates the usefulness of such isolated fractions for the biochemist.

We have already seen how microscopy, phase contrast and particularly electron microscopy, can help assess the state of preservation of cell organelles throughout this process and how it can indicate the degree of purity of isolated fractions. It helps also to emphasize uncertainties, such as the fate of microvilli and Golgi apparatus of the liver cell, and possible losses which may occur as the endoplasmic reticulum is fragmented. It has long been known that a considerable amount of material is lost from nuclei during their isolation in aqueous media. In this connection, it might be worth commenting that the 'supernatant fluid' data are the most difficult, of all the fraction data, to interpret in terms of the living cell. For example, it would be of utmost significance, in terms of *in vivo* function if not in terms of biochemical sequences, to know that the amino acid-activating enzymes discussed by Dr. Stephenson later in this volume (49) are truly in a soluble phase bathing the ergastoplasm and mitochondria. But I believe we cannot categorically assert this to be the case. There remains a possibility that these, like other enzymes of the 'supernatant fluid,' may have leached from the nucleus, endoplasmic reticulum, or some other organelle.

There is, thus, uncertainty about some localizations indicated in figure 8, even for the liver cell. However, there can be little question that the mitochondria are the chief sites of oxidative phosphorylation in the cell. Dr. Allfrey, later in this volume (2), discusses an adenosine triphosphate (ATP) synthesis by isolated nuclear fractions of thymus; but it remains to be seen to what extent the findings regarding thymus and other lymphoid tissues can be generalized to tissues like liver.

The work of Chance and colleagues has demonstrated that isolated mitochondrial suspensions show the same sequence of events in electron transport as do suspensions of *living* yeast and tumor ascites cells. Chance comments on this important achievement in these words: "It is, of course, of considerable reassurance to biochemists that the isolated material does not involve a serious artifact" (5).

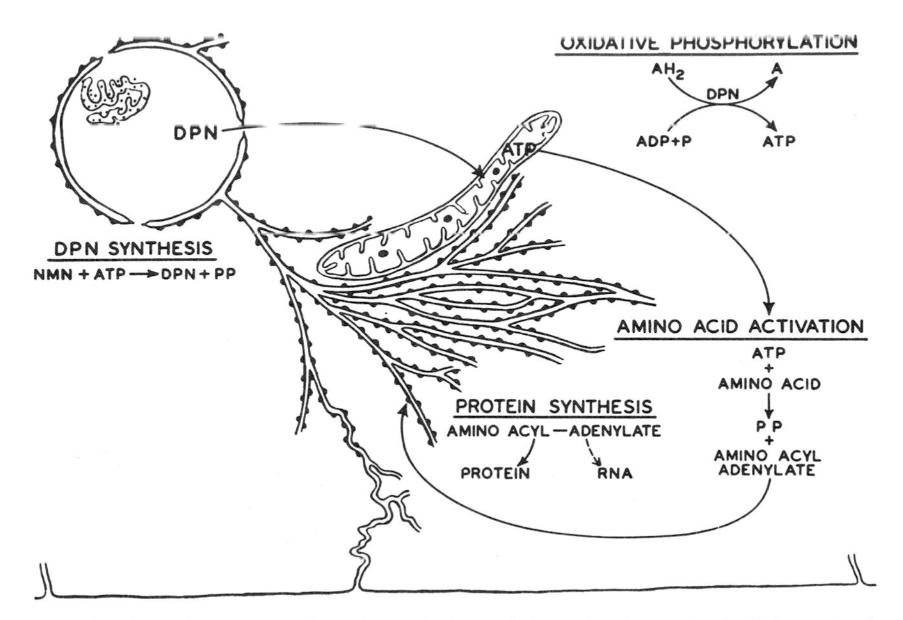

FIG. 8. Schematic representation of complexity and interrelatedness of subcellular units in the rat liver cell. [From (35).] *Abbreviations:* DPN, diphosphopyridine nucleotide; NMN, nicotinamide mononucleotide; ATP, adenosine triphosphate; PP, inorganic pyrophosphate; AH_2, oxidizable substrate; A, oxidized substrate; ADP, adenosine diphosphate; P, orthophosphate; RNA, ribonucleic acid.

The work of Preiss and Handler (44) suggests that perhaps the reaction for DPN synthesis which the diagram (fig. 8) shows, first described by Kornberg (19), may not be the important pathway of diphosphopyridine nucleotide (DPN) synthesis in the cell. However, it is of interest that at least one of the steps of DPN synthesis from free nicotinic acid (44) is also recovered in the nuclear fraction (43).

From the work Dr. Stephenson describes (49) there is little doubt that amino acid incorporation, probably an integral part of protein synthesis, occurs in the microsomal ribonucleoprotein granules, although as Loftfield (22) says in his masterful review, "the final step in forming the protein may be disturbed" in these cell-free systems.

Irrespective of changes which will be required in this diagram, the data from isolated subcellular fractions make the conclusion inescapable that subcellular particles are interdependent metabolically. The diagram does not attempt to show interrelationships among nucleotides, RNA and DNA (deoxyribonucleic acid). Nor does it show lysosomes, dense bodies and other complexities of the liver cell. These are shown diagrammatically in figure 9; this, too, omits some known structures and greatly oversimplifies others. It is based not only upon

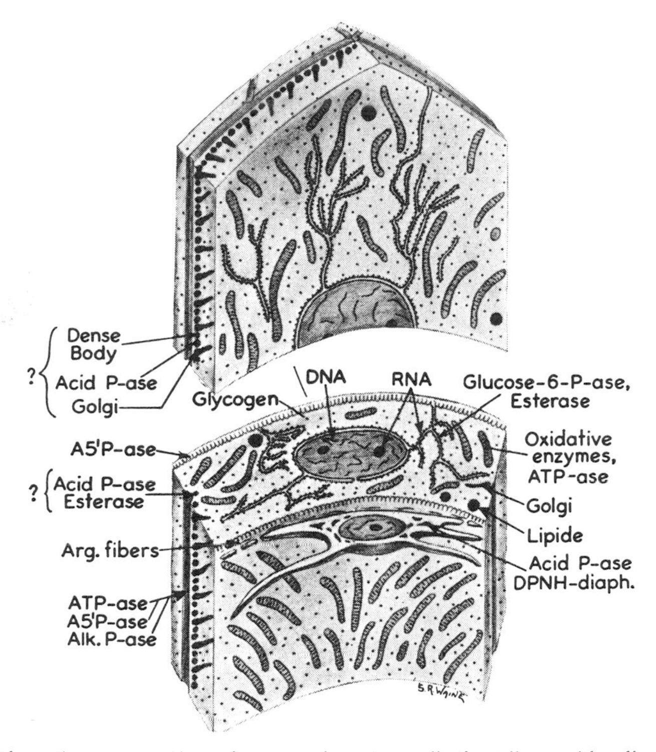

FIG. 9. Schematic representation of a parenchymatous cell of rat liver, with adjacent Kupffer cell (stellate shape). Note orientation of mitochondria (long axes oriented in sinusoid-canaliculi directions). The pericanalicular arrangement of Golgi apparatus, dense bodies, acid phosphatase bodies and esterase bodies is shown; the uncertainty concerning their interrelations is indicated by question marks. *Abbreviations:* Acid P-ase, acid phosphatase; A5′P-ase, 5′-nucleotidase; ATP-ase, adenosine triphosphatase; Alk. P-ase, alkaline phosphatase; Glucose-6-P-ase, glucose-6-phosphatase; DPNH-diaph, DPNH-tetrazolium reductase; DNA, deoxyribonucleic acid; RNA, ribonucleic acid; Arg. fibers, argyrophylic fibers.

biochemical assay of isolated fractions and electron microscopy, but also on the results of specific staining methods.

SPECIFIC CYTOCHEMICAL STAINING METHODS

We will refer to only one cytochemical staining method for nonenzymatic constituents, the Feulgen method for DNA (for a fuller discussion of this and other methods see refs. 26, 30). It has recently been applied to a problem which may be of considerable interest to *in vivo* function. Even if it prove of less physiological interest than now appears, the work illustrates the possibilities of quantitation with some of these staining methods. It is agreed by most that, with but few exceptions, the DNA content of cells is generally constant. Yet, at least in the salivary chromosomes of *Diptera,* at certain stages of development local bursts of activity occur in which the DNA content increases greatly in specific chromosome loci. This has been shown now by three different techniques: two-wavelength microspectrophotometric analysis (36, 40) of Feulgen staining by Stich and Naylor (50), ultraviolet microspectrophotometry by Rudkin and Corlette (46), and tritium-labeled radioautography by Ficq and Pavan (13).

The staining reactions for enzyme activity are generally incapable of true quantitation. However, they can demonstrate intracellular localization, if the organelles under question are preserved, if the enzyme activity is not totally inhibited, and if the product of the enzyme reaction is trapped at its site of formation because it is insoluble or because the site binds it strongly. A procedure currently under investigation in a number of laboratories holds much promise in this area. In the 'freeze-substitution' procedures, tissue is rapidly frozen at low temperatures (−170 to −200°C) and then fixed in nonaqueous fluids like osmium tetroxide in absolute acetone at low temperature (−70°C). It is known that structure is excellently preserved by this procedure, and it is hoped that sufficient enzyme activity will survive to make it useful for enzyme cytochemistry on the intracellular and fine structure levels.

In the past, our work has involved fixation at more usual temperatures, 2–5°C. Figure 10 illustrates the lead method for phosphatases as developed by Wachstein and Meisel (57). In this instance, the tissue was fixed in cold formol-calcium and then cut with a routine freezing microtome. The substrate is ATP. The enzyme, probably an ATPase (9, 33), liberates phosphate ions. These are trapped by lead ions in the medium. The resultant lead phosphate is converted to black lead sulfide by immersing the slide in ammonium sulfide. As figure 10 shows, the bile canaliculi of liver are beautifully delineated by the precipitated reaction product of the enzyme.

By using brief fixation in cold osmium tetroxide and then incubating small blocks of fixed tissue in the ATPase medium, Dr. Edward Essner (9) has been able to visualize the reaction products in electron micrographs. Figure 11 is a low-power electron micrograph. It demonstrates that all the reaction product is *within* the canaliculus. By studying an area with little to moderate enzyme activity, the reaction product can be localized in the cell membrane (fig. 12).

When a similarly fixed liver block is incubated in the same medium with adenosine-5′-monophosphate substituted for ATP, 5′-nucleotidase activity is visualized. This enzyme is also present in the bile canaliculi, but, in addition, it is present in the microvilli of the Disse space. The damage to the Disse space microvilli is a bit too extensive to permit the firm conclusion that the precipitate is in the plasma membrane. If it is, then we may have an interesting enzymic differentiation in different parts of the cell membrane. At the absorptive surface exposed to the blood, ATPase activity is not demonstrable (with this incubation time) but 5′-nucleotidase is. At the secretory surface exposed to the bile canaliculi,

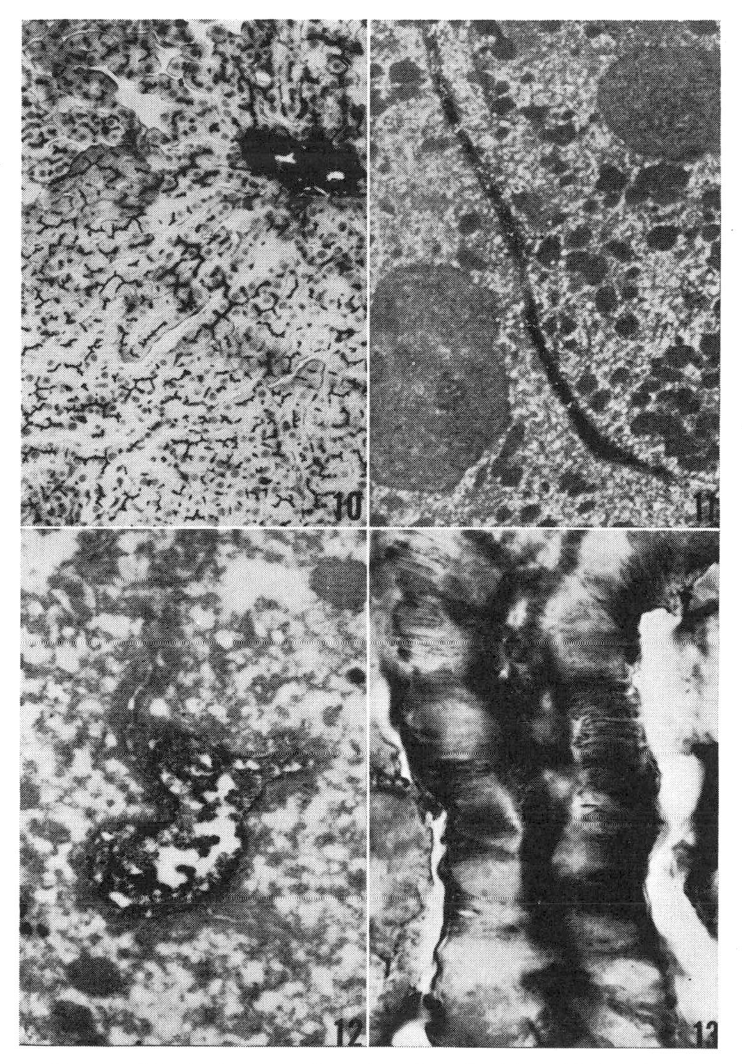

FIG. 10. ATPase activity in frozen section of rat liver fixed in cold formol-calcium. [From (33).] Incubated for 15 min. at 37°C in incubation medium of Wachstein and Meisel (57), with the addition of 2.5×10^{-3} M cysteine hydrochloride. Portal triad in *upper right.* Bile canaliculi of peripheral cells are wider and show more intense ATPase activity than centrolobular cells (*lower left*); cf. fig. 20. × 420.

FIG. 11. Electron micrograph of section of rat liver. [From (9).] Tissue fixed in cold buffered osmium tetroxide for 7 min., then incubated in ATPase medium for 30 min. at 37°C. Note nuclei, mitochondria, and vacuolated cytoplasm. The reaction product is all present inside the bile canaliculus. × 3750.

FIG. 12. Electron micrograph of liver treated as in fig. 11. [From (9).] Note precipitate in the plasma membrane surrounding bile canaliculus and at tips of some microvilli. There is no precipitate in the adjoining regions of the plasma membrane. × 19,200.

FIG. 13. ATPase activity in kidney of a rat made nephrotic by injection of aminonucleoside. [From (51).] In the proximal tubule, cut longitudinally, the indented cell membranes show marked ATPase activity. Activity is also high in the membranes of the capillary endothelium (on either side of the proximal tubule). × 700.

both enzyme activities are visualized, with the level of ATPase apparently higher than 5′-nucleotidase.

We have evidence to suggest that high ATPase activity may be present in the cell membranes of many tissues, particularly where membrane activity is high, as in capillaries (fig. 13) and in the cell membranes of kidney tubule cells (fig. 13). This is a section of rat kidney, from the work of Spater *et al.* (51), to demonstrate high ATPase activity in the membranes at the base of the proximal tubule cells. It is of particular interest that electron microscopy shows these membranes to be in intimate contact with the mitochondria, the sites of ATP generation.

The original lead procedure was that of Gomori (16) for acid phosphatase. It can be used to good advantage with frozen sections of tissue fixed in cold formol-calcium. Figure 14 is a section of kidney from a male rat. The proximal tubule cytoplasm contains a great many 'droplets' with high acid phosphatase activity. Dr. de Duve, in his chapter (8), discusses the possible relation to the 'lysosomes' of acid phosphatase-rich 'droplets' isolated from kidney by Straus (52, 53).

Figure 15 is a similar section of rat liver, demonstrating peribiliary bodies with high acid phosphatase activity. We are currently attempting to ascertain by electron microscopy whether these bodies are identical with the 'dense bodies' seen in figure 7 and discussed by de Duve (8) in relation to 'lysosomes.' We hope in this fashion also to clarify their relation to the Golgi apparatus (figs. 9, 20 and refs. 30, 31).

Kupffer cells, in keeping with their phagocytic character, show high acid phosphatase activity. This is undemonstrable by biochemical assay of tissue homogenates yet is readily seen in stained sections of tissue *in situ* (fig. 15). The value of such staining methods in supplementing biochemical analyses is further emphasized by figure 16, a liver section from a rat fed the carcinogen, 3′-methyl, 4-dimethylaminoazobenzene, for 3 weeks. Its most striking aspect is the marked increase in number of Kupffer cells with very high acid phosphatase activity. After only 2 days on the dye, there is a decided increase in the number of Kupffer cells with high acid phosphatase activity. Such shifts in cell population, enzymically heterogeneous, need to be taken into account in assessing chemical data from homogenates and isolated subcellular fractions of physiologically or pathologically altered tissue. Daoust (7) has plotted the changing numbers of cell types in rat liver following feeding of the carcinogen, 4-dimethylaminoazobenzene, and Abercrombie and Harkness (1) have done so following partial hepatectomy.

The last staining method to be considered briefly is the tetrazolium method for oxidative enzymes, now quite useful for intracellular localization (30). The points at which we believe the tetrazolium links with the electron transport chain of mitochondria and microsomes are shown in figure 17; this is based mostly

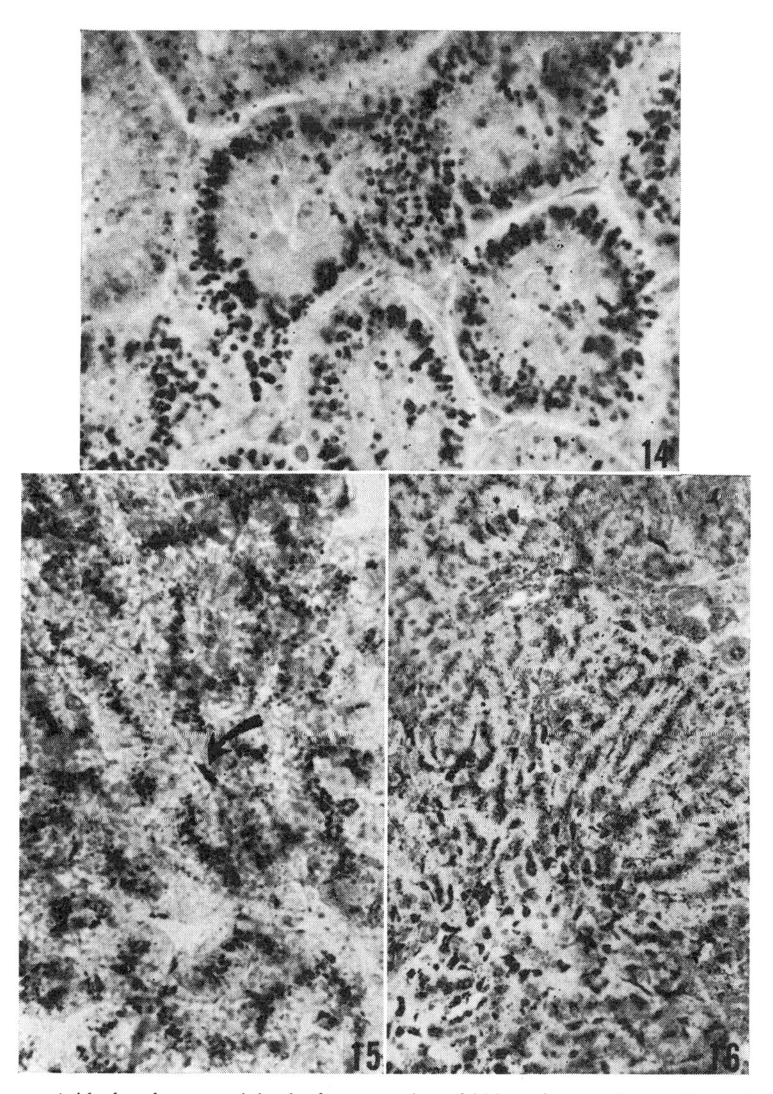

FIG. 14. Acid phosphatase activity in frozen section of kidney from male rat. Tissue fixed in cold formol-calcium and incubated for 30 min. at 37°C, in medium of Gomori (16). Note, in proximal tubule, numerous droplets with high acid phosphatase activity. In distal tubules (*upper left*) droplets are fewer and smaller. × 550.

FIG. 15. Acid phosphatase activity in rat liver. Tissue treated as in fig. 14. Note peribiliary bodies with high acid phosphatase activity. Arrow points to Kupffer cell with intense acid phosphatase activity. × 450.

FIG. 16. Acid phosphatase activity in liver of rat fed 3′methyl, 4 dimethylaminoazobenzene for 3 weeks. Tissue treated as in fig. 14. Some areas show normal peribiliary granules clearly. Particularly in lower part of the photograph, there are a great many Kupffer cells with very high acid phosphatase activity. × 95.

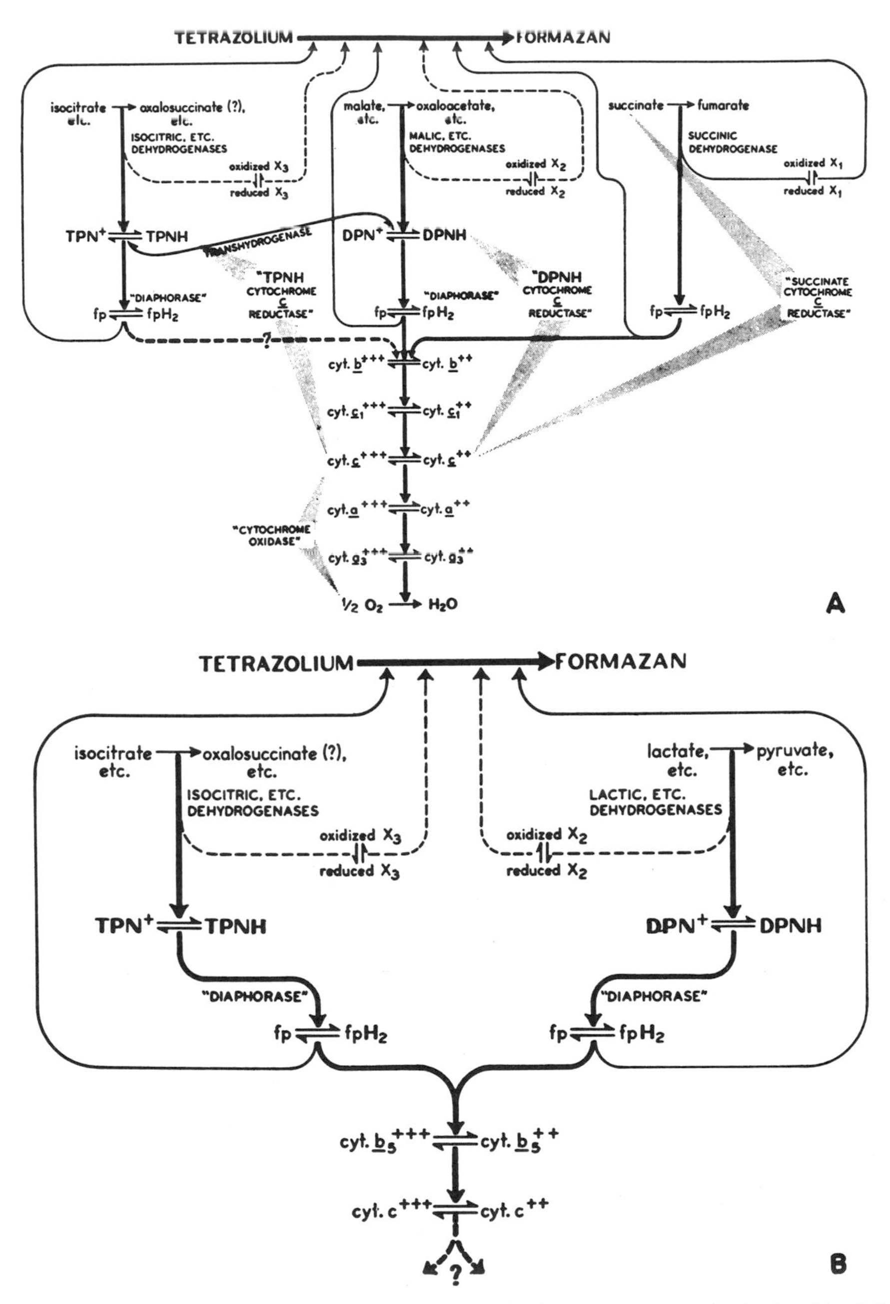

Fig. 17. Probable linkage of tetrazolium salts with electron transport of mitochondria (*A*) and microsomes (*B*). [From (30).] For discussion of the diagram see (30).

on work by Farber and associates (10) with succinic dehydrogenase, and on unpublished work in our own laboratory with DPNH oxidation. When tetrazolium accepts electrons it precipitates as a brightly-colored insoluble formazan.

Figures 18 and 19 are from frozen sections of formol-calcium fixed tissue, incubated with DPNH as substrate and the new 'Nitro-BT' of Tsou, Nachlas and Seligman (56) as the tetrazolium salt. The activity visualized is that portion of DPNH-cytochrome *c* reductase which survives cold formol-calcium fixation. The best name for this portion of the electron transport chain would be the operational term, DPNH-tetrazolium reductase. In heart, vividly-stained mitochondria are readily seen (fig. 18). On the other hand, in liver (fig. 19) mitochondria are difficult to discern, except in areas. We believe this results partly because of damage to the mitochondria, but largely because of the abundant ergastoplasm with high DPNH-cytochrome *c* reductase activity. This produces formazan throughout the cell, obscuring the mitochondria. When liver mitochondria are isolated and then incubated in the same medium, their staining is readily seen. Thus, the staining results agree well with the data on isolated fractions which show DPNH-cytochrome *c* reductase activity in both microsomes and mitochondria.

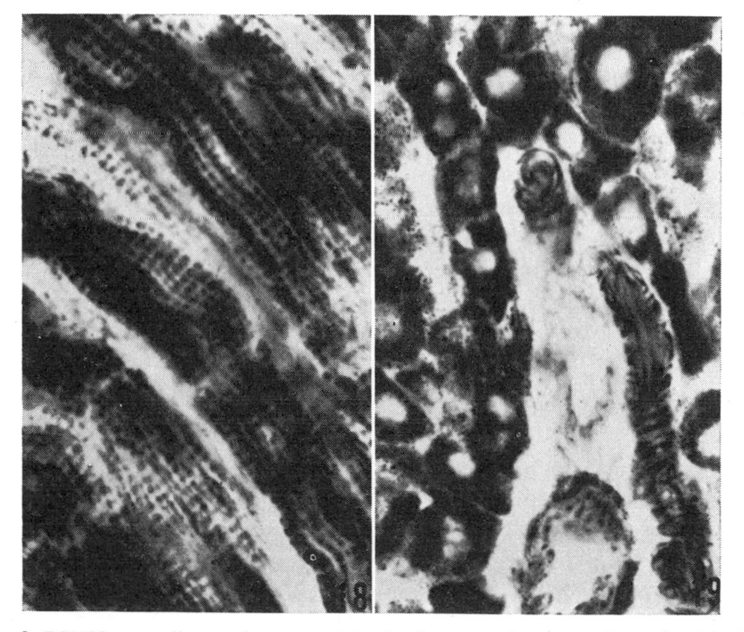

FIG. 18. DPNH-tetrazolium reductase activity in frozen section of rat heart fixed in formol-calcium. Note darkly-stained mitochondria. × 900.

FIG. 19. DPNH-tetrazolium reductase activity in frozen section of rat liver fixed in formol-calcium. The granular precipitate over parenchymatous cells makes mitochondria difficult to see, except in areas. Within the portal space, the arteriole sections show deeply-stained smooth muscle cells. × 580.

POTENTIALITY VS. ACTIVITY

One may raise the question whether tetrazolium salts, added in this artificial manner, truly indicate the intracellular sites of DPNH reduction *in vivo*. This is essentially the question, raised earlier, of potentiality as opposed to actuality. We may ask the same about the apparent ATPase activity shown in figures 10-13. Does the enzyme function, *in vivo,* as a phosphatase; or does it, as the evidence suggests for isolated mitochondria, catalyze a reaction linking oxidation and phosphorylation?

Similar questions may, and should, be raised regarding enzyme activities as measured in isolated subcellular fractions, in submitochondrial fragments, or in purified enzymes. Whether an added dye will accept electrons may, for example, depend upon the degree of coupling of the electron transport chain. In a tightly coupled system, the dye may be unable to reveal the DPNH-cytochrome *c* reductase. Perhaps only if the system is loosened, to begin with, by treatment either with the dye itself or by some other means, will the dye gain access to electron-transmitting enzymes. It would be ironic if only that dye is capable of showing enzyme activity in an organelle which uncouples the organization of that organelle and thereby alters its structure.

We are here in an area where we can do little more than ask questions. Our information is still too meagre with respect to control mechanisms within the cell, or influences of substrate and coenzyme concentrations on rate-limiting reactions and enzyme-forming systems, or effects upon enzyme activity of its integration into a film or membrane within the cell (as Dr. McLaren emphasizes in his chapter (23)) or of the milieu in which it acts (as Dr. Siegel suggests in his chapter (47)). Limitations of thermal collisions of cytochromes by structural factors in the mitochondria are stressed by Green in this volume (17), as is the vital role of lipoprotein in electron transport. These are some of the most fundamental issues in relation to the *in vivo* function of cell particles. In this connection, an article by Korr, "Oxidation-Reductions in Heterogeneous Systems," written some 20 years ago for a Cold Spring Harbor Symposium (20), makes rewarding reading. Consideration of his generalizations is particularly interesting when viewed in current knowledge of multi-enzyme systems of mitochondria, intracellular distributions of enzymes, the fine structure of cells, the capacity of mitochondrial fragments to carry out oxidative phosphorylation, and the 'reconstruction' of the glycolytic sequence with soluble enzymes. It seems to this reader that relatively little advance has been made, in these two decades, toward the 'formulation of the rules,' as Korr (20) puts it, which govern the properties of enzymes and other cell constituents when incorporated in an interface or film.

Another general point may be made in relation to evaluating biochemical data in terms of *in vivo* tissue. I believe we are all aware that 'the liver cell' is

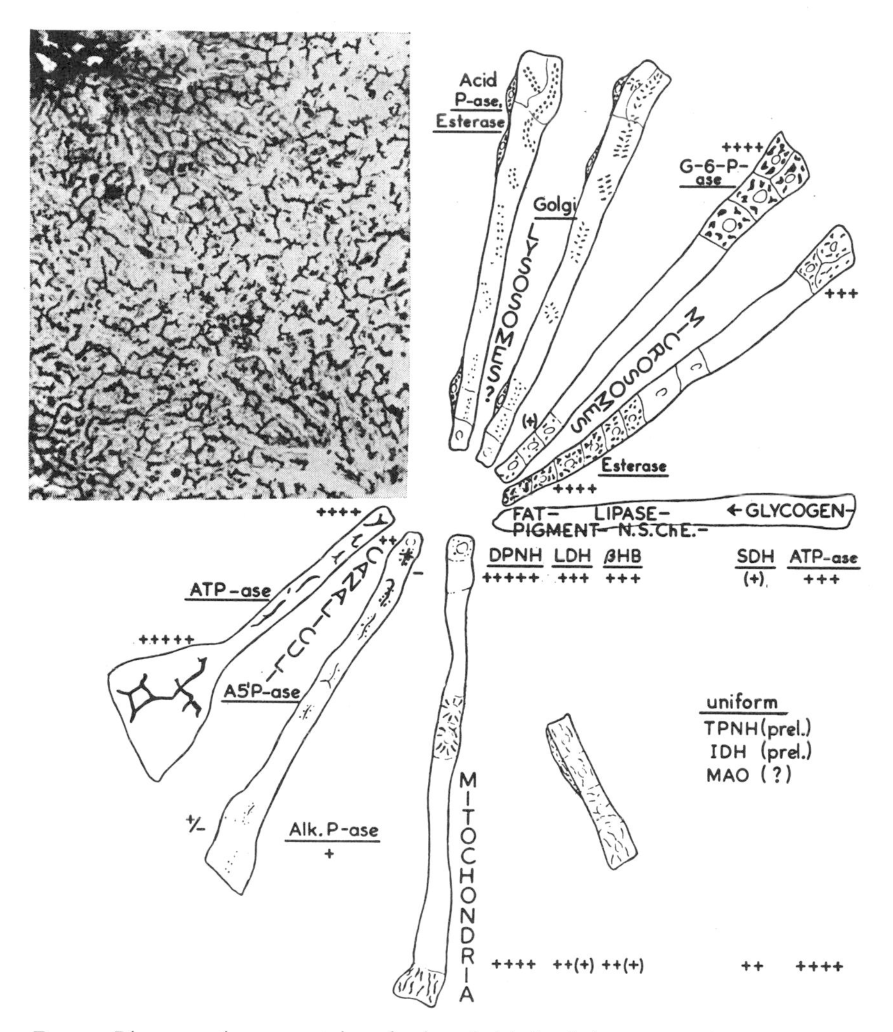

FIG. 20. Diagrammatic representation of a hepatic lobule of the rat.

Upper left quadrant, a photograph shows a portion of the hepatic lobule stained to demonstrate ATPase activity in the bile canaliculi. [From (33).] The quantitative differences between centrolobular cells and peripheral cells are indicated by plus marks (+) and by schematic representation of the cytologic structures. *Abbreviations:* ATP-ase, adenosinetriphosphatase; A5'P-ase, 5'-nucleotidase; Alk. P-ase, alkaline phosphatase; Acid P-ase, acid phosphatase; G-6-P-ase, glucose-6-phosphatase; DPNH, DPNH-tetrazolium reductase; LDH, lactic dehydrogenase-DPNH-tetrazolium reductase; BHB, beta-hydroxybutyric dehydrogenase-DPNH-tetrazolium reductase; SDH, succinic dehydrogenase; TPNH, TPNH-cytochrome *c* reductase; IDH, isocitric dehydrogenase-TPNH tetrazolium reductase; MAO, monamine oxidase; N.S.ChE., non-specific cholinesterase; prel., preliminary observations. Kupffer cells are indicated where they contain high levels of the enzyme activities or large numbers of the cytological structures drawn. (Evidence obtained in our laboratory since this diagram was drawn shows that TPNH-tetrazolium reductase activity is also higher in the centrolobular than in the peripheral cells.)

a concept which, like 'the average man' or 'the beautiful woman,' is useful but somewhat unreal. Yet some may not realize the degree of quantitative heterogeneity, even among homogeneous cells like the parenchymatous cells of liver. Figure 20 is intended to emphasize that every cytological entity and chemical or enzyme studied by *in situ* methods exhibits such quantitative differences between the centrolobular and peripheral cells of the hepatic lobule.[3] It is possible that these differences are related to factors like the quality of blood flowing to the cells (31).

We await with interest the study of these cells in Dr. Oliver Lowry's laboratory. Still another method of biochemical cytology, *micro-techniques applied to tissue sections,* is being employed, in this case to dissected areas of frozen sections. These direct chemical analyses of centrolobular cells and peripheral cells will provide opportunity for evaluating the staining observations.

CONCLUSION

The developments in biochemical cytology show that what seemed simple has become complex, what appeared separate is interrelated, what looked homogeneous is now heterogeneous. Our knowledge of the cell moves towards heterogeneity, but our approach to its study moves towards homogeneity. It would be overstatement to consider that the various approaches of biochemical cytology are the same and that it is therefore difficult, at symposia like these, to distinguish a biochemist from a microscopist. Yet the movement is there—towards removal of barriers, towards a common language, towards common approaches and common concepts.

I am indebted to my colleagues, Dr. Edward Essner, for the electron micrographs in figures 3, 4, 6, 11 and 12; Dr. Herman W. Spater for figure 13; Miss Bertha Masek for assistance in preparing the slides from which figures 14, 15, 16, 18 and 19 were photographed; Mr. L. J. Walker for the photography, including photomicrography; and Mr. Stanley Waine for the art work in figures 8, 9, 17 and 20.

REFERENCES

1. Abercrombie, M. and R. D. Harkness. *Proc. Roy Soc. London, ser. B* 138: 544, 1951.
2. Allfrey, V. G. and I. A. Mirsky. This volume, p. 186.
3. Brachet, J. *Biochemical Cytology.* New York: Acad. Press, 1957.
4. Birbeck, M. S. C., and E. H. Mercer. *Nature* 178: 985, 1957.
5. Chance, B. In: *Enzymes, Units of Biological Structure and Function,* edited by O. H. Gaebler. New York: Acad. Press, 1956, p. 447.
6. Chèvremont, M. *Notions de Cytologie et Histologie.* Liege: Editions Desoer, 1956.
7. Daoust, R. *J. Nat. Cancer Inst.* 15: 1447, 1955.

[3] The evidence for this diagram comes from the work of many laboratories, including our own. It was first presented at a meeting of the New York Pathological Society (31), and will be described in detail elsewhere.

8. DE DUVE, C. This volume, p. 128.
9. ESSNER, E., A. B. NOVIKOFF, AND B. MASEK. *J. Biophys. Biochem. Cytol.* 4: 711, 1958.
10. FARBER, E. AND E. BUEDING. *J. Histochem. Cytochem.* 4: 357, 1956.
11. FAWCETT, D. W. AND S. ITO. *J. Biophys. Biochem. Cytol.* 4: 135, 1958.
12. FERNÁNDEZ-MORÁN, H. AND J. B. FINEAN. *J. Biophys. Biochem. Cytol.* 3: 725, 1957.
13. FICQ, A. AND C. PAVAN. *Nature* 180: 983, 1957.
14. GEY, G. O., P. SHAPRAS, F. B. BANG AND M. K. GEY. *Symp. 8th Congr. Cell Biology,* (Leiden). New York: Interscience, 1956.
15. GOLDSTEIN, L. AND W. PLAUT. *Proc. Nat. Acad. Sci.* 41: 874, 1955.
16. GOMORI, G. *Microscopic Histochemistry: Principles and Practice.* Chicago: Univ. Chicago Press, 1952.
17. GREEN, D. E. This volume, p. 84.
18. ITO, S. AND D. W. FAWCETT. Personal communication. Also, REYEL, J. P., S. ITO AND D. W. FAWCETT, *Biophys. Biochem. Cytol.* 4: 495, 1958.
19. KORNBERG, A. *J. Biol. Chem.* 182: 779, 1950.
20. KORR, I. M. *Cold Spring Harbor Symp. Quant. Biol.* 7: 74, 1939.
21. KUFF, E. L. AND A. J. DALTON. This volume, p. 114.
22. LOFTFIELD, R. B. *Progr. Biophys. Chem.* 8: 347, 1957.
23. MCLAREN, D. AND K. L. BABCOCK. This volume, p. 23.
24. MCMASTER-KAYE, R. AND J. H. TAYLOR. *J. Biophys. Biochem. Cytol.* 4: 5, 1958.
25. MOORE, D. H. AND H. RUSKA. *J. Biophys. Biochem. Cytol.* 3: 457, 1957.
26. NOVIKOFF, A. B. In: *Analytical Cytology,* edited by R. C. MELLORS. New York: McGraw-Hill, pp. 2/1–2/63.
27. NOVIKOFF, A. B. *Science* 124: 969, 1956.
28. NOVIKOFF, A. B. *Symp. Soc. Exper. Biol.* 10: 92, 1957.
29. NOVIKOFF, A. B. *Cancer Res.* 17: 1010, 1957.
30. NOVIKOFF, A. B. In: *Analytical Cytology* (2nd ed.) edited by R. C. MELLORS. New York: McGraw-Hill 1959. In press.
31. NOVIKOFF, A. B. *Bull. New York Acad. Med., 2nd ser.* 35: 67, 1959.
32. NOVIKOFF, A. B., H. BEAUFAY AND C. DE DUVE. *J. Biophys. Biochem. Cytol.* 2: suppl.; 179, 1956.
33. NOVIKOFF, A. B., D. H. HAUSMAN AND E. PODBER. *J. Histochem. Cytochem.* 6: 61, 1958.
34. NOVIKOFF, A. B. AND E. F. NOE. *J. Morphol.* 96: 189, 1955.
35. NOVIKOFF, A. B. AND E. PODBER. *J. Histochem. Cytochem.* 5: 552, 1957.
36. ORNSTEIN, L. *Lab. Invest.* 1: 250, 1952.
37. PALADE, G. E. *J. Biophys. Biochem. Cytol.* 1: 59, 1955.
38. PALADE, G. E. This volume, p. 64.
39. PALAY, S. L. In: *Frontiers of Cytology,* edited by S. L. PALAY. New Haven: Yale, 1958, p. 305.
40. PAUTAU, K. *Chromosoma* 5: 341, 1952.
41. PEACHEY, L. Unpublished observations.
42. PORTER, K. R. *Harvey Lect.* 51: 175, 1957.
43. PREISS, J. AND P. HANDLER. *J. Biol Chem.* 233: 488, 1958.
44. PREISS, J. AND P. HANDLER. *J. Biol. Chem.* 233: 493, 1958.
45. ROSE, G. G. *J. Biophys. Biochem. Cytol.* 3: 697, 1957.
46. RUDKIN, G. T. AND S. L. CORLETTE. *Proc. Nat. Acad. Sci.* 43: 964, 1957.
47. SIEGEL, S. M. This volume, p. 37.
48. SJÖSTRAND, F. *Internat. Rev. Cytol.* 5: 456, 1956.
49. STEPHENSON, M. *et al.* This volume, p. 160.
50. STICH, H. F. AND J. M. NAYLOR. *Exper. Cell Res.* 14: 442, 1958.

51. SPATER, H. S., A. B. NOVIKOFF AND B. MASEK. *J. Biophys. Biochem. Cytol.* 4: 765, 1958.
52. STRAUS, W. *J. Biophys. Biochem. Cytol.* 2: 513, 1956.
53. STRAUS, W. *J. Biophys. Biochem. Cytol.* 3: 933, 1957.
54. TAYLOR, J. H. AND P. S. WOODS. This volume, p. 172.
55. TOBIOKA, M. AND J. J. BIESELE. *J. Biophys. Biochem. Cytol.* 2: Suppl.; 319, 1956.
56. TSOU, K. C., S. S. CHENG, M. M. NACHLAS AND A. M. SELIGMAN. *J. Am. Chem. Soc.* 78: 6139, 1956.
57. WACHSTEIN, M. AND E. MEISEL. *Am. J. Clin. Path.* 27: 13, 1957.

DISCUSSION

R. E. Beyer, A. B. Novikoff, Lars Ernster, Alfred Marshak

DR. BEYER: I would like to ask a teleological question, for the physiologist must live with this mistress. What cellular function would you assign to the specific phosphatases and ATPases which you have demonstrated in the bile canaliculi and cell surface? Do you think, for example, that the ATPase is competing with hexokinase for ATP? And what does this mean in terms of cellular function?

DR. NOVIKOFF: In the bile canaliculi, one thinks at once of secretion of bile constituents from the cell, but movement of molecules into the cell is not excluded. It is also possible to conceive of the enzyme as being involved in movement of microvilli or similar cell membrane phenomena. On the biochemical level, we are equally ignorant of the enzyme's function. If it functions as an ATPase, then competition for substrate with hexokinase is an interesting possibility. As suggested in the presentation, it is possible that *in vivo* it is one of the enzymes involved in oxidative phosphorylation. There is as yet too little indication of the enzyme's role, on either the cytological or biochemical level.

DR. ERNSTER: I don't know whether or not the dye used by Dr. Novikoff uncouples oxidative phosphorylation; we do know that certain dyes, such as 2,6-dichlorophenol-indophenol or methylene blue, interfere with mitochondrial phosphorylation, but whether this is due to a disorganization of the mitochondrial structure or to a competitive type of enzyme-inhibition is not clear.

DR. NOVIKOFF: Thank you very much, Dr. Ernster.

DR. MARSHAK: It is true, as Dr. Novikoff has pointed out, that separation and study of cell particulates received its current impetus from Bensley and Hoerr, but this is only for our generation, for Miescher, Brunton and some of their predecessors studied properties of isolated nuclei almost 100 years ago.

DR. NOVIKOFF: It is good that Dr. Marshak points to the importance of the predecessors, later and early, of Bensley and Hoerr. Even the separation of cytoplasmic particles ('grana') had been used by Otto Warburg some 20 years earlier. However, the first to employ a method essentially like the modern complete cell fractionation were Bensley and Hoerr, and, one should add, Albert Claude.

Some Characteristics of Enzyme Reactions at Surfaces[1]

A. D. McLAREN AND K. L. BABCOCK

College of Agriculture
University of California
Berkeley

It has long been recognized that enzyme reactions may be influenced by the structural heterogeneity and surface properties of cells. The nutrition of cells, as of microbes and plant roots in soil or of bacteria on teeth, for example, also involves enzyme activity at interfaces. Since natural interfaces are often charged, the effective concentrations of hydrogen ions, sulfhydryl groups and anions at interfaces are generally different from those in adjacent bulk media. Thus, enzyme reaction rates involving requisite concentrations of ions or redox potentials for the enzyme will be quantitatively different for bulk and interfacial systems. In structured systems such as mitochondria one may ask, for example, whether for the electron transport chain from succinate to cytochrome *c* the spatial arrangement in the original subcellular particle is so exacting that random collision between the component proteins, or even coadsorption on a suitable carrier, will be able to re-establish the original sequence of events with anything approaching the efficiency of the natural practiculate complex (45).

Although the theory of enzyme reactions *in vitro* has progressed phenomenally in the past decade, the biological implication of this progress is not straightforward and an even greater effort will have to be placed on the *in vivo* aspects before these theories are fully justified. A few schools have been keeping the goal in sight, among which are A. Rothstein and co-workers (18, 41) with cell surfaces and B. Chance (5) with intracellular reactions.

SIGNIFICANCE OF A DIFFERENCE BETWEEN SURFACE pH AND BULK pH

In 1937 Danielli wrote, "The bulk of the fluid contents of the cell are presumably of fairly uniform reaction, but the surfaces of granules, oil globules, mitochondria, and gel particles may well differ from the bulk reaction by up to 2 pH units, according to the constitution of the surfaces concerned. The cell may thus offer a much more diverse environment for enzyme reactions than has hitherto been supposed." Also, with an acid interface, variation of cation concentration "may produce an effect very similar to variation of the pH" (7).

[1] Supported in part by a research grant (G-4236) from the National Institutes of Health.

This conceptual scheme does not seem to have been explored extensively during the past 20 years, although at present enormous effort is being expended on examining the enzyme chemistry of cell surfaces and cellular particles. Let us examine the basis of Danielli's assertion.

It had been known for some time that the interfacial tension (I.T.) between nonaqueous solutions of long-chain acids, or amines, and aqueous solutions, is much lowered when the pH of the aqueous phase is such that the polar groups of the solute at the interface are electrolytically dissociated. However, the range of pH over which the I.T. change occurs with a fatty acid is more alkaline by as much as 3 pH units than the titration curve of the acid (HA) in the bulk aqueous phase. (The choice of buffer in these and related experiments is very important, since buffer cations, such as acetate, may also accumulate in an interface, particularly if an association with H^+ ions is extant.) The change is more marked with lower concentrations of cation. A simple assumption to account for this pH shift phenomenon is that the pH at the interface is less than that of the bulk aqueous phase because of the concentration of charge (minus) at the interphase and a consequent concentration of H^+ ions at the interface to form an ionic double layer of thickness δ.

Danielli derives an expression for the pH-shift by a consideration of a Donnan equilibrium involving 'activities' of ions, which is

$$\frac{[H_s^+]}{[M_s^+]} = \frac{[H_b^+]}{[M_b^+]} \tag{1}$$

where M^+ is cation other than hydrogen, and the dissociation of the fatty acid at the interface which is given by

$$[H_s^+]\,[A_s^-] = K_s[HA_s]. \tag{2}$$

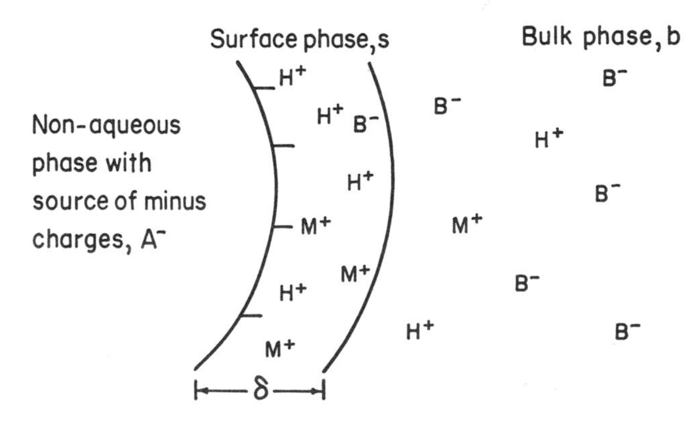

Fig. 1. Relations of pH and I.T. change with fatty acids. M^+ = cations other than H^+, and B^- = anions other than those from the fatty acid, A^-.

He introduces the assumption that the additional lowering of I.T. below the I.T. given by the undissociated acid is exactly proportional to the fractional dissociation (α) in the surface phase,

$$\alpha = \frac{[A_s^-]}{[HA_s] + [A_s^-]}. \tag{3}$$

The sum $[HA_s] + [A_s^-]$ was calculated from a knowledge of the surface area per polar group at an interface and an assumed value of δ. Although one arrives at $[A_s^-]$ from *equation 3*, $[H_s^+]$ cannot be evaluated from *equation 2* since K_s may not be assumed to be equal to the dissociation constant (K_b) in bulk phase. Instead $[H_s^+]$ is obtained from *equation 1* by further assuming that $[M_s^+] = [A_s^-] + [B^-]$, which is a reasonable assumption near neutrality. An example is the following:

PH VALUES FOR 1% PALMITIC ACID IN A BROMOBENZENE-WATER SYSTEM
(buffer 0.02 M in cation)

pH_b	7	8	9	10	11
$pH_b - (pH)_s$	1.4	2.1	2.5	2.7	2.7

The values of ΔpH are significant (about 1 pH unit) even in 0.4 M buffers.

Danielli pointed out that his approach fell short of providing a theoretical relationship between K_s and K_b. This problem has since been reexamined by Hartley and Roe (20). They suggested that the electrokinetic potential (ζ) of the colloidal chemist can be identified with the potential ψ in the neighborhood of a simple ion at the distance of closest approach of another ion, as considered by Debye and Hückel. In this sense the ζ-potential determines the local concentration of ions near the surface of a particle. The potential near the surface of a particle with ionized acidic groups is greater than the average for the bulk solution by an amount ζ, and the hydrogen ion concentration near the surface will be $e^{-\epsilon\zeta/kT}$ times the H^+ concentration in bulk. The effective dissociation constant according to Hartley and Roe becomes

$$K_s = Ke^{-\epsilon\zeta/kT} = Ke^{-F\zeta/RT} \tag{4}$$

where K is the thermodynamic dissociation constant in bulk, ϵ is the electronic charge, F is the faraday, T the absolute temperature, and k the Boltzmann constant.

At 25°, *equation 4* may be rewritten as

$$pH_s = pH_b + \zeta/60 \tag{5}$$

The difficulties in defining pH_s in a suitable manner in order to be consistent with pH_b in the usual sense has been thought through by Craxford *et al.*(6). We will use the Gibbs-Guggenheim approach to show that at a charged interface one sees concentrations, whereas partitioning takes place according to chemical potentials.

The chemical potential for hydrogen ions in bulk is given by

$$\mu_b = \mu_{0_b} + RT\, ln\, A_b = \mu_{0_b} + RT\, ln\, f_b C_b$$

and near the surface, at some point in the double layer, by

$$\mu_s = \mu_{0_s} + RT\, ln\, A_s = \mu_{0_s} + RT\, ln\, f_s C_s$$

where $\mu_{0_b} = \mu_{0_s}$ is the chemical potential of a standard state and A_b, f_b, C_b and A_s, f_s, C_s are activities, activity coefficients and concentrations in bulk and surface volumes respectively. At equilibrium, according to Gibbs,[2] $A_b = A_s$ and

$$\frac{C_b}{C_s} = \frac{f_s}{f_b}.$$

In dilute solutions $f_b \rightarrow 1$, so that $C_s \cong \frac{C_b}{f_s}$.

Equation 5 can be evaluated via electrophoretic measurements by substituting, for *large* particles, the Smoluchowski relationship $u = \frac{\zeta D}{4\eta\pi}$. We thereby arrive at the experimentally useful equation

$$pH_s = pH_b + 0.217u. \qquad (6a)$$

The mobility of a particle u is reckoned negative for motion toward an anode, in microns per second per volt per centimeter; D is the dielectric constant and η is the viscosity of the disperse medium at the same temperature.

In table 1 are some values for $\Delta pH = pH_b - pH_s$ evaluated by means of the equation of Hartley and Roe. Included are some data on roots obtained by still another approach, which will not be discussed here (27).

We may now inquire as to some of the biochemical and biological consequences of the existence of ΔpH.

Action of Proteolytic Enzymes on Proteins. *Equation 1* may be written as

$$pH_s - pH_b = -\log \frac{[M_s^+]}{[M_b^+]} = \log \frac{[B_s^-]}{[B_b^-]} = -\Delta pH \qquad (7)$$

and Danielli (8) pointed out that the pH at the surface of a protein would therefore be different from that in bulk, and to an extent determined in part by the ionic strength of the salts present. For *small* particles Hartley and Roe give, at 25°,

$$pH_s - pH_b = \zeta/60 = 0.325u = -\Delta pH. \qquad (6b)$$

[2] μ_{0_b} is set equal to μ_{0_s} by choice of a reference state such that $\lim_{C_b \to 0} \frac{A_b}{C_b} = f_b = 1$ and as C_b approaches zero so does C_s. Since $A_b = A_s$ and $C_b \neq C_s$, it is clear that any difference between pH_s and pH_b reflects differences in concentrations of H^+_s and H^+_b.

TABLE 1. VALUES OF Δ pH $=$ pH$_b$ — pH$_s$ FOR SOME COLLOIDAL AND BIOLOGICAL SURFACES IN AQUEOUS SYSTEMS AT ROOM TEMPERATURE

SURFACE	MOBILITY, M/SEC/V/CM *	I	ζ-POTENTIAL, MV	pH$_b$	Δ pH	REF.
Lysozyme	4.0	0.05	52	8.05	—0.87	(7)
Kaolinite	—4.8	0.05	—62	8.05	1.1	(44)
Lysozyme on kaolinite	—2.5	0.05	—32	8.05	0.54	(44)
Pseudomonas aeruginosa	—2.0	.02		6.9	0.44	(25)
Yeast	—1.2	0.01		4.1	0.30	(47)
Erythrocytes	—1.3	.13		7.4	0.3	(10)
Mitochondria (kidney)				7	$>$0	(2)
Roots		.003		7.1	1.1	(3)

* The ionic strength i is of fundamental importance in governing, in part, these quantities. They are lower the higher the ionic strength.

The value ΔpH has been found to be virtually identical for ovalbumin between pH 3 and 6 by either method of calculation. This is remarkable when one remembers that the first approach requires an assumption about δ (based on Debye-Hückel theory) and the results of the second approach give the surface pH essentially at the plane of shear, and this plane may be several Ångstroms away from the surface ionogenic groups (9). In solutions between 0.1 N and 0.001 N, δ varies from about 10 Å to 100 Å, so the attack on a substrate molecule by an enzyme of molecular weight of about 25,000 most certainly involves an environment characterized more by pH$_s$ than by pH$_b$ in such solutions.[3]

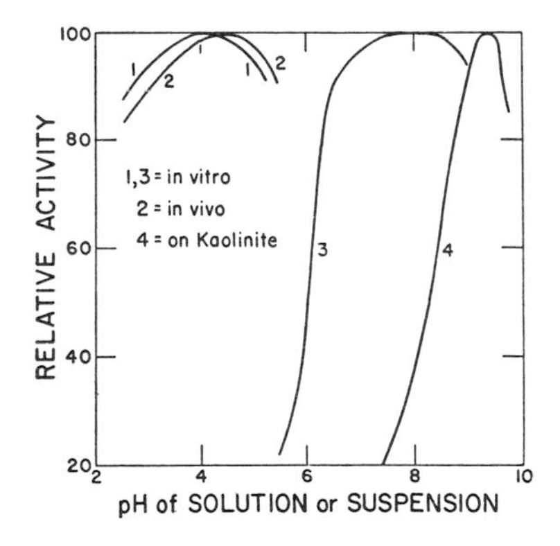

FIG. 2. Effect of pH on invertase activity of yeast cells and isolated enzyme [1,2] and on chymotryptic activity in solution or adsorbed on kaolinite [3,4]. (Refs. 29, 48.)

A dramatic example of the influence of pH$_s$ on the hydrolysis of lysozyme (denatured) is shown in figure 2. A comparison of the action of chymotrypsin on lysozyme in solution and on the surface of kaolinite particles (about 1 μ in size) in suspension reveals that the pH$_b$ of half maximum activity for the suspension is shifted about two units toward higher pH, showing that chymotrypsin behaves in

[3] The protein error of indicators has been semiquantitatively handled from this point of view (8).

accordance with a concentration of hydrogen ions at the surface which is greater than in the surrounding buffer medium (29). The chemical potentials of the hydrogen ions in the ambient solution and in the double layer about the kaolinite particles are of course the same.

Actually, a ΔpH of this magnitude may also be calculated from the data in table 1. Alderton *et al.* (1) give moving boundary values for the mobility of lysozyme in bulk at $pH_b = 8.05$ of about 4μ/sec/v/cm, giving $pH_s = 8.05 + 0.87 = 8.9$. For kaolinite, $pH_s = 8.05 - 1.05 = 7.0$, and for lysozyme on kaolin $\Delta pH = 0.53$ at an ionic strength of 0.05. Thus the effective pH at the surface of lysozyme molecules in solution is 8.9, whereas on kaolin it is somewhere between 7.0 and 7.5. The *zeta* potential measurements serve to show that there should be a pH shift of between 1.4 and 1.9 units of pH between the surfaces of adsorbed and unadsorbed lysozyme.

Apparently the action of an enzyme at an interface can serve the role of a 'molecular pH meter.' The following considerations will show that this action can be used to give an idea of the activity coefficient of hydrogen ions at the interface of lysozyme-on-kaolinite and an aqueous solution. It has been shown that the influence of hydrogen ion concentration on chymotrypsin activity, with an inflection point at about pH 6, may be attributed to the dissociation of histidine residues in the enzyme molecule (30). Histidine is part of the active center of chymotrypsin (19), so the hydrogen ion concentration at the surface or in bulk solution determines the degree of dissociation of histidine residues and hence the fraction of maximum activity of the enzyme, the left hand portions of the activity curves in figure 2.

In dilute solutions $f_b \rightarrow 1$, so that $C_s \cong C_b / f_s$. In the experiment cited, C_b is known and the action of chymotrypsin on adsorbed substrate shows a shift of 2 pH units compared with activity in solution. Now $pH_s - pH_b$ for lysozyme in solution was 0.87, which leaves about 1.1 units of ΔpH for the substrate-clay surface, or in other words $C_s \cong 10\ C_b$ and $f_s \cong 0.1$. In such experiments the order of addition of enzyme and substrate to kaolinite greatly influences the rate of reaction. At pH $= 8.5$ the rate is slower if the enzyme is adsorbed first (31). This could mean that the H^+ ion concentration is higher nearer the surface, as is to be expected, or that the enzyme is not oriented with active centers all outward toward the substrate, or that the mobility of the enzyme is reduced. The first reason must be important since the difference in rates becomes less at $pH_b = 9.1$, at which the pH of the surface of the kaolin must be high enough to support nearly a maximum enzyme activity by an almost fully active population of enzyme molecules regardless of the order of addition of enzyme and substrate to kaolin (40).

A locality in nature where the above phenomena are probably important is the soil. In soil, microorganisms liberate enzymes which hydrolyse organic compounds of many varieties. If such compounds, or the enzymes, are adsorbed on

TABLE 2. SITUATIONS IN WHICH ONE FINDS AN INFLUENCE OF Δ pH ON ENZYME ACTIVITY IN SOLUTION COMPARED WITH ACTIVITY AT A SURFACE *

ENZYME ON PARTICLE OR SURFACE	DISPLACEMENT OF pH OPTIMA FOR ENZYME ACTION	REF.
Chymotrypsin on adsorbed protein	2.0	(30)
Yeast surface		
Invertase	0.3	(29, 48)
'Phosphorylase'	see text	(18)
Surfaces of other microorganisms		
Ascorbic acid oxidase of *M. verrucaria* (spores)	0.0	(34)
Invertase of *M. verrucaria* (spores)	—0.4	(33)
Roots		
Barley-cell wall ascorbic acid oxidase (homogenates vs root segments)	—0.2	(22)
Wheat-cell wall invertase	see table 3	(3)

* Activity at surface — activity in bulk: Δ pH.

soil structural elements one must consider that the activity of the soil enzymes will not be of the same relative reactivity as would be found for the study of the same enzymes in solution. A comparison of chymotryptic activity in solution versus that on a surface (cf. fig. 2) at $pH_b = 7$ could lead one to conclude that adsorbed enzyme is inactive, or nearly absent (see ref. 32 for a study of soil urease). Failure to take this phenomenon into consideration may lead to questionable conclusions about the degree of enzyme activity (16). Zittle has reviewed this subject (49).

Action of Cell Surface Enzymes in Vivo and in Vitro. For the yeast *Saccharomyces cerevisiae,* ΔpH is calculated to be 0.30 (in M/100 acetate or phthalate); table 2 (26, 47).

A number of enzymes are supposed to be near or at the cell wall of yeast (42); table 2. For one of these, invertase, a ΔpH of 0.3 has been determined from rate studies of yeast and cell free enzyme; see figure 1 (48). A difference in pH_s and pH_b for *Bacterium coli* has been computed from microphoretic measurements (fig. 3) and such differences may apply to 'permease,' dehydrogenase, and other enzymes which may be acting at bacterial cell surfaces.[4] It is clear from tables 1 and 2 that the displacement of pH optima for enzyme action at cell surfaces is not always as expected; i.e., is either zero or in the opposite direction. Unknown factors other than a negatively charged surface must be involved. (The direction of displacement could be toward lower pH for a positively charged surface; however, such surfaces seem to be rare or as yet infrequently observed in nature. They have been achieved artificially, however, and with the expected influence on I.T. (7).)

[4] For cations, the 'reversal of charge concentrations' has been plotted in the form of spectra for *B. coli* and compared with similar spectra for naturally occurring high polymers. The exterior of cells has thereby been surmised to contain polysaccharide.

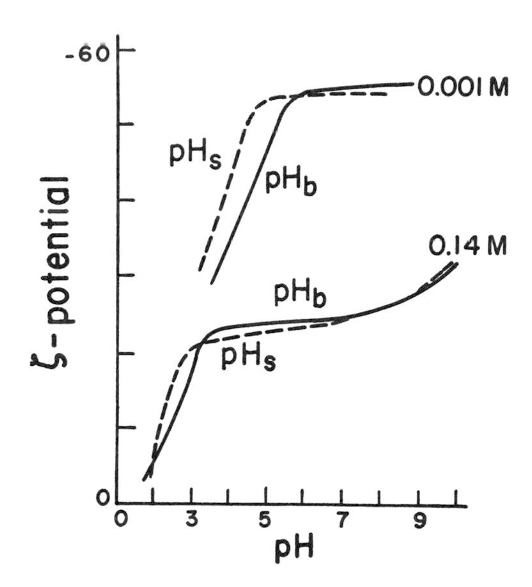

FIG. 3. *Zeta* potentials of *B. coli* as a function of pH and sodium chloride concentration (9).

Phosphate is actively transported into yeast by a mechanism involving glycolysis reactions and the pH_b optimum for the phosphate uptake of 6.5 is shifted to the acid by nearly two units by 0.02 M K^+ (18). A possible explanation is that an increase in extracellular K^+ results in alkalinization of the cell surface by exchange reaction (cf. *eq. 1*).

Burström (3) has observed a splitting of sucrose by wheat roots in external solution 20 times as rapidly as the absorption of hexoses under the same conditions. The hydrolysis proceeds by enzyme action at the root surface and is a decreasing function of pH between 3.7 and 7.4 at high salt concentrations where $pH_b \approx pH_s$. The root surface is negatively charged, and one way of decreasing ΔpH is by increasing the external salt concentration at constant pH_b. A comparison of *columns 3* and *4* in table 3 shows that the rate of hydrolysis closely follows the hydrogen ion concentration on the root surface, independently of the external pH (3).

It is worth noting that Burström suggested that probably one could adapt the rate of sucrose inversion to a quantitative method of determining the charge of the root surface.

TABLE 3. INFLUENCE OF Δ PH ON INVERSION OF SUCROSE BY WHEAT ROOTS (3)

$CaSO_4$+NaCl, EA.	pH_b	pH_s	SUCROSE HYDROLYZED, mM
0 M	6.9	4.5–5.0	0.085
10^{-4} M	7.1	5.6	0.079
[illegible] M	[illegible]	[illegible]	0.056
10^{-2} M	7.0	6.8	0.039

In this connection it is of interest to note that the formation of new cell wall material must be confined to the plasma surface, and hence enzyme systems involved in carbohydrate metabolism are present in the surface layer.

SOME REMARKS ON INTRACELLULAR ENZYMES

Enzymes in cells are probably associated for the most part with specialized structures, the inner cell membranes, reticular networks (giving rise to microsomes by rupture), mitochondria, etc. (21). If this were not the case, it is difficult to see how reaction sequences could be controlled (43). The state of the enzyme in or on such a particle may depend on the available hydrions near by and on the orientation of the enzyme. The orientation with respect to adjacent protein molecules may determine the amount of intermolecular protein bonding which exists and hence the H^++enzyme equilibria. Huennekens has compared the pH optimum of conjugated (pH 7–8) and dissociated (pH 9.5) malic oxidase still attached to particles of the cyclophorase system (23), and found a difference which may depend in part on this factor (see also Dickman and Speyer (10)). Also, the degree of swelling of mitochondria influences cytochrome activity (43).

In very small intact cells, such as those of bacteria, the concept of pH is without useful meaning (14). Thimann cites the interesting example that a 0.5 μ diameter microbial cell with a continuum of pH throughout the cell and its surroundings of pH=7 would only have room for 3.6 hydrions. What about the chances for such a free ion in a similar cell at pH 8! Under such circumstances, with the activity of an enzyme depending on the dissociation of say 1 H^+ per molecule, the observed dissociation may actually involve a switch of 1 H^+ from one protein molecule to another, or displacement by another cation. For example, in the utilization of potassium by *B. lactis aerogenes,* potassium appears to play the part of an enzyme-activator. Eddy and Hinshelwood based a quantitative treatment of the competition between K^+ and H^+ for an array of negative sites on an enzyme surface, on the assumption that a certain critical area of K^+-activated sites is necessary for growth to continue (12).

In spite of the fact that the idea of a pH inside a bacterial cell is nebulous, one must ultimately explain differences among bacteria. For example, Gale (17) has suggested that the difference in pH_b optima for amino acid decarboxylases acting in bulk and in intact washed cells arises because the value of pH_b for cells is necessary in order to have an intracellular pH equal to the true pH of optimum activity. By contrast, Few *et al.* (13) believe that there is a constancy of pH at the site of the intracellular catalase in *M. lysodeikticus* despite changes in pH of the external medium.

For cells the size of yeast, intracellular pH (pH_i) begins to take on some meaning. The pH_i of (resting) *S. cerevisiae* is 5.8 as a whole and the buffering power of the cell is considerable. Thus the enzyme system fermenting glucose is nearly independent of pH_b over a wide range (24). The buffering power resides more in salts than in proteins, and on prolonged fermentation the interior pH value may exceed 6 whereas at the outer layers a drop to 4.2 may occur. An example wherein local, point-to-point variations of $[H^+]$ may play a part in the rate of a reaction is the steady state of reduced pyridine nucleotides in yeast (5). Assuming that K for the reaction $K = \frac{[H^+]\,[DPNH]\,[acetaldehyde]}{[DPN^+]\,[ethanol]}$ is the same *in vivo* as *in vitro*, Chance calculated an intracellular 'pH' about two units higher than expected from solution studies.

Enzyme Reactions in Gels and at Liquid-Liquid Interfaces. With such problems in mind it is clear that the study of enzyme reactions in solution, although a preliminary step, cannot be expected to be sufficient for a thorough understanding of the enzymology of a living cell. Enzymology must eventually develop more closely in companionship with cell morphology. Cytochemical localizations of enzymes represent a primitive beginning in this direction; the effort must be made to correlate reaction rates with the ion-exchange properties and three-dimensional arrays of macromolecules as gels and membranes (4).

Katchalsky and colleagues (37) have been studying the potentiometric behavior of simple gels which can be characterized by two factors—the electrostatic interaction among the ionic constituents and the contractility of the polymer network. These studies should provide useful models for describing cell structures of interest to the enzymologist. In substance, in order to relate the pH of bulk solution to the degree of ionization, a, of the gel network and the number of small ions in the gel per monomer unit, p, *equation 7* is revised to give

$$pH_b - pH_g = \tfrac{1}{2} \log \frac{[X_g^+]}{[X_g^-]} = \tfrac{1}{2} \log \frac{p + a}{p - a}$$

where the subscript g applies to the gel and $X^{\pm}$ represents molal fractions of univalent small ions. The pH diffefences between the two phases can thus be evaluated from ionic concentrations. The differences were found to be of the order of 0.2 to 1.2, depending on the ionic strength of the external solution. Although the Donnan theory cannot be expected to apply well to living cells, since they are not at thermodynamic equilibrium but rather in steady state equilibrium (4), such equations may be pertinent to two-phase systems within a cell. Mazia (35) has prepared molecular fibers of albumin plus pepsin which undergo self-digestion at about the same pH_b optimum at which pepsin digests albumin in solution, and the theory could presumably be checked enzymatically by careful quantitative comparisons.

If, in the organized cell, enzymes operate as parts of structures, then a new kind of enzyme kinetic theory must be formulated. The theory must take into account the diffusion of substrate to and from the structure, or else the diffusion of the enzyme in and about the substrate structure. Very little seems to be known about these phenomena. The action of chymotrypsin on substrate adsorbed on kaolinite was shown to involve the preliminary formation of a reactive enzyme–substrate–kaolinite complex, and proteolysis of the adsorbed complex occurs at a rate comparable to the action of chymotrypsin on the same substrate in solution. It would seem that the enzyme is able to move about on the face of the adsorbant at a rate comparable to that in solution. Addition of substrate to chymotrypsin previously adsorbed on kaolinite resulted in a slower reaction rate, however, showing that structural details are important. Trurnit (46) studied the proteolytic activity of chymotrypsin on adsorbed serum albumin at a solid-liquid interface and found that the reaction velocity increased with increasing substrate thickness. He also concluded that the various theories developed for the kinetics of enzyme reactions in solution could not be applied to a system where one of two reaction partners is in a solid phase. By introducing diffusion as the rate-limiting factor it was possible to derive equations which described the initial phase of adsorption and reaction. Experimentally, enzyme reactions at surfaces or in gels may not go to completion for structural reasons; these observations have so far been given *ad hoc* explanations (31, 36).

Mazia and Hayashi (35, 36) found albumin fibers were hydrolyzed by added pepsin in solution faster than albumin in solution, and that 20:1 albumin-pepsin fibers were hydrolyzed extremely rapidly. Since it does not seem likely that a pepsin molecule can be in contact with 20 equal-in-size substrate molecules in a fiber, this rapid rate is not easily explained within the framework of contemporary conceptual schemes. It has also been established that the enzyme activity of a trypsin ergosterol complex is higher than that of pure trypsin (39), where a catalase-cellulose derivative is less active than the soluble enzyme (38). Taken all in all, we may infer that the amount of an enzyme in a structured system does not alone dictate the reaction kinetics, since the rate will depend on the structural restrictions and on the relative amounts of enzyme and substrate (36, 46).

Finally, unlike adsorption of a globular protein at a solid-liquid interface (28), adsorption at an oil-water interface involves a drastic reorientation of polypeptide chains, with the breaking of many intramolecular bonds (15). Presumably a rigid structure as one moiety of an interface prevents tangential motion of the interface as adsorption takes place. The *zeta* potential of an enzyme at an oil-water interface may be 2–3 times greater than in solution (11) and, through an influence on interfacial pH, can contribute to apparent differences on activities of enzymes in solution and at these interfaces (15). The situation is enormously complicated when more than one interfacial layer of adsorbed enzyme is present.

SUMMARY

Many of the enzyme reactions in nature take place on surfaces or in ordered structures. At interfaces the 'concentrations' of reactants generally differ from those in solution, and one such difference may be revealed by study of pH optima for enzyme reactions. In gels and at interfaces in cells the terms 'concentration,' 'diffusion' and 'pH' cannot be readily applied and must eventually be replaced by conceptually clear notions amenable to mathematical treatment before the cell physiologist can hope to deal quantitatively with the microheterogeneity of the cell.

The authors are indebted to Dr. G. V. F. Seaman of Cambridge University and Dr. Eva Estermann for the electrophoretic data on the kaolin-lysozyme systems, and for many stimulating discussions.

REFERENCES

1. Alderton, G., W. H. Ward and H. L. Fevold. *J. Biol. Chem.* 157: 43, 1945.
2. Bartley, W. and R. E. Davies. *Biochem. J.* 57: 37, 1954.
3. Burström, H. *Ann. Agric. Coll. Sweden* 9: 264, 1941.
4. Caldwell, P. C. *Internat. Rev. Cytol.* 6: 229, 1956.
5. Chance, B. *Harvey Lect.* 1953–54, p. 145.
6. Craxford, S. R., O. Gatty and T. Teorell. *Phil. Mag. ser.* 7, 25: 1061, 1938.
7. Danielli, J. F. *Proc. Roy. Soc. London ser. B* 122: 155, 1937.
8. Danielli, J. F. *Biochem. J.* 35: 470, 1941.
9. Davies, J. T., D. A. Haydon and E. Rideal. *Proc. Roy. Soc. London ser. B* 145: 375, 1956.
10. Dickman, S. R. and J. F. Speyer. *J. Biol. Chem.* 206: 67, 1954.
11. Douglas, H. W. and D. J. Shaw. *Trans. Faraday Soc.* 53: 512, 1957.
12. Eddy, A. A., and C. Hinshelwood. *Proc. Roy. Soc. London ser. B* 136: 544, 1949.
13. Few, A. V., M. H. Fraser and A. R. Gilby. *Biochim et biophys. acta* 24: 306, 1957.
14. Fraser, M. J. *J. Pharm. and Pharmacol.* 9: 497, 1957.
15. Fraser, M. J., J. G. Kaplan and J. H. Schulman. *Disc. Faraday Soc.* 20: 44, 1954.
16. Fraser, M. J. and J. H. Schulman. *J. Colloid Sci.* 11: 451, 1956.
17. Gale, E. F. *Bact. Rev.* 7: 139, 1943.
18. Goodman, J. and A. Rothstein. *J. Gen. Physiol.* 40: 915, 1957.
19. Hartley, B. S. *Ann. Rep. Chem. Soc.* 51: 303, 1955.
20. Hartley, G. S. and J. W. Roe. *Trans. Faraday Soc.* 36: 101, 1940.
21. Hodge, A. J., E. M. Martin and R. K. Morton. *J. Biophys. Biochem. Cytol.* 3: 61, 1957.
22. Honda, S. I. *Plant Physiol.* 30: 174, 1955.
23. Huennekens, F. M. *Exper. Cell Res.* 2: 115, 1951.
24. Ingram, M. *An Introduction to the Biology of Yeast.* London: Pitman, 1955.
25. James, A. M. *Progr. Biophys. Biophys. Chem.* 8: 95, 1957.
26. Jansen, H. E. and F. Mendlick. *Proc. European Brewery Convention, Brighton.* Amsterdam: Elsevier, 1951, p. 59.
27. Lundegårdh, H. *Biochem. Z.* 298: 51, 1938.
28. McLaren, A. D. *Proc. Soil Sci. Soc. Am.* 18: 170, 1954.
29. McLaren, A. D. *Science* 125: 697, 1957.
30. McLaren, A. D. and E. F. Estermann. *Arch. Biochem. Biophys.* 68: 157, 1957.
31. McLaren, A. D. and E. F. Estermann. *Arch. Biochem. Biophys.* 61: 158, 1956.
32. McLaren, A. D. *Soil Sci.* 83: 497, 1957.
33. Mandels, G. R. *J. Bact.* 71: 684, 1956.
34. Mandels, G. R. *Arch. Biochem. Biophys.* 42: 164, 1953.

35. MAZIA, D. *Ann. New York Acad. Sci.* 50: 954, 1950.
36. MAZIA, D. AND T. HAYASHI. *Arch. Biochem. Biophys.* 43: 424, 1952.
37. MICHAELI, I. AND A. KATCHALSKY. *J. Polymer Sci.* 23: 683, 1957.
38. MITZ, M. A. *Science* 123: 1076, 1956.
39. OPARIN, A. I., N. S. GELMAN AND G. A. DEBORIN. *Arch. Biochem. Biophys.* 69: 582, 1957.
40. PETERSON, G. H. Doctoral Diss. Univ. of California, Berkeley, 1957.
41. ROTHSTEIN, A. *Disc. Faraday Soc.* 21: 229, 1956.
42. ROTHSTEIN, A. *Protoplasmatologia* 2, E 4: 1, 1954.
43. SCHNEIDER, W. C. *Proc. Third Internat. Congr. Biochem., Brussels* 1955, p. 305.
44. SEAMAN, G. V. F., E. F. ESTERMANN AND A. D. MCLAREN. Unpublished results.
45. SINGER, T. P., E. B. KEARNEY AND V. MASSEY. In: *Enzymes: Units of Biological Structure and Function* (Henry Ford Hospital Internat. Symp.). New York: Acad. Press, 1956, p. 417.
46. TRURNIT, H. J. *Arch. Biochem. Biophys.* 51: 176, 1954.
47. WILES, A. E. *Proc. European Brewery Convention, Brighton.* Amsterdam: Elsevier, 1951, p. 84.
48. WILKES, B. J. AND E. T. PALMER. *J. Gen. Physiol.* 16: 233, 1932.
49. ZITTLE, C. A. *Advances Enzymol.* 14: 319, 1953.

DISCUSSION

A. M. Chase, A. D. McLaren, L. Lorand, A. Marshak, W. D. McElroy, K. Paigen

DR. CHASE: The enhanced activity of invertase at the surface of plant cells where the local hydrogen ion concentration was actually greater than in the bulk medium reminds me of an old observation by Bertrand and Rosenblatt in volume 158 of the *Comptes rendus.* They reported that yeast suspension lost all invertase activity when heated for 1 minute at 80°, but regained it if the temperature was raised to 90° or 100°. I have repeated their experiment and got the same result. Could this phenomenon be explained in terms of some localized effect?

DR. MCLAREN: Undoubtedly, but I have no idea how.

DR. LORAND: I should like to raise two questions briefly: *a*) In your discussion you seem to have tacitly assumed that the same active center (identical in its details) functions on the free and adsorbed enzyme. *b*). Secondly, if the state of H_2O around the active center is different in the case of adsorbed enzyme, would you not expect the type of results you presented?

DR. MCLAREN: *a*) Trypsin on kaolin is inhibited by crystalline soybean-trypsin-inhibitor in the same way and to the same extent as in solution. Also, both trypsin and chymotrypsin are known to have only single active centers per molecule (E. JANSEN *et al. J. Biol. Chem.,* 1949). *b*) The thickness of the layer of strongly bound water on kaolin is doubtless much thinner than the diameter of the protein molecules (MCLAREN, PETERSON AND BARSHAD. *Proc., Soil Sci. Soc. America,* 1958).

DR. MARSHAK: How do you explain the mobility of the enzyme molecules on the surface of kaolin? Would you expect in terms of this interpretation that the mobility on the surfaces would be the same as that in bulk, as I understood you to say?

DR. MCLAREN: It has been shown that the adsorption of an enzyme on kaolin involves an exchange of surface cations by the enzyme (MCLAREN, *J. Phys. Chem.,* 1954). The polycationic protein can also be eluted from the surface by M/1 salt. At low salt concentrations the protein does not leave the surface but is loose enough to move from one exchange site to another. The mobility on the surface is perhaps 60 per cent of that in solution (*Proc. Soil Sci. Soc. America*, 1954).

DR. MCELROY: Are there any examples where mechanism rather than rate might be affected by the absorption of enzymes on surfaces?

DR. MCLAREN: None that I know of. See, however, Dr. Siegel's paper on the polymerization of eugenol (this volume, p. 37).

DR. PAIGEN: Can you give an approximate value of the double layer of a biological membrane at an ionic strength equivalent to isotonic salt?

DR. MCLAREN: Such values may be found in the manuscript.

Structural Factors in Polymerization: The Matrix in Aromatic Biopolymer Formation

S. M. SIEGEL

Union Carbide Research Institute
White Plains, New York

ALTHOUGH THE HIGHEST EXPRESSION of biological specificity may reside in cellular polynucleotides, an important mode of expression of genetic and physiological uniqueness may also be found in biochemical products somewhat removed from the immediate necessities for life, namely the 'secondary' or 'metaplasmic' derivatives of the cell. Indeed, the subtleties of nucleic acid structure and function, now in the most elementary stages of elucidation, are expressed with great amplification in the specific syntheses associated with formation of melanin, lignin, rubber, and other polymeric materials. It is, therefore, of no little importance to recognize that the biosynthetic pathways for the manufacture of some of these by-products are dependent upon specific structures other than those ordinarily involved in enzymic catalysis. It is hoped that the investigations and findings to be detailed here will, in fact, contribute to a broadening of the concept of 'biocatalysis' to include the reaction and polymerization-directing ('matrix') properties of non-enzymic macromolecules.

Development of the matrix concept has been intimately associated with studies on the biosynthesis of lignin[1] and other di- or polymeric compounds of aromatic derivation. An important part of this association has been the use of model systems which trace their origin to the usual organ and tissue systems whose behavior is difficultly interpretable at best, and whose reduction to the present minimal form is in itself an object of interest from the viewpoint of the experimentalist.

EVOLUTION OF A MODEL SYSTEM: LIGNIN SYNTHESIS AND THE POLYSACCHARIDE MATRIX

Behavior of Peroxidase In Situ and In Vitro. The demonstration of a system in plants able to convert appropriate aromatic compounds into lignins grew out of initial observations which dealt with the differences in enzymatic peroxidation of phenols and aromatic amines by crystalline horseradish peroxidase and by peroxidases retained *in situ* in tissue slices from a variety of plant species; color and solubility of product were initially noted, hence non-chlorophyllous

[1] Brauns (4) reviews the chemistry of lignins; Siegel (30) emphasizes the physiological and biochemical aspects of lignin formation.

embryo and root tissues were employed. Thus, phenol added to peroxidase-H_2O_2 yields orange-brown, water-soluble products which finally become black, highly insoluble substances; phenol supplied to slices of embryonic bean hypocotyl together with peroxide yields instead yellow, pink, and finally gray-brown products progressing from the soluble to the highly insoluble condition. The product of *p*-toluidine peroxidation is deep red-orange when formed with the isolated enzyme, but yellow when formed in the slices themselves. Similar results were obtained with a number of peroxidase substrates, including eugenol, 1-hydroxy-, 2-methoxy-, 4-allyl-benzene, whose *in vitro* and *in situ* products differed principally in the far lower solubility of the latter in ethanol and chloroform. Eugenol and related hydroxyphenylpropane derivatives have long been regarded as similar to the fundamental building stones of lignin (4), and indeed, have been isolated from native lignins by reductive degradation procedures. With knowledge of the generally accepted relationship between eugenol and lignin, application of the standard phloroglucinol-HCl test for the latter followed. This test, which yields a red to magenta color with lignins, was positive for the ethanol- and chloroform-insoluble peroxidation products of eugenol.

Biochemical Characteristics of the Lignifying System. Examination of a number of plant parts and species showed that the capacity for conversion of eugenol to lignin was not limited, but internodes of the aquatic angiosperm, *Elodea,* normally unlignified (through loss of lignifying ability, presumably), exhibited an exceptionally high rate of lignin deposition. In the study of lignin deposition in *Elodea* tissue, the Klason technique for isolation of the product was employed; the procedure involved depends upon the insolubility of lignins in strong (70-75%) sulfuric acid and hot dilute mineral acids, both of which are applied in the removal of cellulose and other wall and protoplast components (24).

Lignin is formed rapidly in moderately acid media, especially in the region of pH 4.5. At pH 3 or below, and above pH 8.5, no lignin is produced (fig. 1; ref. 28). In the alkaline range, the autoxidation of eugenol competes with the tissue lignifying system.

Qualitatively, detectable amounts of lignin were formed from 10–60°C, although in greatest yield in the region of 20–35°C.

No lignin is formed in the absence of peroxide, and in general the peroxide requirement exceeds the eugenol supply. Using young pea root tips, another active tissue in lignin formation, it was found that the yield of lignin increased linearly with increasing peroxide until attainment of a ratio of about 2 moles of peroxide per mole of precursor. Measurement of eugenol consumption concurrently with peroxide disappearance yielded molar ratios of somewhat less than 2:1. A possible objection to these approximations, that catalatic peroxide decomposition may increase the calculated mole ratio, can be countered with the

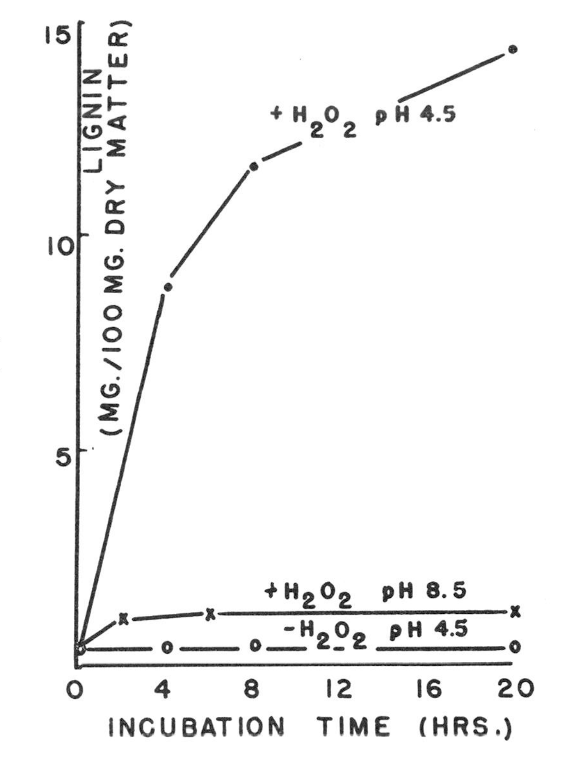

FIG. 1. Peroxide and pH dependency of lignin synthesis by *Elodea.*

observation that peroxidase substrates in general suppress or inhibit completely the activity of catalase (14).

Although it had been assumed from the outset of this investigation that peroxidase was involved in lignin formation, it was necessary, as the point of emphasis shifted toward the aromatic polymer rather than substrate for a particular enzyme, that the participation of this enzyme be established more thoroughly. In addition to the already apparent peroxide dependency of the system, it was subsequently shown that boiling of tissues, cyanide (28), azide and such conventional peroxidase substrates as guaiacol and pyrogallol (29) all inhibited conversion of eugenol to lignin. Finally, the distribution of peroxidase in bean embryo, *Elodea,* pea root and other tissues as elucidated with pyrogallol coincided with the regions in which eugenol lignin was deposited. The fibrovascular system, a natural center of lignification, was one of the principal sites both for peroxidase and synthetic lignin deposition. In view of the suggested role of mushroom phenol oxidases in forming dehydrogenation polymers from substances similar to eugenol (9), both isolated mushroom tyrosinase and *in situ* potato phenolases were tested with eugenol. In the former system, resinous, chloroform-soluble products distinct from lignin were formed; and in the latter system, which also contains peroxidase, lignin-like products were formed only on addition of hydrogen peroxide. It was later found, however, that some bryophytes possessing normally little or no lignin can form lignin-like products from eugenol in the absence of peroxide (31); these observations do not eliminate conclusively the peroxidases, as the formation of hydrogen peroxide via phenol autoxidation is well known (22, 38).

More than 30 compounds have been tested in various systems as lignin precursors. These substances have ranged from simple phenols such as catechol and pyrogallol through phenols with sidechains of varying length, degree of unsaturation, and oxidation level (hydrocarbon, alcohol, aldehyde, ketone, etc.). The more complex phenols include eugenol, isoeugenol, caffeic acid, ferulic acid, cinnamic acids, vanillin, flavonoids, etc. (29); hydroxycinnamyl alcohols, coniferyl alcohol (8, 9); and, in long-term studies, the labeled compounds shikimic acid, sinapic acid and tyrosine (5). Structural requirements are least rigid when lignin formation is followed in long-term experiments with still growing plants, and it is to the model systems which form lignin within minutes, making use of high peroxide and precursor levels, that one must turn for a more definitive picture of ultimate or penultimate precursors. Using tissue slices from embryonic bean hypocotyl, pea root tips, and *Elodea* stem, as well as segments of celery vascular strands, it was established that the lignin precursor possessed a phenylpropane (C_6-C_3) carbon skeleton with a free hydroxyl group *para* to the sidechain. Blockage of the OH in this position by methylation or glucosylation renders otherwise suitable molecules inert as precursors. Suitable sidechains occurred as unsaturated hydrocarbons with or without oxygen functions. Eugenol, its isomer, isoeugenol, the hydroxylated derivative of the latter, coniferyl alcohol, and *p*-hydroxypropiophenone, with a beta keto group in the side chain, are representative precursor molecules. It is of interest that isoeugenol in some systems (with celery vascular tissue, for example) is a far poorer precursor than eugenol, yielding one-seventh as much lignin.

Inhibitory precursor analogs include those substances which form little or no lignin alone, but are capable of blocking the formation of lignin from suitable precursors without inhibiting peroxidase (36). Examples of such substances are phenyl-2-propanone, cinnamaldehyde, and 3-(chloropropenyl-) benzene.

Although the conversion of eugenol to a lignin-like substance in plant tissues was undeniable, more compelling evidence for its relation to native lignin was required than that afforded by color and solubility tests alone. Isolated synthetic lignins were therefore compared with native lignins from various plant groups for common physical and chemical properties, including ultraviolet spectra (fig. 2), elementary composition, as well as solubility and color reactions (table 1). Of the synthetic lignins tabulated, the product isolated from celery

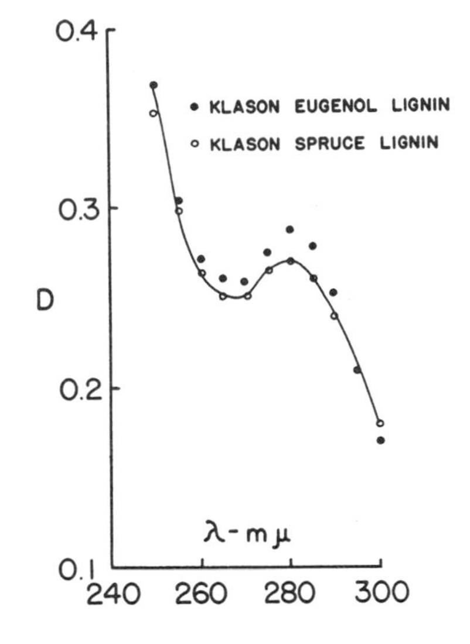

FIG. 2. Ultraviolet absorption by natural (gymnosperm) lignin and synthetic formed from eugenol.

vascular strands could be extracted only with ethanol-HCl, and is in a partially depolymerized state with a contribution to apparent methoxy content derived from the solvent. Molecular weight determinations (Rast) were carried out with success only on the solubilized celery lignin and yielded a value of 667 ± 17, corresponding to a partially ethoxylated trimer. Eugenol, although the precursor of these lignins, is not itself to be regarded as a monomer. Clearly, the differences in composition presented show that eugenol is first transformed (peroxidized)

TABLE 1. COMPARISON OF NATURAL AND SYNTHETIC LIGNINS

PROPERTY	NATURAL LIGNIN			EUGENOL	EUGENOL LIGNIN FORMED IN		
Composition, %	Oak	Spruce	Pine		Pea Root	Elodea Stem	Celery
C	58–60	65–66	62–67	73.2	62.8	63.5	67.1
H	5	6	5–6	7.31	6.64	6.15	6.38
OCH_3	20–22	15–16	14–16	18.9	15.0	14.7	28.8
Solubility							
Water	—	—	—	(+)	—	—	—
KOH	+	+	+	+	+	+	+
Ethanol	—	—	—	+	—	—	—
Ethanol-HCl	+	+	+	+	+	+	+
Acetone	—	—	—	+	—	—	—
Dioxane	+	+	+	+	+	+	—
U. v. spectrum							
Max., mμ	275	281	278	282	280	280	286
Min., mμ	265	270	267	252	270	270	273
Molar extinction	—	—	—	3150	6700	—	5600
Color with $Cl_2 + Na_2SO_3$	Red	Red	Red	Yellow	Red	Red	Red

into an intermediate of increased oxygen content, possibly corresponding to a monomer radical. Thus eugenol and the other precursors recognized could be more correctly termed 'premonomers.'

Although the present paper was not intended as a treatise on the physiology and biochemistry of lignification, its proper subject matter grew out of a physiological problem and cannot attain its full significance divorced from considerations at the cellular and organismal level. It is therefore of value to consider briefly some of the chemical factors in the cell that might contribute to the regulation of lignin deposition.

Among active substances, 3-indoleacetic acid, the plant elongation hormone, is of uncommon interest. This substance has been reported to promote regeneration of xylem, the most highly lignified of plant tissues (16), and it is further known to induce the formation of peroxidase in vascular tissue (11, 17). In contrast, it has been reported (29) and confirmed (39) that indoleacetic acid can inhibit lignification when supplied at concentrations somewhat higher than those in the stimulatory range. In addition to the growth hormone, reducing compounds such as cysteine and ascorbic acid can inhibit the conversion of eugenol to lignin (29), as can common components of the metabolically active young cell. Among the ordinary metabolites, the following produce sizeable inhibitions when supplied in concentrations equimolar with eugenol: *a*) aspartic acid, 90%; *b*) arginine, lysine, glycine, 35-40%; *c*) cadaverine, 60%; *d*) glycerol, 60%; *e*) Krebs cycle acids, 50-90%; *f*) adenylic acid, 90%; *g*) glucose-1-phosphate, 50%; and *h*) Mg(II), Ca(II), 50%. Several esters and terpenes were without activity. In contrast, the inhibitions produced by indoleacetic acid, from 25 to 100% depending upon the tissue, were effected with only 1 molecule for every 20 of eugenol. Thus, regulation of lignin synthesis can be linked to normal hormonal and metabolic components of the plant cell. Although these factors remain to be evaluated as to comparative significance, the dual role of indoleactic acid, together with the lower effective levels needed, makes it most prominent as a hormonal regulator of lignification. Indoleacetic acid is particularly concerned with elongation of the young post-mitotic cell and is a factor of importance in the etiology of plant neoplasms such as crown gall (20). It is a hormone of importance in maintenance of a relatively juvenile, although postembryonic, physiological state, and its decline is particularly associated with cellular differentiation and senescence (10). Its role in the promotion of lignification may begin with the already established ability of indoleacetic acid to induce peroxidase synthesis, especially in vascular tissue. In spite of increased enzyme, oxidation of eugenol and other substrates is not immediately accelerated, as indoleacetic acid is also a competitive inhibitor with these substrates for peroxidases (28), and is itself slowly destroyed by the enzyme. Hence, as the level of induced peroxidase rises, the concentration of indoleacetic acid declines and the peroxidation of other substrates, lignin precursors included, begins, leading to lignification and other oxidative changes characteristic of cellular differentiation and senescence.

Capacity for induction of peroxidase by indoleacetic acid is not uniformly distributed among tissues, but is greatest in the region in which vascular differentiation begins. In young apical tissues, therefore, a high level of hormone would serve only to inhibit peroxidation, hence to maintain the relatively undifferentiated condition characteristic of immature cells.

When *Elodea* internode sections were lignified in eugenol-peroxide media, both walls and protoplast of stem cells accumulated a brown coloration; extraction with organic solvents removed most of the protoplast pigmentation. Color tests for lignin applied were positive only in cell walls, although tests for peroxidase showed that enzyme to be of general cellular distribution (29). These findings prompted an examination of the distribution of peroxidase and lignifying ability among cellular constituents, and the fractionation which was subsequently carried out with chloroplast-free pea root tissue yielded the following pattern:

	FRACTION			
ACTIVITY, %	WHOLE	MITOCHONDRIAL	CYTOPLASMIC	WALL
Peroxidative	100	0	94-97	3-6
Lignifying	100	0	< 0.3	75

Save for treatments destroying its activity (8M urea, for example) the wall peroxidase was firmly bound and could not be eluted by ordinary salt, buffer, or organic acid solutions. Hence, although the oxidative polymerization of eugenol to lignin was clearly established as a peroxidase-dependent process, it did not depend upon this enzyme alone, but upon a cell wall system of which peroxidase was only a part. It was surmised that the peroxidative step in conversion of eugenol to lignin might be of a 'preparative' nature, transforming premonomer into monomer and presumably monomer radical. There remained then the question as to the exact role of the cell wall in completion of the polymerization. Two experimentally verifiable possibilities presented themselves: *a*) a specific polymerase or polymerase system is localized in the wall, a not unreasonable premise when the importance of lignin in the vascular plant is considered; and *b*) polymerization of peroxidized eugenol involves ordering of activated monomer on cell wall macromolecules without participation of additional enzymes. The probability that activated monomer units will build up a polymer would be increased if they were oriented along wall polysaccharide chains; activated monomer released onto an aqueous medium high in eugenol concentration would be more likely to undergo terminal dimerization reactions with the more reduced precursor. A test for the second premise was devised that would, if positive, eliminate the need for a wall polymerizing enzyme, and it was through this experimental study, to be discussed below, that development of the matrix concept became possible.

Formation of Lignin in Matrix Systems. Cellulose in the form of analytical grade filter paper, a tentative cell wall model, was incubated with eugenol, peroxide and peroxidase. Within 20 hours, detectable amounts of lignin-like product were found in the paper, but not in the ambient medium; approximately 1 milligram per gram of paper was formed. Although this finding tended to confirm the postulated role for cell wall substance in polymer formation, the low yield rendered the system nearly impracticable for extensive and critical experimentation. It was recalled, however, that the peroxidase in the cell wall was tightly bound, hence that a filter paper system with peroxidase in solution failed to duplicate a wall condition of possible importance. Paper was accordingly infiltrated with peroxidase solution (2×10^{-8} moles/gm) and dried under reduced pressure at room temperature (32) or dried under normal atmospheric conditions at 0°C (33). It was correctly surmised that the enzyme might be sufficiently strongly adsorbed on the cellulose to render its elution slower and more difficult when returned to an aqueous environment. The peroxidase-paper in a eugenol-peroxide solution formed 12–25 milligrams of lignin per gram of paper, amounts of product that rendered further experimentation feasible. The product formed, in part soluble in dioxane, in part in ethanol-HCl, possessed the characteristic ultraviolet absorption spectrum of a gymnosperm lignin (see fig. 2). The dioxane-soluble fraction on analysis yielded C, 63–64%; H, 6–7%; OCH_3, 14–16%, typical values, and gave positive color tests for lignin.

In addition to a number of variations on the basic experimental design, including grade and area of paper, efforts were made to introduce a chemical block into the cellulose matrix. Paper acetylated sufficiently to block 25 per cent of the cellulose hydroxyl groups yielded 53–69 per cent less lignin than untreated paper (33), and when increased to a 34 per cent block, yielded 73–90 per cent less product. Thus, even when most of the cellulosic OH is free, lignin polymer formation is greatly inhibited, suggesting that more than one OH is involved in the orientation of each monomer, and evoking a picture of monomer units forming a continuous file along the polysaccharide chain prior to polymerization. An unexpected additional evaluation of the acetyl block was obtained when chitin from the egg case of *Busycon* was tested as a matrix. Because it is a 2-amino-β-*d*-glucopyranoside derivative, hence an analog of cellulose with similar molecular and crystallographic properties (18), chitin provided an exceptionally useful material for comparison with cellulose; it was found to yield about 5 milligrams of lignin per gram of matrix. In the natural state, the 2-amino-group of chitin is acetylated and, assuming the H-bond donating amino group to be equivalent to a hydroxyl group, native chitin should correspond to the cellulose with a 34 per cent block described above. Upon deacetylation of chitin with alkali, its activity as a matrix increased strikingly, with as much as 50 milligrams of lignin now being deposited per gram.

Following these preliminary studies of matrix activity, a number of substances was surveyed for suitability and yield (table 2). Of the substances listed, only the high molecular weight polysaccharides direct the formation of lignin. It was of interest to find activity at a high level to be associated most with the less ordered, more dispersible polysaccharides such as starch and methylcelluloses. Most attention was given to the methylcelluloses, which were effective in concentrations of 10^{-7} to 10^{-6}M; concentrations on the order of 10^{-5}M and above, on the other hand, were inhibitory to peroxidation of eugenol. Methylcellulose lignin, like cellulose lignin, was separable into dioxane- and ethanol-HCl-soluble fractions. The dioxane-soluble fraction yielded, on analysis, C, 62.7%; H, 6.9%; OCH_3, 15.9%; the fraction extractable on ethanolysis yielded C, 63.8%; H, 6.4%; OCH_3, 15.4%. The latter, again in a state of depolymerization, yielded for molecular weight a value of 763 ± 79, corresponding to a degree of polymerization of 3 to 5.

When the products obtained with various matrices were compared as to solubility classes and ultraviolet spectra, differences observed suggested the existence of a certain degree of specificity. Recognizing three general spectral types (fig. 3), the matrices tested (tables 3 and 4) show considerable variation with respect to detail of absorption and further distinctions attributable to differences between water-soluble and insoluble polysaccharides. Such spectral distinctions are probably based principally upon degree of polymerization, heterogeneity of product, and, to a lesser extent, upon isomerism.

It was anticipated when matrix studies were first begun that cellulose would be the most suitable matrix, and indeed, it was assumed that the correctness of this view would constitute a test of the biological validity of a matrix system. After study of the far superior methyl-cellulose matrix it seemed possible that part of its greater efficacy might be associated with its dispersion in aqueous media. Of the soluble polysaccharides that would be widespread in young cells and

TABLE 2. MATRIX ACTIVITY OF VARIOUS SUBSTANCES IN LIGNIN FORMATION

SUBSTANCE	LIGNIN FORMED	YIELD, MG/GM	SUBSTANCE	LIGNIN FORMED	YIELD, MG/GM
Methylcellulose	+	1240–5140	Deacelytated chitin	+	73
Starch	+	6000	Fibrin	—	0
Sorbitan esters	—	0	Hair	—	0
Raffinose	—	0	Collagen	—	0
Sucrose	—	0	Peroxidase (plant)	—	0
Cellulose			Lactoperoxidase	—	0
Filter paper	+	12–25	Gelatin	—	0
Cotton	+	10–45			
Milkweed fiber	+	16			

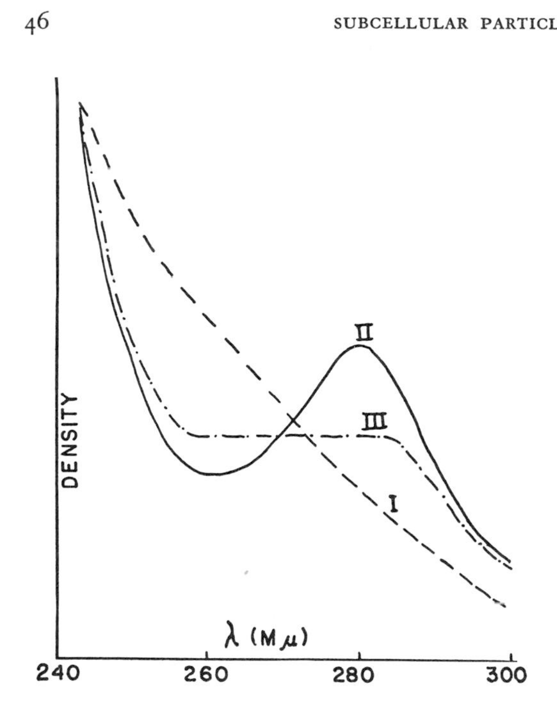

FIG. 3. Ultraviolet spectral types in synthetic lignins.

TABLE 3. SPECTRAL FEATURES OF LIGNINS FORMED ON WATER-SOLUBLE MATRIX SUBSTANCES

MATRIX	CONC., MOLES/ML	SPECTRAL CLASS * FRACTION SOLUBLE IN	
		Dioxane	Ethanol-HCl
Methylcellulose	2–10 × 10^{-7}	II or III	II or III
Starch (amylose)	2 × 10^{-7}	II	II

* As defined by fig. 3.

TABLE 4. SPECTRAL FEATURES OF LIGNINS FORMED ON WATER-INSOLUBLE MATRIX SUBSTANCES

MATRIX	QUANTITY, MG/ML	SPECTRAL CLASS * FRACTION SOLUBLE IN	
		Dioxane	Ethanol-HCl
Cotton cord	10.0	I	III (280)†
Cotton (absorbent)	1.0	I	III (260–75)
Milkweed fiber	1.0	I	III (265–80)
Filter paper (no. 1)	10.0	I	II (280)
Filter paper (no. 40)	5.3	I	II (280)
Filter paper (acetylated no. 40)	6.3	I	II (280)
Chitin (acid washed)	1.0	I	III (260–80)
Chitin (deacetylated)	1.0	I	II (270)
Chitin (alkali washed)	1.0	I	II (270)

* As defined by fig. 3. † Number in parentheses indicates position of maximum or range of shoulder.

specifically associated with the cell wall, the pectic substances, polygalacturonic acids of about 20,000 molecular weight, which may exceed cellulose in amount (2) offered a further material for comparison. The pectic acid matrix was approximately 100-fold greater in yield than the cellulose system, and considerably more active than methylcelluloses. It was further noted that gelation of pectic acid with Ca(II) reduced its activity substantially. Recently it has been observed that the region of young wood fiber cells staining with Ruthenium Red corresponded to the region first showing deposits of strongly ultraviolet-absorbing substance (40, 41) and that the intensity of the Ruthenium Red reaction diminishes as lignification proceeds (1). Although this dye may be bound by many polymeric acids, its reaction in young cell walls is limited almost completely to pectic acid (19), whence it may be concluded that the differences observed between cellulosic and pectic acid matrix systems constituted a reasonable reflection of an actual histophysiological pattern of lignification to be found under natural conditions.

Additional evidence suggesting the importance of pectic substances in lignification was obtained by treatment of celery vascular strands with a selection of enzymes prior to incubation with eugenol-peroxide solutions. After exposure of tissue to 1 per cent pectinase (20 hr., 25°C), all rigidity was lost and lignin formation was reduced to 30 per cent of the control yield. With cellulase, 60–65 per cent of the original activity was retained; and with pepsin, only 15–25 per cent of the initial lignifying ability remained. Thus, the native cell wall matrix is primarily susceptible to attack on its protein (peroxidase?) and pectic components, secondarily by disturbance of at least the superficial layers of cellulose.

Variations on the Biopolymer Matrix. The nature of eugenol, its probable derivatives and the polysaccharide matrix emphasize hydrogen bonding as the principal intermolecular force involved in orientation of the lignin monomer. It was therefore of interest to test as matrices substances somewhat removed from the general polysaccharide type. In the presence of the adsorbents alumina and silica gel, eugenol was not converted into lignin (32), but lignin or lignin-like products were formed in the presence of the minerals amphibole, serpentine and kaolin (table 5). Products formed in the presence of amphibole possessed an absorption

TABLE 5. SPECTRAL FEATURES OF PRODUCTS FORMED ON MINERAL MATRICES

MATRIX	QUAN. MG/ML	SPECTRAL CLASS * FRACTION SOLUBLE IN		OTHER PEAKS
		Dioxane	Ethanol-HCl	Ethanol-HCl
Amphibole	2.8	III	I	315mμ
Amphibole	5.6	III	I	315mμ
Serpentine	2.8	I	I	
Kaolin	5.0	II	II	

* As defined by fig. 3.

maximum at 315 mμ, in addition to other features. These mineral substances have in common hydroxyl groups and electronegative oxygen atoms capable of acting as H-bond acceptors, but differ in their spatial arrangement, and include the random structure of silica gel; the sheets of hexagonally assembled Si-O tetrahedra with superimposed OH in kaolin; and the hexagonally arranged chains of Si-O tetrahedra in the amphiboles and serpentines (3).

The matrix activity of mineral substances was further studied under different physical conditions omitting peroxidase from the system. First, it was shown that when eugenol, water and air are incubated at moderately elevated temperatures and pressures (at 125°C, 5 atm, for example) a variety of polymeric products is obtained, among them dark, spongy, inert substances high in C (50–60%) low in H (2–3%), and, in general, melanin-like in nature. If, however, chrysotile (serpentine) fibers are present, either in the liquid or vapor phases of the system, the products formed thereon include lignin-like polymers. Even under mild conditions (25°C, 1 atm) chrysotile and other minerals, including amphibole and mica, can form a lignin-like polymer if peroxide is provided but peroxidase omitted (34). In the absence of minerals, substances resembling the naturally occurring dimeric lignanes (12) are formed in eugenol-peroxide solutions at 25°C. Thus, products representative of three groups of natural substances can be formed under comparatively controlled conditions, the nature of the matrix serving as a principal determinant of reaction product, with oxidant and physical conditions as contributing factors (fig. 4).

The investigations under consideration have emphasized the matrix properties of natural polymers, both inorganic and organic. A precise knowledge of the mechanism of matrix action requires both adequate information about the sur-

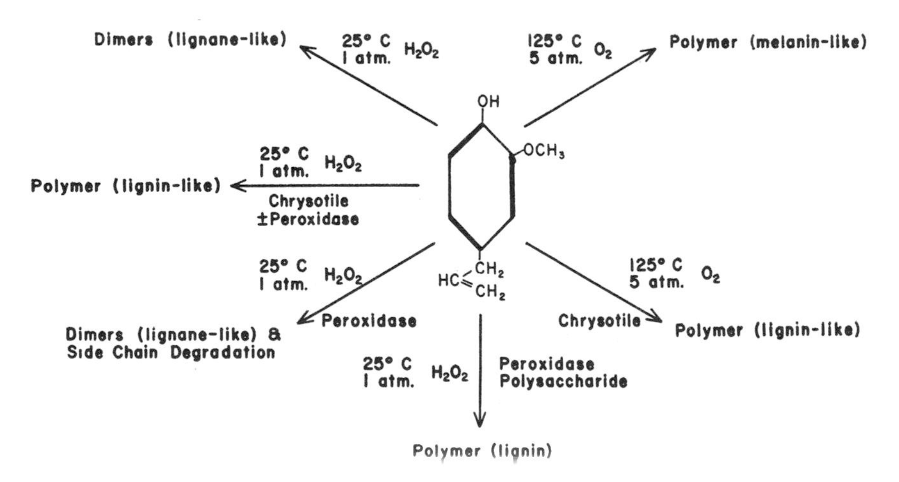

FIG. 4. Summary of transformations of eugenol under various conditions.

face properties of matrix substances and more exact control over the structure of active materials. Such control may be derived in part from experimental modification of already-formed molecules but may benefit from the use of selected synthetic products with matrix activity. The possibilities for fruitful application of synthetic organic polymers as 'tailor-made' matrix substances are virtually without limit. Investigations intended as an initial effort in this direction have been carried out and even in an early stage of development have expanded further the scope of the entire matrix study (26). Using Dowex-50, a sulfonated polystyrene, with the usual reactants, it was first observed that peroxidation proceeded rapidly without peroxidase, providing a matrix satisfying in its structure the additional requirement of substrate activation. Further experimentation showed that Dowex was also selective, polymerizing isoeugenol far faster than eugenol. Several reaction products were obtained, but attention was focused upon one of these, a comparatively soluble substance of molecular weight ca. 520, which yielded on analysis C, 66.8%; H 6.7% (compare with ethoxylated celery trimer, M.W. *ca.* 667, C 67.1%, H 6.4%). Analysis of the Dowex system utilized a controlled sulfonic acid block with *p*-toluidine and indicated operation of a multiple-site mechanism; that is, that products released from the matrix already possess a degree of polymerization of 2 or more. This concept has been implicit throughout the consideration of natural matrix substances, but is here established experimentally. The exact manner in which the matrix influences polymerization remains unknown, but it was suggested by Ridgeway that if it is assumed that the individual monomers adsorbed on the matrix surface are arranged approximately as they would be in the finished polymer, the entropy decrease associated with polymer formation will be small relative to the entropy decrease associated with adsorption, hence to the over-all entropy change for the reaction. It is not the object of the present discussion of matrix substances and polymer formation to develop a theoretical physical-chemical treatment. Nevertheless it is clear from the foregoing consideration of Dowex activity that a method of experimental and theoretical attack upon the detailed mechanism of matrix action is available.

Although methodology in science is often associated with experimental detail, it possesses a broader aspect as well. Thus it was pointed out initially that the development of the matrix concept involved an investigation of lignification. Elucidation of the mechanism whereby eugenol underwent transformation into lignin depended upon development of a model system which could, in effect, reduce to its essentials the active fraction of the cell. The matrix concept was thus a natural development of the effort directed toward evaluating the role of the cell wall. During the foregoing discussion of lignin synthesis by model systems, the pattern of development and refinement may have been obscured by consideration of results as they pertain to lignin and lignification per se. The essentials of the various experimental systems have therefore been abstracted and summarized

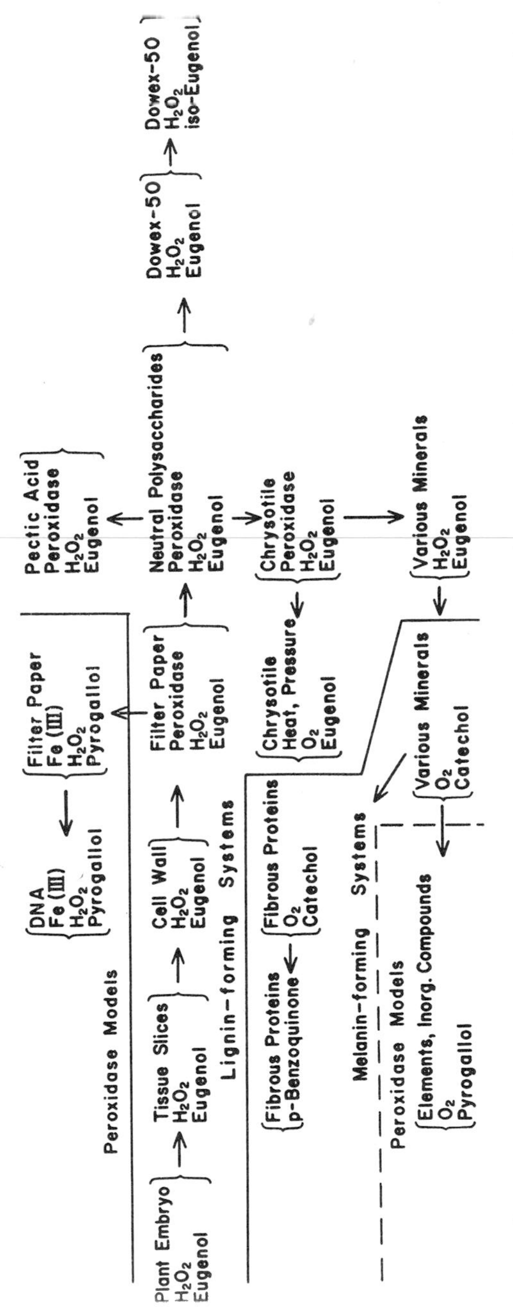

Fig. 5. Summary of model systems used in matrix investigations.

in the sequence of their introduction into experimental work (fig. 5), and both the pattern of investigations already considered and of those to be treated in following sections may be seen. Although models could conceivably be fabricated *de novo* by a fortunate selection of component parts, it is more probable that a biologically accurate and acceptable analog be forthcoming if the materials and phenomena under investigation are subjected to a careful, stepwise reduction in complexity. It is reasonable to expect that any biological problem definable in chemical terms treated in this fashion will in the end be sufficiently grounded in principle so that it will lead to applications far beyond its original scope. Thus the study to follow of the protein matrix as a factor in formation of polyquinones, a 'by-product' of the study of lignin synthesis, has so far required less than one-thirtieth of the time involved in arriving at the present picture of lignin synthesis, yet is in some respects fully as well established.

AN ANALOGY: THE PROTEIN MATRIX IN POLYQUINONE SYNTHESIS

Application of the Matrix to Quinone Polymerization. Save for one instance, the term 'melanin' has not been employed in the preceding discussion. This omission has been deliberate, in spite of the obvious relationship between quinone polymerization and melanization, inasmuch as it was desired that a test of matrix function be carried out objectively with a model substrate selected for chemical and analytical simplicity. *o*-Benzoquinone would be the ideal substrate if it were stable, but its para-isomer was selected as a reasonably satisfactory substitute. Nuclear coupling of *p*-quinones to form polymers is known (6). Although experiments with catechol and tyrosine are in progress, it was deemed advantageous to avoid the complications that might arise during the initial phase of precursor oxidation and restrict preliminary studies as much as possible to the polymerization phase.

The primary criteria established for recognition of directed polymerization were: *a*) change in color and visible spectrum as related primarily to degree of conjugation, hence degree of polymerization; *b*) change in solubility; *c*) minimal changes and minimal differences in elementary composition.

The basis for selection of proteins as matrix substances was essentially biological; namely, the comparatively greater abundance of melanins in animal tissues lacking the highly developed polysaccharide products of the plant cell wall. It cannot be assumed, of course, that substances such as chitin play no role in melanization, and it is recognized that otherwise the criterion of distribution is far from absolute. The selection of protein was justified, however, by tests made with cellulose and pectic acid, neither of which had any discernible effect upon the behavior of quinone solutions under any of the conditions described below.

Oxdiative Polymerization Without Matrix. *p*-Quinone forms yellow solutions with a single, distinct visible absorption maximum (fig. 6); solubility in water corresponds to a concentration of approximately 0.02 M; *p*-quinone yields, on analysis, C 66.8%, H 3.7%. Under moderately acid conditions (pH 4–5), it is stable for approximately an hour, but darkens rapidly in alkaline media. Under acid conditions solutions undergo color changes toward red-orange and red-brown hues, but yield little or no NaCl-precipitable product, even after 75–100 hours; under alkaline conditions (pH 8.8), solutions develop a deep red-brown color and form a brown precipitate when saturated with NaCl. Precipitates formed at pH 5.5 and pH 8.8 show a slight decrease in percentages of C and a sizeable decrease in percentages of H, which is indicative of polymerization with some introduction of oxygen into the product molecules. Decrease in H is more pronounced at pH 8.8 than in acid media. The products formed in these systems exhibit neither the parent spectrum nor any other distinctive maxima, although a certain amount of analytically useful detail is present (fig. 7, table 6).

Effect of the Protein Matrix. When fibrin (100 mg/20 ml quinone) is incubated with fresh quinone solution, evidence for its effect on behavior of the quinone may be obtained by spectrophotometric examination of the supernatant (water-soluble) phase also (fig. 8, table 6). Thus the comparatively undifferentiated spectrum of a pH 5.5 control is modified to one with a new distinct maximum

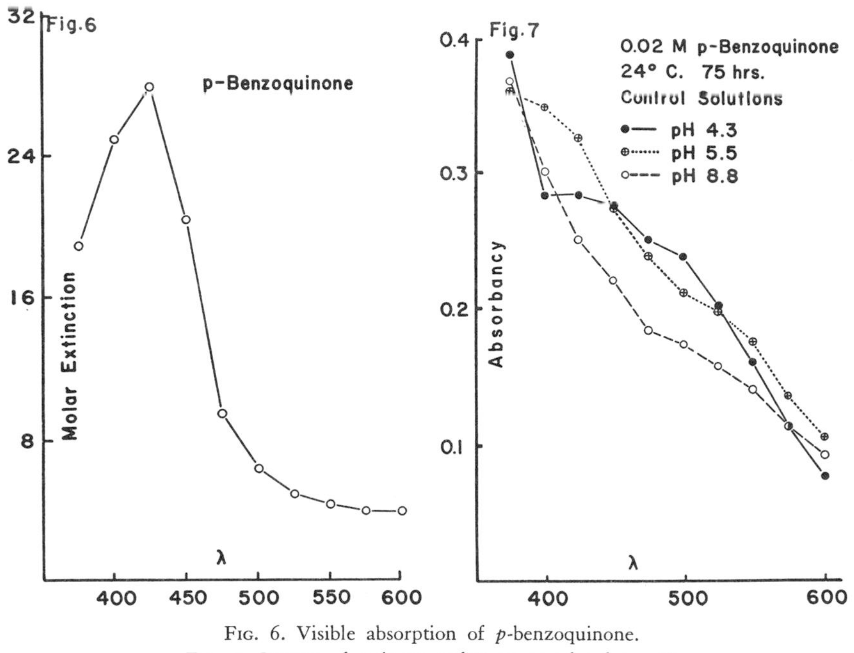

FIG. 6. Visible absorption of *p*-benzoquinone.
FIG. 7. Spectra of quinone polymers as related to pH.

at 500 mμ and which is otherwise grossly different in form. Assuming that a shift of absorption bands toward longer wavelengths accompanies polymerization, and that a more heterodisperse polymer system will possess a more amorphous spectrum, it is reasonable to conclude that polymerization, which proceeds with or without fibrin, has been directed by the protein toward formation of a decidedly less heterogeneous array of products. Comparison of the effects of fibrin under acidic and alkaline pH conditions suggests that it only functions well as a matrix in acidic media. At pH 8.8, fibrin would be expected to carry a largely negative charge, and at pH 5.5, a positive charge. More properly, in the mosaic of charged regions comprising the protein surface, negative sites will outnumber positive ones at high pH and conversely at low pH. The effect of an immobile ionic surface upon small charged molecules, although generally predictable, was tested specifically by comparison of dye adsorption by fibrin at pH 5.5 and 8.8. Acid fibrin removed methylene blue (cation) from solution, but not eosin (anion), whereas the converse was true for alkaline fibrin. The significance of this behavior for quinone polymerization derives from the polarization of the carbonyl group (25), a condition which would direct the strongly electronegative quinone oxygen atoms toward cationic regions on the matrix, and repel them from anionic sites. The exact mode of quinone orientation will depend upon the geometry and pattern of the charged surface. Again an avenue for combined theoretical and experimental attack upon the mechanism of matrix action is evident, although the fibrin surface is undoubtedly too complex to qualify as a subject for detailed investigation.

In addition to the matrix effect as seen in the supernatant phase, quinone derivatives were deposited in the protein itself. Fractionation of these products permitted recognition of at least two modes of association between polymers and matrix; first, those products bound by weak forces (presumably H-bonds in most cases) which were extracted readily by solutions of urea or LiCl; and second, those products held by covalent bonds, (quinone tanning) thus solubilized only by proteolysis (with trypsin). The latter were isolated as addition compounds with water-soluble peptides. Water, urea and LiCl-insoluble products soluble in KOH, but not $KHCO_3$, presumably contained weakly acidic phenolic hydroxyl groups which would contribute to the total strength of hydrogen bonds.

The spectral characteristics of polyquinones formed in various media, without matrix, with fibrin, or with collagen have been summarized in table 6, where it may be seen that

TABLE 6. EFFECT OF MATRIX AND pH ON SPECTRAL CHARACTERISTICS OF *p*-BENZOQUINONE POLYMERS

REACTION SYSTEM		SUPERNATANT				8M UREA				PIGMENT EXTRACTED 5M LiCl				0.2M KOH			
Matrix	pH	Max.*	Infl.*	Shld.*	Col.†	Max.	Infl.	Shld.	Col.	Max.	Infl.	Shld.	Col.	Max.	Infl.	Shld.	Col.
Fresh	*p*-benzo-quinone	425	—	—	Y												
None	4.3	—	475	400–25	R												
	5.5	—	425, 475	—	RB												
	8.8	—	475	—	RB												
Fibrin	4.3	500	425, 575	—	P	475, 575	—	400–25	PB	550	—	475–500	PB	—	—	500–25	YB
	5.5	500	425	—	P	550	—	425–75	PB	—	475–550	—	YB	—	—	525–50	OB
	8.8	500	—	—	R	—	450	—	B	—	500	400–25	OP	—	—	—	OB
Collagen	4.3	400–25	525	—	O	400–25, 550	—	—	OP	400	—	550–75	OP	—	450	525–50	OB
	5.5	400	—	475–500	RO	—	525	—	B	—	500	—	OB	—	—	525–50	OB

* Spectral features: position (mμ) of maxima, inflections, and shoulders. † Colors: B, brown; O, orange; P, pink; R, red; Y, yellow.

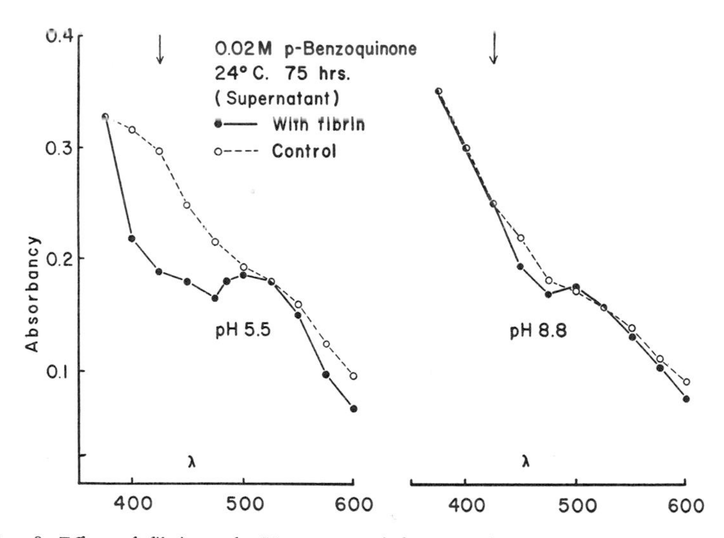

FIG. 8. Effect of fibrin and pH on spectral features of quinone reaction products.

unique products or mixtures are associated with each of the proteins used, and with specific fractions as well.

Relation of Synthetic Polyquinones to Melanins. The absorption curves of several polyquinone fractions resembled the spectrum of pigment extracted from a poriferan, *Euspongia,* the similarity prompting a broader comparison of polyquinones with natural melanins. The spectrum of the sponge pigment is distinct from polyquinones formed in matrix-free systems and all fractions formed under the influence of fibrin, but is approximated in varying degrees by three fractions from the collagen system (fig. 9), a finding of interest in view of the occurrence of collagen in the porifera (27). All of the synthetic products appear to be less homogeneous than the natural product, a condition also to be met with in comparison of natural and synthetic lignins.

Other similarities noted were: *a*) between an ethanol fraction formed with fibrin at pH 8.8 and black guinea pig melanin (13); and *b*) between aqueous fractions formed with fibrin at pH 5.5 and the pigment from the endoskeleton of the alcyonarian, *Pterogonia* (fig. 10).

In no instance has it been claimed that exact replication of a native melanin has been accomplished. Nevertheless, when the several kinds of analytical and comparative evidence are taken together it is clear that substances fitting the generic concept of melanins (13, 23, 7) can be formed, particularly under the influence of proteins. It is further gratifying to note that the possible significance of a polymerization-ordering protein surface has already been recognized in relation to the question of pigment granule formation (21), and it is perhaps not unreasonable to suggest that a biologically meaningful model of the melanin

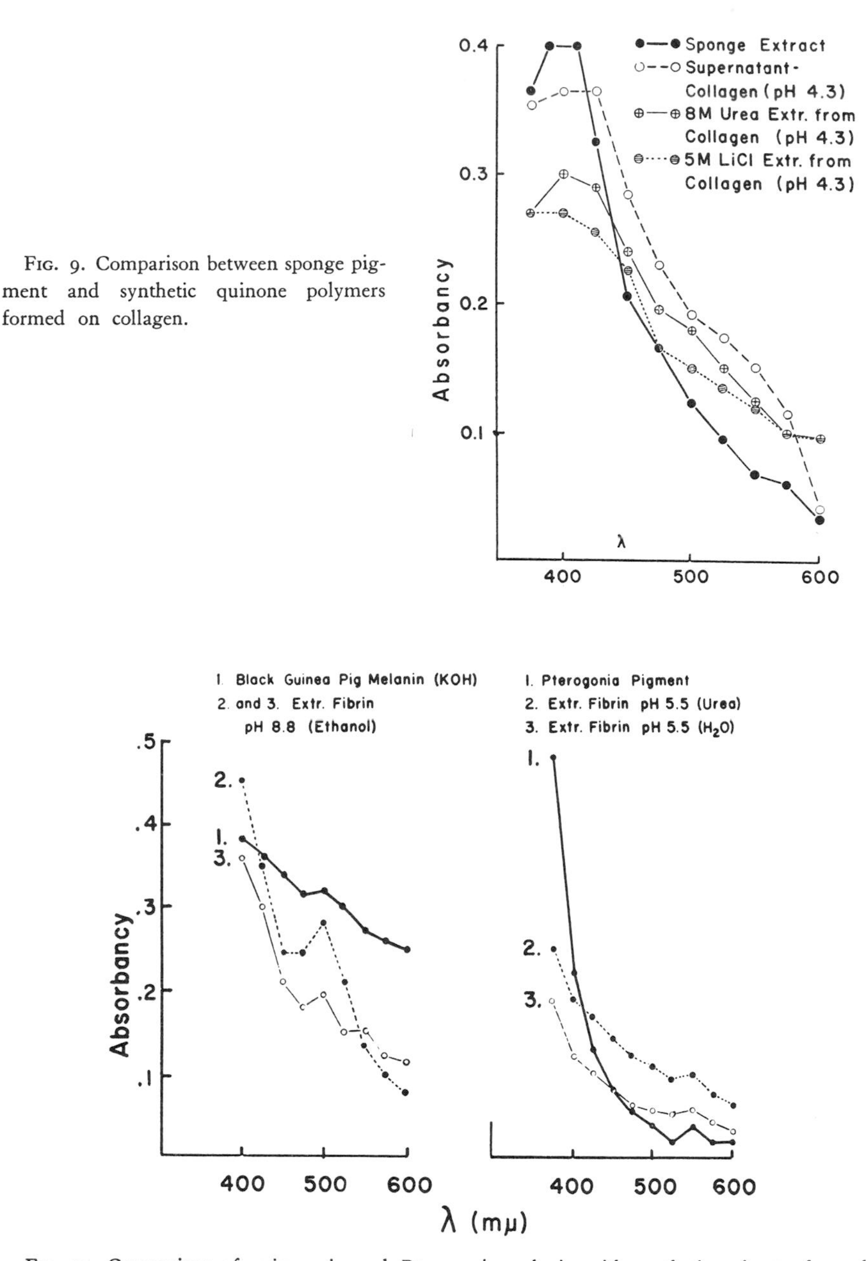

Fig. 9. Comparison between sponge pigment and synthetic quinone polymers formed on collagen.

Fig. 10. Comparison of guinea pig and *Pterogonia* melanin with synthetic polymer formed on fibrin.

granule might be derived by application of the matrix concept to the chemical and physical constitution of the melanoblast.

Oxidative Polymerization of Catechol in Mineral Systems. A catechol-protein system antecedent to the study of polyquinones is still under investigation, presenting more complexities in analysis than did the latter. It may be pointed out, however, that even at pH 8.8, where catechol oxidation has been followed, the polymeric products thus far isolated from fibrin, collagen and gelatin systems differ little from one another but markedly from material formed by protein-free controls in yield, visible absorption spectra and magnitude of spectral shifts between pH 1.5 (orange color) and pH 8.8 (green color). There are two features of interest in association with the catechol-mineral system. First, it provides a three-way connection, linking the eugenol-mineral system, from which it was derived, both to quinone-protein systems just considered and to pyrogallol-inorganic substance systems, one of the classes of peroxidase models yet to be discussed (fig. 5). Second, the catechol-mineral system provides additional evidence for the matrix activity of inorganic substances, suggesting a role of possible geochemical importance for them in the formation of organic polymers and the origin and antiquity of specificity in polymer synthesis.

The NaCl-precipitable products formed when 0.1M catechol solutions were incubated at 25°C for 100 hours were all dark-brown substances insoluble in aqueous and neutral organic solvents (hence, originally dispersed as a hydrosol, not as a true solution). Products formed in the mineral-free control system comprised 3 per cent by weight of the original catechol and averaged on analysis, C, 60%; H, 3.6%; those formed in the presence of minerals comprised 27–32 per cent of the original catechol and averaged C, 47–54%; H, 3.0–3.3% (34). Ultraviolet absorption characteristics were as follows:

MINERAL	SPECTRAL FEATURES	$E_{1cm}^{1\%}$
None	shldr. 275–280 mμ	260
Chrysotile	shldr. 265–270	125
Granite	max. 265	103
Hornblende	shldr. 275–280	411

The study of mineral-catalyzed and directed polymerization has been shown to be of utility in development of the matrix concept, and prompted further examination of the catalytic oxidation of phenols. Because it is more readily oxidizable than the other phenols studied, pyrogallol was introduced as a substrate. At the same time, the desire that the matrix itself be simplified prompted the introduction of free elements as well as inorganic compounds. The new experimental system thus constructed led to the development of one of the two classes of peroxidase models now to be described. The other class of peroxidase models arose earlier in this investigation when the original filter paper matrix system for lignin synthesis was modified by replacement of eugenol and peroxidase with pyrogallol and Fe(III) respectively.

PEROXIDASE MODELS AND STEREOSPECIFIC SYNTHESIS

Pyrogallol Oxidation in the Fe(III)-Biopolymer System. Study of the effect of cellulose was originally directed toward a better understanding of the polysaccharide matrix, but developed a second, no less important objective, investigation of the nature of peroxidation reactions. Cellulose affects both the rate of iron-catalyzed peroxidation and the array of products formed (15); its effectiveness in increasing the rate of oxidation depends upon the concentration of Fe(III) provided (fig. 11). That the presence of cellulose also modifies the course of pyrogallol oxidation is shown by differences in relative proportions of water- and organic solvent-soluble fractions, particularly in the considerably increased chloroform-soluble fraction found when systems without and with filter paper are compared.

Another biologically important macromolecule capable of enhancing the catalytic effectiveness of iron is deoxyribonucleic acid (37), which at very low concentrations more than doubled the rate of pyrogallol peroxidation measured with Fe(III) alone (fig. 12). Between the two active substances noted were several other macromolecules of varying effect on pyrogallol oxidation with iron, including fibrin, which promoted, and gelatin and methyl cellulose, which inhibited, even at concentrations of the order of 10^{-7}M.

In the light of the various systems discussed in connection with the matrix problem, it is not surprising to find those effects described here for cellulose

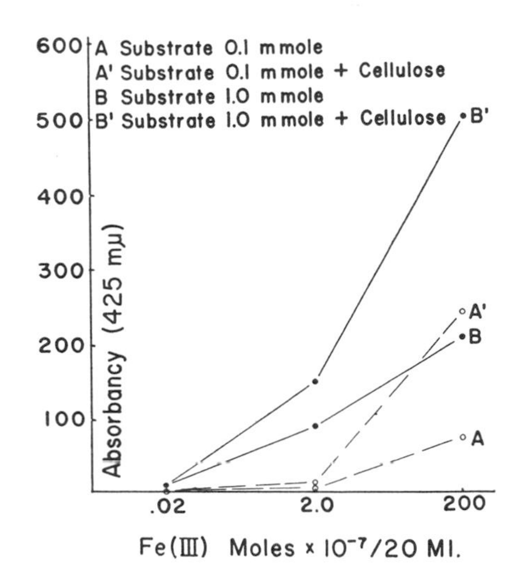

FIG. 11. Effect of cellulose and Fe(III) on rate of pyrogallol oxidation.

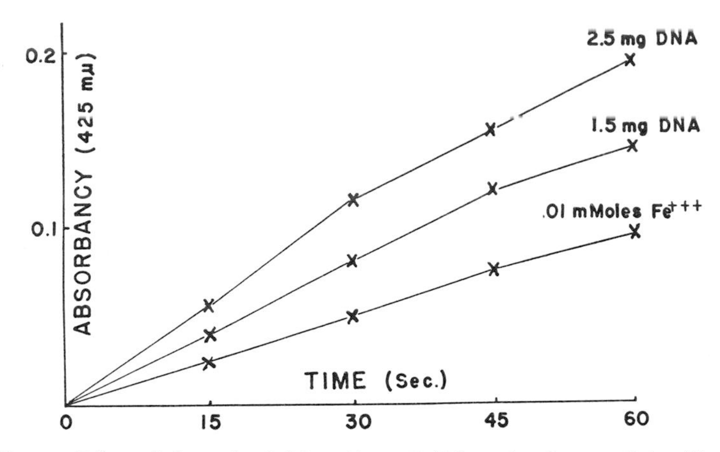

FIG. 12. Effect of deoxyribonucleic acid on Fe(III)-catalyzed pyrogallol oxidation.

and DNA, but it is difficult to select the interaction of greatest influence on the rate of oxidation from among hydrogen bonding of pyrogallol to macromolecule, complexing of iron with macromolecule, and complexing of iron with pyrogallol. Although the problem may be treated in part as one involving the behavior of concentrating surfaces—increased probability that the necessary collisions will occur between reactants—qualitative differences among products and variation in activity among the macromolecules tested suggest the operation of other factors, possibly surface structure and geometry as well. Just as the catalytic effectiveness of heme is enhanced and specificity conferred by conjugation with the appropriate protein moiety to form a particular hemoprotein enzyme, so there is suggested here an analogous system, with Fe(III) replacing heme and non-protein macromolecules serving in place of the appropriate enzyme protein, or even serving in a dual role, replacing both porphyrin and protein. In addition to their significance as models reflecting diversity among hemoproteins, the cellulose and DNA systems open the possibility that many more catalytically active associations exist in cells than are encompassed in the formal recognition of enzymes, including those containing an immobile member, hence effecting a localization of the catalytic process involved.

Inorganic Catalysis and Stereospecificity. Pursuing the problem of phenol oxidation catalysts has entailed the use of some 70 inorganic substances, including 29 elements, 8 metal oxides, and 34 simple salts. The elements tested for their effect on the autoxidation of pyrogallol—Al, Sb, As, B, Cd, C, Cr, Co, Cu, Ga, Au, I, Fe, Pb, Mg, Mn, Hg, Ni, Nb, Pd, Se, Si, Ag, S, Ta, Te, Sn, Zn and W—cover a wide range with respect to physical and chemical properties (36). With comparatively small surface areas, 20–30 cm^2, some of these elements affected autoxidation of pyrogallol profoundly. Manganese and cobalt were most effective in accelerating oxidation, with iron and copper next in stimulatory activity;

arsenic, antimony and carbon were most active as inhibitors; cadmium, aluminum, sulfur, silicon, tellurium, lead, tantalum and gold were among the inactive elements tested. Efforts toward relating physical and chemical properties to catalytic activity were for the most part unsuccessful, but some degree of correlation was obtained for hardness, specific gravity and electrical resistivity. In addition, it was observed that virtually all elements increasing oxidation rate occurred in Periodic Groups I, II, VI, VII and VIII (1st transition—Fe, Co, Ni) whereas those inhibiting oxidation fell into Groups III, IV and V.

During the study of Fe(III)–biopolymer models and the first of the investigations with elementary surfaces, it was assumed that the product of pyrogallol oxidation was in all cases identical with the product formed by the action of peroxidase, the benztropolone, purpurogallin. When the ultraviolet spectra of products formed in various systems were determined, however, the characteristic two maxima of purpurogallin (in the regions of 270 and 315 μ, the exact position depending upon solvent) were almost consistently lacking. Among all systems with biopolymers or pure elements, the only exceptions were cobalt and manganese, whose products yielded a strong purpurogallin spectrum. More extensive study of the autoxidation of pyrogallol confirmed the absence of this specific reaction product, or its presence only in trace amounts (36). Various modes of oxidation—anodic, hypochlorite, peroxidic—all yielded highly polymerized, brown to black products, insoluble in purpurogallin solvents, devoid of its spectral features, and yielding, on analysis, hydrogen contents of 2–3% (pyrogallol, 4.75%; purpurogallin, 4.5%). The products of cobalt and manganese catalysis yielded hydrogen contents of 4.3–4.5 per cent, values close to those for purpurogallin.

The peroxidase-mimicking metal catalysts exhibited stereospecificity only in sufficiently polar reaction media, water, and methanol. In the homologous alcohol series, from methanol to octanol, the distinguishing second ultraviolet maximum of purpurogallin becomes reduced to an absorption shoulder (C_2), progressively weaker inflections (C_3–C_6), and finally disappears (C_8).

A study of the catalytic properties of oxides (of Al, As, Cu, Mg, Mn, Hg, Si and Zn) in aqueous media, and of various salts (mainly the phosphates, halides, sulfates, and carbonates of Groups Ia and IIa) in ethanol and chloroform demonstrated a number of catalytic properties of interest, including *a*) the great catalytic efficiency of silica gel, but the complete inactivity of powdered quartz; *b*) the sometimes opposed activities of metals and their oxides; and *c*) the stereospecific (purpurogallin-synthesizing) activity restricted to lithium halides and carbonates among the simple compounds tested.

Turning once again to the more complex silicates, stereospecificity was lacking in all cases save for glass fiber, which catalyzed purpurogallin synthesis in non-aqueous media.

The investigation of model systems and matrix activity has thus taken a new turn toward the study of enzyme-mimicking models. The matrix concept as it has been hitherto employed should not be applied to the peroxidase models, as the highest degree of specificity and the point of greatest interest involve formation of a product with lowest degree of polymerization possible. On the other hand, the importance of spatial orientation in phenol dehydrogenation reactions has been recognized (6). The lack of structural similarity among the several substances forming purpurogallin makes impossible any conclusion about surface structure requirements for its synthesis. Nevertheless, it will be possible in the future to explore in detail the specific catalysts, to modify constitution, crystal structure, and the characteristics of the reaction medium, with the hope of arriving at inorganic catalytic models accounting for the properties of an enzymic surface.

CONCLUSIONS

The development of model systems making use of reaction-directing surfaces has revealed a powerful tool for investigation of biopolymer synthesis and the nature of stereospecific synthesis by enzymes. In principle, no surface upon or within a cell can be assumed a priori to be inert from the standpoint of matrix or catalytic activity. Indeed, it would be difficult to prove that any macromolecule, crystal surface, or, for that matter, phase boundary, within the cell is genuinely devoid of such properties. Among the consequences of such widespread reaction-directing properties will be a far more commonplace localization of chemical reactions than may be represented by those associated with organellar systems, and a dependency of some biochemical reactions upon catalytic entities of a non-protein (hence nonenzymic) character or upon proteins not now associated with enzyme activity. Viewed in another manner, distinctions between structural and functional cellular components must become highly arbitrary, and possibly misleading, and in effect reduce many biochemical problems to questions of molecular morphology and molecular interaction.

The flexibility of the matrix concept encompasses a host of interactions of organic or inorganic surfaces, crystalline or polymeric, with organic substrates, and may be extended to systems including inorganic substrates whose behavior is determined by organic surfaces, as in the mineralization of cartilaginous skeletal substances, or secretion of highly intricate cell walls among diatoms, Radiolaria, etc.

The matrix and catalytic systems investigated determine the synthesis of lignin, melanin, or purpurogallin, hence have substrates or monomers of a particularly reactive type from the standpoint of free radical formation and ease of activation for nuclear or nucleus-sidechain coupling. In principle, however, appropriate systems can be developed to serve as models for directed condensation polymer formation, thereby extending further the scope of the matrix concept. The matrix-substrate and peroxidase-mimicking systems discussed here show that the constitution of the matrix may be of importance in specific cases, but that equivalent activity may be exhibited by surfaces very different in composition, suggesting that such activity may eventually be expressable solely as a function of the electrical properties of such surfaces and their geometry.

The author wishes to acknowledge with gratitude the support which made possible the work upon which this paper has been based: Grant G-329, National Science Foundation; The Dr. Wallace C. and Clara A. Abbott Memorial Fund of the University of Chicago; Research Grant C-2730, National Cancer Institute; and a Fellowship from the John Simon Guggenheim Memorial Foundation.

REFERENCES

1. ALLEN, C. E. *Bot. Gaz.* 32: 1, 1901.
2. BONNER, W. *Plant Biochemistry.* New York: Acad. Press, 1950.
3. BRAGG, W. L. *Atomic Structure of Minerals.* Ithaca, N. Y.: Cornell Univ. Press, 1937.
4. BRAUNS, F. E. *Chemistry of Lignins.* New York: Acad. Press, 1952.
5. BROWN, S. A. AND A. C. NEISH. *Can. J. Biochem. Physiol.* 34: 769, 1956.
6. ERDTMAN, H. AND C. WACHTMEISTER. In: *Festschrift, Arthur Stoll.* Basel: Sandoz A. G., 1957.
7. FIGGE, F. H. J. In: *Biology of Melanomas,* edited by R. W. MINER. New York: New York Acad. Sci., 1948.
8. FREUDENBERG, K. AND W. HEEL. *Chem. Ber.* 86: 190, 1953.
9. FREUDENBERG, K., H. REZNICK, H. BOESENBERG AND D. ROSENACH. *Chem. Ber.* 85: 641, 1952.
10. GALSTON, A. W. In: *3rd Internat. Plant Growth Substance Symp.,* Wye College, England, 1955.
11. GALSTON, A. W. AND L. Y. DALBERG. *Am. J. Bot.* 41: 373, 1954.
12. GEISSMAN, T. AND E. HINREINER. *Bot. Rev.* 18: 77, 1952.
13. GINSBURG, B. *Genetics* 2: 176, 1944.
14. GOLDACRE, P. L. AND A. W. GALSTON. *Arch. Biochem. Biophys.* 43: 169, 1953.
15. GOODMAN, N. S. AND S. M. SIEGEL. *Nature.* In press.
16. JACOBS, W. *Am. J. Bot.* 39: 301, 1952.
17. JENSEN, W. A. *Plant Physiol.* 30: 426, 1955.
18. KENT, P. W. AND M. W. WHITEHOUSE. *Biochemistry of the Amino Sugars.* New York: Acad. Press, 1955.
19. KERR, T. AND J. W. BAILEY. *J. Arnold Arbor.* 15: 327, 1934.
20. KLEIN, R. M. AND G. K. K. LINK. *Proc. Nat. Acad. Sci.* 38: 1066, 1952.
21. KOPAC, M. J. In: *Biology of Melanomas,* edited by R. W. MINER. New York: New York Acad. Sci., 1948.
22. MAEHLY, A. C. In: *Methods of Biochemical Analysis,* Vol. I, edited by D. GLICK. New York: Interscience, 1955.
23. MASON, H. S. In: *Biology of Melanomas,* edited by R. W. MINER. New York: New York Acad. Sci., 1948.
24. NORMAN, A. G. *Biochemistry of Cellulose, Polymonides, Lignin, etc.* Oxford: Clarendon, 1937.
25. PAULING, L. *The Nature of the Chemical Bond.* Ithaca, N. Y.: Cornell Univ. Press, 1948.
26. RIDGEWAY, D. Doctoral dissertation (Part B), Univ. of Rochester, Rochester, N. Y., 1957.
27. RUDALL, K. M. In: *Fibrous Proteins and Their Biological Significance* (Symp. Soc. Exper. Biol. IX), edited by R. BROWN AND J. DANIELLI. New York: Acad. Press, 1955.

28. SIEGEL, S. M. *Physiol. Plant.* 7: 41, 1954.
29. SIEGEL, S. M. *Physiol. Plant.* 8: 20, 1955.
30. SIEGEL, S. M. *Quart. Rev. Biol.* 31: 1, 1956.
31. SIEGEL, S. M. Unpublished observations.
32. SIEGEL, S. M. *J. Am. Chem. Soc.* 78: 1753, 1956.
33. SIEGEL, S. M. *J. Am. Chem. Soc.* 79: 1628, 1957.
34. SIEGEL, S. M. *Proc. Nat. Acad. Sci.* 43: 811, 1957.
35. SIEGEL, S. M. Unpublished observations.
36. SIEGEL, S. M. *J. Am. Chem. Soc.* In press.
37. SIEGEL, S. M. AND B. Z. SIEGEL. *Nature* 179: 421, 1957.
38. SIEGEL, S. M. AND B. Z. SIEGEL. *Nature* 181: 1153, 1958.
39. SOLBERG, R. AND N. HIGINBOTHAM. *Am. J. Bot.* 44: 704, 1957.
40. WARDROP, A. B. Personal communication.
41. WARDROP, A. B. *Tappi* 40: 225, 1957.

DISCUSSION

L. Lorand, S. M. Siegel, A. Marshak, D. A. Marsland, A. D. McLaren

DR. LORAND: I wonder if the melanin isolated from quinone-fibrin is free of protein. The tanning effect of quinone could perhaps be eliminated by blocking the free amino group of fibrins (MIHALYI AND LORAND, *Hung. acta physiol.*, 1948).

DR. SIEGEL: Permit me to comment first that I would prefer to retain the term 'polyquinone' for these products; hence reserving judgment on the polymers as melanins, although they are undeniably melanin-like. All extracted polyquinones have proven to be N-free whereas residual pigment solubilizable only by proteolysis (trypsin) is firmly associated with peptides or amino acids, hence contains organic N. An amino block would be useful, if matrix activity is not destroyed.

DR. MARSHAK: Does the distribution of lignin formation within the protoxylem elements follow a pre-existing pattern (e.g., annuli and helices of varying pitch) of pectic acid distribution on the walls of cells of developing embryos and seedlings?

DR. SIEGEL: The one serious limitation to the lignin model system lies in the fact that all cells in a tissue slice are flooded with reactants, hence any active surface will participate in lignin deposition, even if in a region not normally receiving precursor. Thus any detailed vascular architecture may be obscured. With respect to such a fine adherence to pattern in nature, I know of no observations, although I expect that Wardrop's group (CSIRO, Australia) will have an answer shortly.

DR. MARSLAND: *1*) I seem to remember that eugenol is listed as displaying an unusually high compressibility in the range of pressure up to about 10,000 atmospheres. Do you think that this might indicate polymerization by pressure? *2*) As to the high activity of starch as the catalyst of lignin formation, is it true that the envelope which naturally covers the starch grain may have a lignin component in its structure?

DR. SIEGEL: *1*) Presumably, pressure alone could serve as an orienting factor, as could shear or other mechanical agents, but in the ordinary chemical sense, I doubt that pressure alone could bring about polymerization, as the energy would involve at least meeting the level of C-H bond dissociation energies for homolytic cleavage. In the broad sense, including H-bonded structures and crystals in the term 'polymer,' as does Pauling, the super-compressed eugenol may be in a reversible state of polymerization. 2) There is no lignin in starch plastid membranes as these are, presumably, not polysaccharide in nature, hence not suitable as matrices. In fact, one may suppose that they would prevent starch from becoming lignified if plastids co-existed with a heavily lignified cell wall. I rather think that the starch would be long since depleted in the aging cells undergoing lignification.

DR. McLAREN: What range of molecular weights do you find for your synthetic lignins?

DR. SIEGEL: Published figures for isolated derivatives of native lignins range from 1,000 to 11,000, with values on the order of 1,000, probably representing a pentamer, in greatest abundance. Conceivably a fundamental polymeric unit may exist as a primary product which secondarily is built into a larger, randomly arrayed three-dimensional entity. Using ethanolic-HCl as a solubilizing agent, a terminal degradation product falling in the range of 650–700 is obtained. Taking account of ethoxy groups derived from the solvent, a trimer of oxidized eugenol is indicated. Considering the terminal nature of this product, it is reasonable to propose a minimum DP of 6 for the original product.

Functional Changes in the Structure of Cell Components

GEORGE E. PALADE

Rockefeller Institute for Medical Research
New York, N. Y.

PHYSIOLOGICAL EVENTS THAT OCCUR at the intracellular level are frequently accompanied by structural changes which deserve careful study because they may suggest, and sometimes indicate, the role played by the affected structures in the general economy of the cell. As the functional significance of many cell components is still uncertain or entirely unknown, suggestions or indications of this kind can be particularly valuable. Changes or modulations in cell structure occur at various dimensional levels and some of them are so striking that they were noted early in light microscopy and studied with considerable profit. A conspicuous example is represented by the extensive changes in form and distribution undergone by the nuclear material during cell division. Our knowledge of the mechanisms operating in hereditary transmission has, in fact, been derived from a detailed analysis of such structural changes, correlated with a careful study of the qualities of the products, in this case the offspring.

FUNCTIONAL CHANGES IN EXOCRINE CELLS OF PANCREAS

Heidenhain's Hypothesis. Another example, closer to the subject to be discussed in the following pages, concerns the exocrine cells of the pancreas. As early as 1875, Heidenhain (11) noted that the numerous granules which occupy the apical region of these cells disappear shortly after food intake, to be replaced by apparently new granules a few hours later. By following in time the changes occurring in the apical pole of the exocrine cells, on the one hand, and the variations in the enzymatic activity of the pancreatic juice, on the other hand, Heidenhain arrived at the conclusion that the granules consist of digestive enzyme precursors. His conclusion rested on the finding that the disappearance of these intracellular bodies, which he called zymogen granules (12), coincided in time with the appearance of proteolytic enzymes in the pancreatic juice. According to his interpretation, the zymogen granules represent a temporary intracellular storage of digestive enzymes which will be released from the cell at a future food intake. For many years the cyclic variation in the number of zymogen granules discovered by Heidenhain remained the only well established and clearly understood event in the physiology of the pancreatic exocrine cell. No real progress was achieved by further observations because the structural modulations involved were too subtle for the resolving power of the light microscope and because correlated morphological and biochemical studies, like the one Heidenhain had carried through, had to be shifted inside the cell. For a long time such an operation was impossible and, as a result, the intracellular part of the secretory process inevitably became a matter of speculation rather than a topic of factual research.

At present, however, we can take advantage of the higher resolving power of the electron microscope in the hope that, at the dimensional level it explores, some structural modulations will be distinct enough for clear interpretation. Of course the electron microscope has its own limitations. Many structural changes, and probably the most significant ones, remain beyond its present resolving power, but what has been gained over the light microscope is already impressive. It can be said, without exaggeration, that the instrument can become an important and efficient tool for research in general and special cell physiology, just because it can be used to analyze naturally occurring or experimentally induced structural modulations. If, in addition, cell fractionation procedures are concurrently used, complementary information can be obtained about the chemistry and the biochemical activity of the cell components studied. Finally, if the structural changes, chemical constitution, and biochemical activity of the various cell components are followed in time during a significant period of the activity of the gland, and if the results are integrated, one may hope to find answers to such questions as: where are the digestive enzymes produced inside the cell and how are they handled therein before release? Prompted by such hopes, Dr. Philip Siekevitz and I decided to undertake such a project which, as can be seen, combines new techniques with old and simple experimental approaches (36–39). It is, one could say, a collaboration over almost a century between Rudolf Heidenhain, Philip Siekevitz, and myself.

I have chosen three examples, taken from our study of the secretory cycle of the pancreatic exocrine cell, to illustrate the type of information that can be obtained at present by electron microscopy, either alone or in combination with cell fractionation procedures.

Association of Mitochondria With Lipid Inclusions in Fasting Animals. Under normal conditions the exocrine cells of the pancreas are poorly synchronized: some of them have completed the storage of new zymogen granules, while others are still at the beginning of this operation. We tried various means to bring in step the cell population of the gland, and the best we found was to starve our experimental animals, the guinea pigs, for 48 hours. At the end of this period, all the exocrine cells were loaded with zymogen granules and at the following food intake most of them simultaneously discharged their secretory products. In addition to a relatively good synchronization of the acinar cells, the fasting has yielded an interesting byproduct which will be presented as a first example of structural modulation.

Under normal feeding conditions, the exocrine cells contain none or very few lipid inclusions and their elongated mitochondria appear distributed at random throughout the cytoplasm without any preferred relationship with the other cell components (cf. 40). After a fast of 48 hours, however, most cells contain large lipid inclusions which appear to be in close relationship with one or more mitochondria (29). Usually an incomplete mitochondrial ring is found around a lipid droplet (fig. 1),[1] but frequently the ring is complete (fig. 2), and occasionally complex conglomerates occur in which more than one lipid droplet and more than one mitochondrion are involved. If the fast is prolonged for 3 to 4 days, the number of lipid inclusions with associated mitochondria increases noticeably. Refeeding slowly brings back the original disposition of the mitochondria, apparently by the gradual disappearance of the associated lipid droplets.

By comparison with the topographical changes just described, structural modifications incurred by the mitochondria are less striking. Sometimes the organelles in contact with lipid inclusions increase in size, take bizarre forms (fig. 3), and lose the regular arrangement of their cristae, but many retain a normal appearance. Changes of probably greater significance occur at the periphery of the mitochondrion along the zone of contact with the adjacent lipid inclusion. In some cases there is no resolvable space left between the mitochondrion and the inclusion, the lipid mass abutting directly against the outer mitochondrial membrane. In other cases, the outer membrane is no longer visible and the lipid extends across the outer mitochondrial chamber up to the inner mitochondrial membrane. Finally, the periphery of the lipid droplet usually differs in density and texture from the rest of the inclusion and appears as a denser shell with punctate deposits of high density scattered throughout it.

What we have in this close association of lipid inclusions and mitochondria is, in all probability, an expression of the fact that the fasting animal is obliged to oxidize its reserve fat to cover the energy requirements of its important cell types, i.e., the cells that constitute its 'vital organs.' Indeed, a comparable association is encountered under similar conditions in many other cells, especially in the muscle fibers of the heart and of the diaphragm (29) and, to a lesser extent, in the parenchymal cells of the liver and in the nephron epithelium of the kidney. As expected, the animals lose weight during the fasting period and their adipose tissue dwindles. In capillaries throughout the body the blood plasma appears loaded with small ($\sim$50 mμ) lipid droplets comparable to the chylomicrons found in the circulating blood during intestinal fat absorbtion. Such observations suggest that at least part of the mobilized fat is transported in relatively large droplets from the adipose tissue to the sites of oxidation.

[1] All figures are electron micrographs of thin sections of tissue fixed in buffered osmium tetroxide (pH 7.6) and embedded in n-butyl methacrylate. For general preparatory techniques, see references 24 and 28.

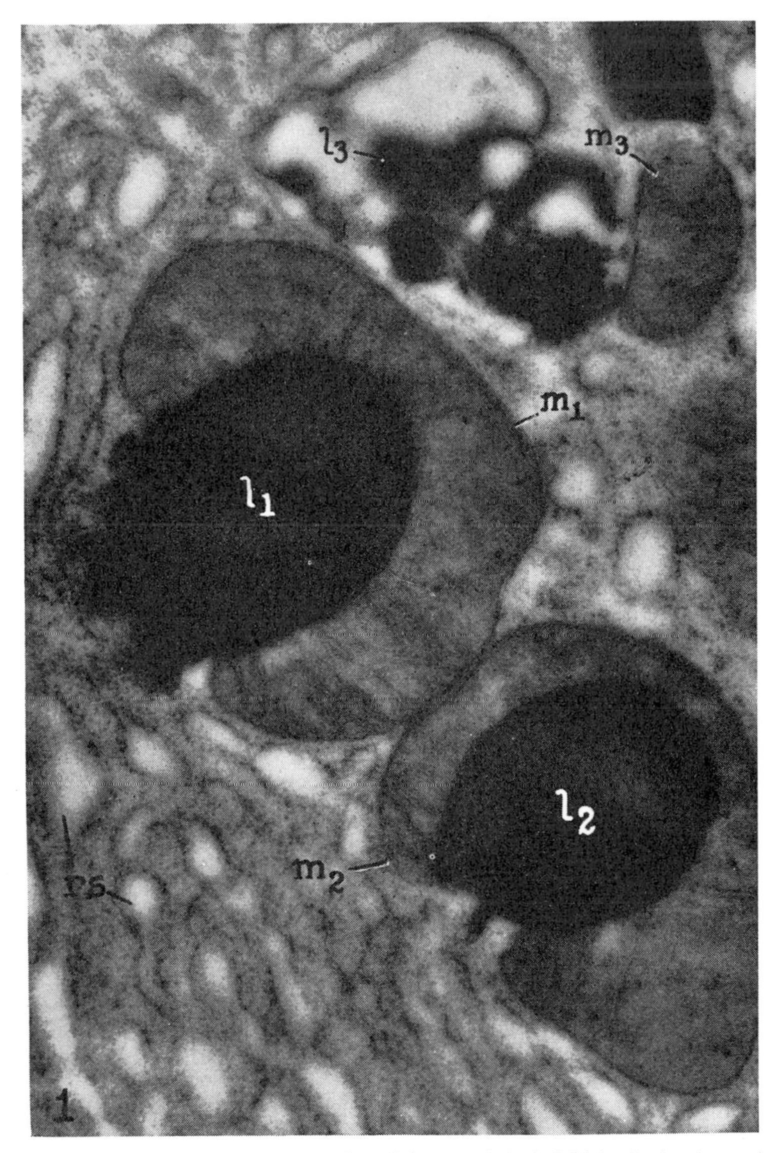

FIG. 1. Pancreas of guinea pig starved for 48 hours. Limited field in the basal cytoplasm of an acinar cell. Two lipid inclusions (l_1, l_2) are surrounded by incomplete mitochondrial rings (m_1, m_2). Two other mitochondrial profiles (one of them marked m_3), the polymorphic residue of a 'burnt-out' lipid inclusion (l_3), and numerous rough-surfaced profiles of the endoplasmic reticulum (*rs*) can be seen in the rest of the figure. × 31,000.

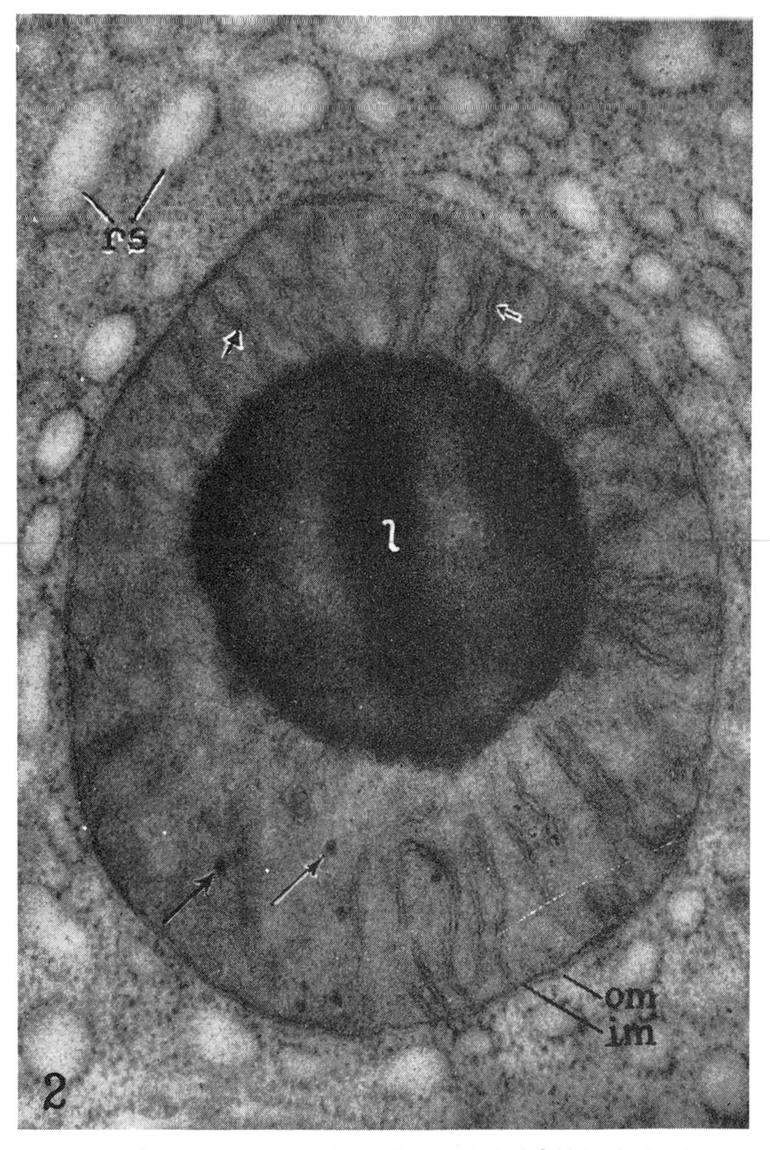

FIG. 2. Pancreas of guinea pig starved for 48 hours. Limited field in the basal cytoplasm of an acinar cell. A lipid inclusion appears surrounded by a complete mitochondrial ring. The lipid mass is in direct contact with the mitochondrion over its entire perimeter. At the periphery of the mitochondrial ring the two mitochondrial membranes can be distinguished; the inner membrane (*im*) appears thicker and denser than the outer membrane (*om*). Radially disposed cristae mitochondriales (*short arrows*) and intramitochondrial granules (*long arrows*) can be seen within the mitochondrial profile. Rough surfaced elements of the endoplasmic reticulum (*rs*) surround the lipid-mitochondrial complex. × 47,000.

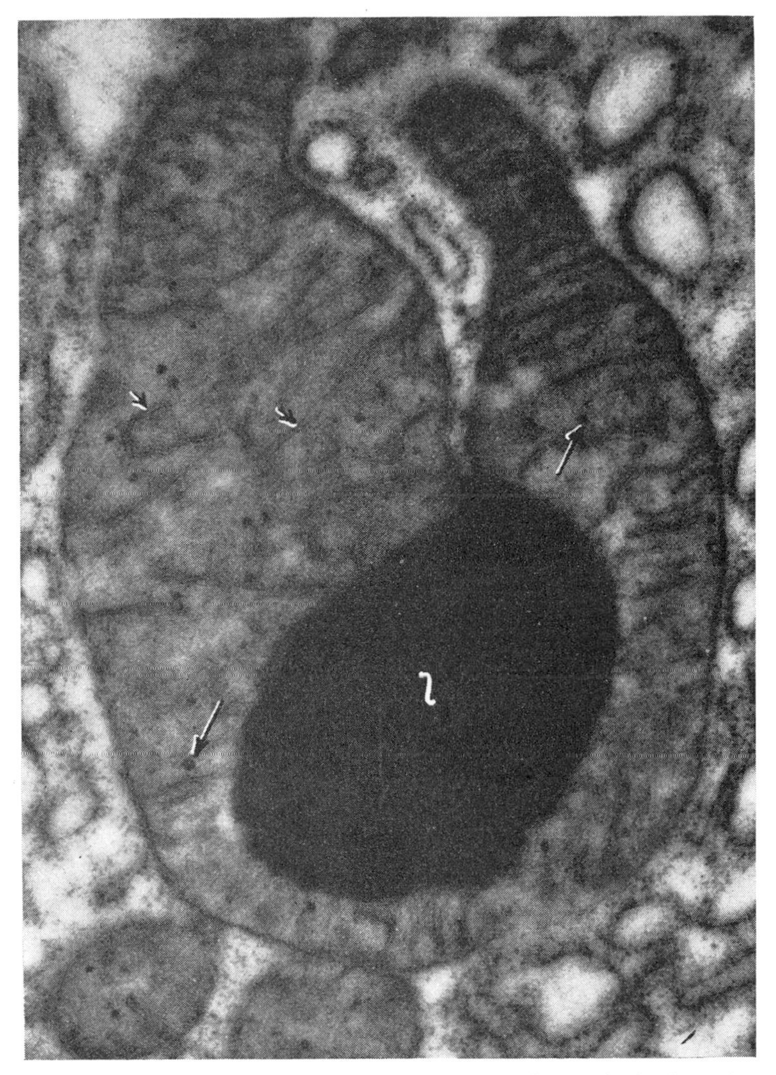

FIG. 3. Pancreas of guinea pig starved for 48 hours. Limited field in the basal cytoplasm of an acinar cell. A lipid inclusion (*l*) appears almost completely encircled by an enlarged and deformed mitochondrion. The cristae (*short arrows*), still disposed in orderly fashion in the right arm of the mitochondrial profile, are markedly disturbed in the left arm. Numerous intramitochondrial granules (*long arrows*) appear scattered throughout the mitochondrial matrix. × 35,000.

Spectacular as they are, these morphological changes are not entirely unexpected. It is already known from the initial work of Schneider (33) and of Lehninger and Kennedy (18), that mitochondria can oxidize long chain fatty acids, and more recently Green (10) and his collaborators have shown that the numerous enzymes involved in fatty acid oxidation are located in the mitochondria. This fact, and the limited solubility of the lipids involved (mostly triglycerids), can well account for the peculiar relationship established between mitochondria and lipid droplets. In this respect, the morphological findings represent only supporting evidence for well established biochemical data. Certain details of the structural changes described raise, however, a number of questions, for which—to my knowledge—there is no answer at present. We may ask, for instance, by what mechanism are the triglycerids hydrolyzed? If a lipase is involved, is it located, like the oxidative enzymes, in the mitochondrion? We may also wonder about the means by which structural damage by fatty acids and soaps is prevented, and finally, we may note that the two mitochondrial membranes are not affected to the same extent in this circumstance: the outer membrane apparently can be disposed of, while the inner membrane is retained. This finding suggests that the oxidative enzymes are located, as already postulated (24, 25), in the inner mitochondrial membrane and in its infoldings or cristae.

Changes Incurred by Endoplasmic Reticulum. The second example of functional modulation in the organization of the pancreatic exocrine cell is encountered at the level of the endoplasmic reticulum. As is known, the term describes an extensive system of membrane-bound vesicles, tubules, and flat vesicles or cisternae interconnected into a more or less continuous network (32, 28, 27). The membrane limiting this system separates two distinct phases in the cytoplasm: one is represented by the material inside the cavities of the network, the other by the cytoplasmic matrix surrounding the elements of the endoplasmic reticulum. In the acinar cell, the system is characterized by: *a*) a large relative volume; *b*) preferred orientation (its elements are disposed in successive, parallel planes at more or less regular intervals); and *c*) an extensive association with small dense particles which appear to be attached to the outer surface of the limiting membrane of the system (27, 30, cf. also 44, 42, 7). The features mentioned can be seen to advantage in the basal region of the exocrine cell, in which the endoplasmic reticulum reaches its highest intracellular concentration. Light microscope studies have shown that the cytoplasm of this basal region is intensely basophilic, and histochemical tests have demonstrated that the basophilia is due to the presence of ribonucleic acid (RNA) in relatively high concentrations (2, 5). From cell fractionation studies it is known that the endoplasmic reticulum breaks down during tissue homogenization into closed vesicles which constitute the bulk of the microsomal fraction (30). And, finally, from experiments carried out with isolated microsomes, it appears that the small particles attached to the outer surface of the microsomal membrane are ribonucleoprotein (RNP) particles (30).

As is generally known, a considerable body of circumstantial evidence suggests that the cytoplasmic RNA is involved in protein synthesis (cf. 5, 3) and points to the microsomes (cf. 3, 21) and to their attached RNP particles (20, 38) as the probable sites of the process. For these reasons, it has already been postulated (27, 30, 44) that the voluminous endoplasmic reticulum of the exocrine cell is connected with the large-scale synthesis of proteins which is carried out by this cell, and which results in the production of relatively large quantities of digestive enzymes. After being synthesized, the enzymes are temporarily stored, as assumed by Heidenhain, within the zymogen granules.

In our study of the exocrine pancreas of the guinea pig, we looked for structural modulations at the level of the endoplasmic reticulum and found that in the starved animal the system is characterized by tight packing, preferred orientation and light content. One hour after feeding, extensive changes appear in a large proportion (~40–60%) of the exocrine cell population. The cavities of the system are distended, the preferred orientation is lost, and relatively large, dense granules are found within the cavities of its distended cisternae (fig. 4). These intracisternal granules are similar in density and fine texture to the zymogen granules of the apical region of the cell, but they are much smaller in size and different in location (26). To find out what the intracisternal granules contain, we decided to fractionate the pancreas of fed guinea pigs 1 hour after food intake[2] and to compare the results with those obtained by fractionating the gland of starved animals. In both cases we isolated from the pancreatic breis: *1*) a heterogeneous nuclear fraction; *2*) a zymogen fraction made up primarily of zymogen granules; *3*) a mitochondrial fraction; *4*) a microsomal fraction which consisted of fragments of the endoplasmic reticulum; and *5*) a final supernatant fraction supposedly representing the cytoplasmic matrix (36). In starved guinea pigs we found that the zymogen fraction accounted for ~ 40 per cent of the trypsin-activatable proteolytic activity of the cell (mainly trypsinogen and chymotrypsinogen) and ~ 40 per cent of its ribonuclease activity. In this situation the enzymatic activity of the microsomes was low, but in fed animals it approached both in total amount and in concentration the activity found in the zymogen fraction (37). The finding was evidently in agreement with the assumption that the endoplasmic reticulum is involved in the production of digestive enzymes, and that the intracisternal granules, like the zymogen granules, are temporary deposits of the enzymes produced. To explore further this possibility, we subfractionated the microsomes by differential centrifugation after treating them with low (0.1%) concentrations of Na deoxycholate. In the case of fed animals, we obtained a heavy subfraction containing intracisternal granules totally or

[2] In all experiments the animals were fed after a fast of 40 to 48 hours.

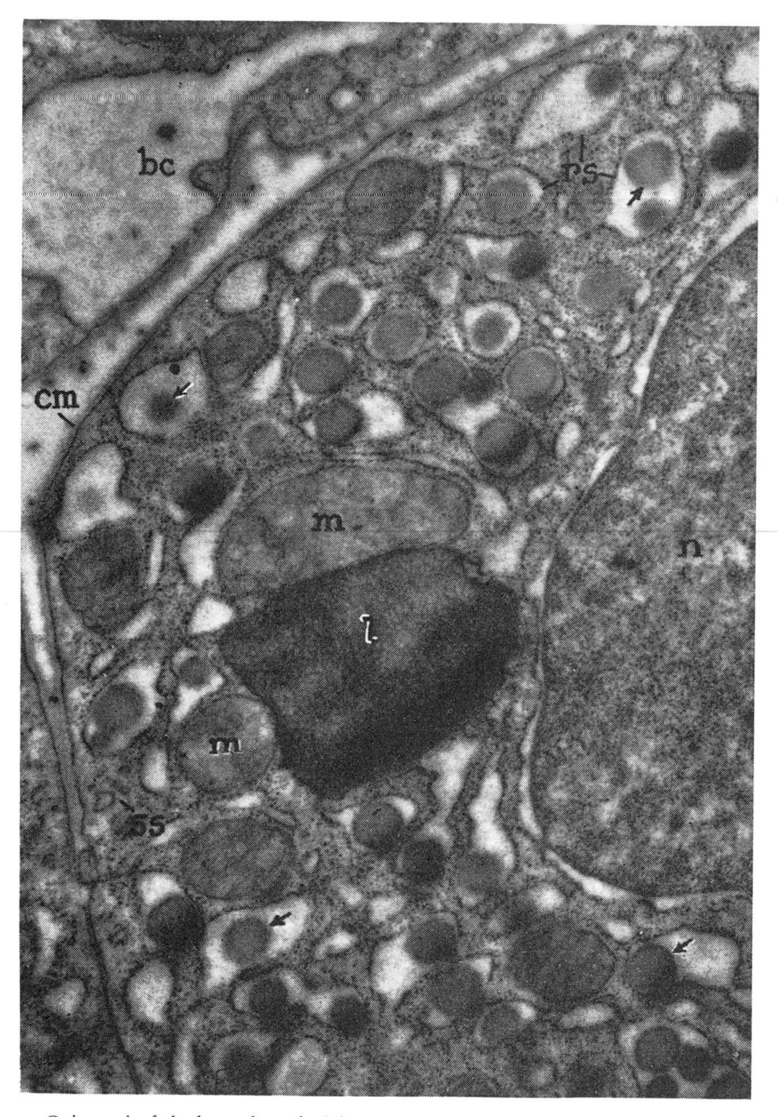

FIG. 4. Guinea pig fed after a fast of 48 hours. Pancreas fixed 1 hour after beginning of meal. The micrograph shows a relatively large field in the basal cytoplasm of an exocrine cell. The cell membrane can be seen at *cm* and part of the nucleus at *n*. A lipid inclusion (*l*) appears in close contact with two mitochondrial profiles (*m*). The rough-surfaced elements of the endoplasmic reticulum (*rs*) show distended cavities and many of them contain 1–4 intracisternal granules (*arrows*). A small cluster of smooth-surfaced vesicles is marked *ss*. A blood capillary (*bc*) can be seen in the upper left corner of the figure. × 25,000.

partially freed from the surrounding membranes. To be sure, this heavy subfraction is a heterogeneous preparation which contains, in addition to intracisternal granules, various microsomal detritus, mainly damaged membranes. We also obtained an intermediary subfraction made up primarily of detached RNP particles and a light subfraction representing the deoxycholate-soluble components of the microsomes, primarily their liquid content and their solubilized membranes. In fed animals, proteolytic and ribonuclease activities were more concentrated in the heavy microsomal subfraction than in the parent microsomes. In starved animals, the corresponding subfraction showed no increase in specific activity over the microsomes (37). These findings clearly indicate that the intracisternal granules are masses of segregated digestive enzymes. To my knowledge, this is the first instance in which a product of the endoplasmic reticulum has been demonstrated in the form of well defined granules within the cavities of the system, and has been identified biochemically.

The study of the microsomal subfractions has revealed another feature worth mentioning. The intermediary subfractions, which primarily consist of detached particles, contain proteases and ribonuclease in remarkably high concentrations. If we assume that the finding reflects the situation *in situ,* then we may have reached here, at the level of the attached RNP particles, the site, or at least one of the sites, of protein synthesis in the cell. To verify this assumption we must demonstrate that the enzymes in question are new proteins still attached to their site of synthesis, not old enzymes relocated by adsorption during tissue homogenization. This important distinction remains to be established by future work. For the moment we can strengthen the first alternative by some evidence derived from experiments in which the incorporation of leucine-1-C^{14} into the mixed proteins of various cell fractions was followed with time. The curves (fig. 5) show that the highest early incorporation takes place in the attached particles and the crossings on the graph are compatible with a transfer of labeled proteins from the particles to the microsomal content, that is, the intracisternal granules, and from the latter to the zymogen granules. It should be stressed that the results of these experiments do not validate our hypothetical pathway; they are only compatible with it. A more convincing test can be obtained by following with time the radioactivity of a single protein, chymotrypsinogen for instance, produced by the cell. Information of this kind is not yet available.

Membrane Exchange During Zymogen Discharge. The third example concerns the membrane of the zymogen granules. It is finally known, as a result of the work carried out by Marshall with fluorescein-labeled antibodies (23), and by Hokin (13) and us (36) with cell fractions, that Heidenhain's hypothesis is correct and that the zymogen granules deserve their name. Indeed, they contain trypsinogen and chymotrypsinogen—the classical zymogens—and in addition procarboxypeptidase, ribonuclease, lipase and amylase. All these hydrolytic enzymes,

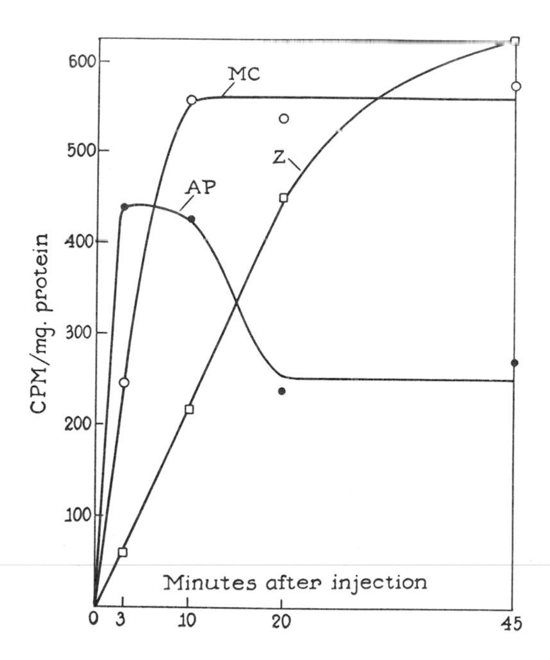

FIG. 5. Variation with time in the specific activities of protein of attached particles (*AP*), microsomal content (*MC*), and zymogen granules (*Z*) of pancreas after injection of DL-leucine-1-C^{14} into guinea pigs 1 hour after refeeding. For further details see (38).

temporarily stored in the apical region of the cell, are dangerous products which could easily wreck the cell. To handle them without mishap, the cell uses a number of protective devices. One is represented by the fact that some of the enzymes involved, namely the proteases, are produced and stored in the form of inactive precursors. Another consists of the isolation of the enzymes from the rest of the cytoplasm by a membrane barrier, which is clearly visible when the granules are normally sectioned, measures ~70 Å in thickness, and has a smooth surface: it does not have attached particles on the side that faces the cytoplasmic matrix. This latter finding introduces a complicating element in our general hypothesis. We have postulated, on the basis of the previous example, that the digestive enzymes are produced by the endoplasmic reticulum, presumably by its attached RNP particles, and are subsequently segregated in the form of intracisternal granules. These granules were found within the cavities of the endoplasmic reticulum surrounded by a membrane bearing attached particles and separated from it by a relatively large, light halo. If the intracisternal granules are the direct morphological precursors of the zymogen granules, then we must assume that they grow within the cisternae by continuous accretion until they fill a whole cisterna and reach the dimensions of the zymogen granules. At that time, we must further postulate that the membrane becomes smooth by shedding its attached particles. Such a sequence of events is, however, highly improbable because the intracisternal granules usually remain below [illegible] in diameter and never reach sizes comparable to those of the zymogen granules. An alternative course could involve the transport of the intracisternal granules, or of their material, to other parts of the endoplasmic reticulum free of attached particles. Such a part exists in the centrosphere region (the 'Golgi zone') of the cell where piles of smooth surfaced cisternae and large numbers of smooth surfaced vesicles (fig. 6) are regularly encountered (41, 30). At the periphery of the centrosphere region, there are junctions between the rough- and smooth-surfaced parts of the system, as indicated by the presence of elements of mixed appearance which could be used to gain access from one part of the reticulum to another. Within the region itself, many smooth-surfaced vacuoles or cisternae appear to be in the process of filling (fig. 7) and all gradations are encountered between still flattened cisternae, partly filled vacuoles, and fully packed, well rounded zymogen granules (8, 26). The morphological evidence indicates clearly that the membrane of the zymogen granules is derived from the centrosphere region, but is less informative about the mechanisms whereby intracisternal granules gain access to the cisternae of the Golgi zone. As already mentioned, there are connections between the rough-surfaced parts of the reticulum and the membrane-bound spaces of the centrosphere region, but intracisternal granules are rarely seen in transit through such junctions. For the moment, what appears to be of particular interest is the fact that, upon discharge, the membrane of the zymogen granules becomes continuous with the cell membrane at the apical pole of the exocrine cell. Through the exit thus created, the content of the granule is poured out into the acinar lumen, which frequently appears to be filled with discharged zymogen (fig. 8). By this simple device the 'granules' can be discharged without any break in the continuity of the cell membrane and without the risks involved by any membrane discontinuity.

It appears, therefore, from these observations on the formation and discharge of zymogen granules that membranous material picked up in the centrosphere region of the cell is continuously relocated in the cell membrane at the apical pole of the cell. The implications of this finding are worth considering in some detail. To begin with, it is highly improbable that the membrane moves only from the centrosphere to the surface. An unidirectional movement would soon result in considerable enlargement of the lumen and in exhaustion of the intracellular membranous material. It is reasonable to assume that a concomitant movement, from the surface to the centrosphere region, takes place, and the presence of small 'empty' vesicles below the luminal membrane is compatible with this assumption. Observations made on other cell types, particularly on macrophages (19, 9, 31) and amebae (14, 6, 4) clearly indicate that membrane material can be moved from the cell surface to the interior. We may conclude that we 'see' the centrifugal arc of this circular movement because the membrane is marked for its duration by the characteristically dense content of the zymogen granules. And we may assume that we cannot visualize the centripetal arc because in its case we lack a natural marker. In keeping with these general assumptions, we may further surmise that

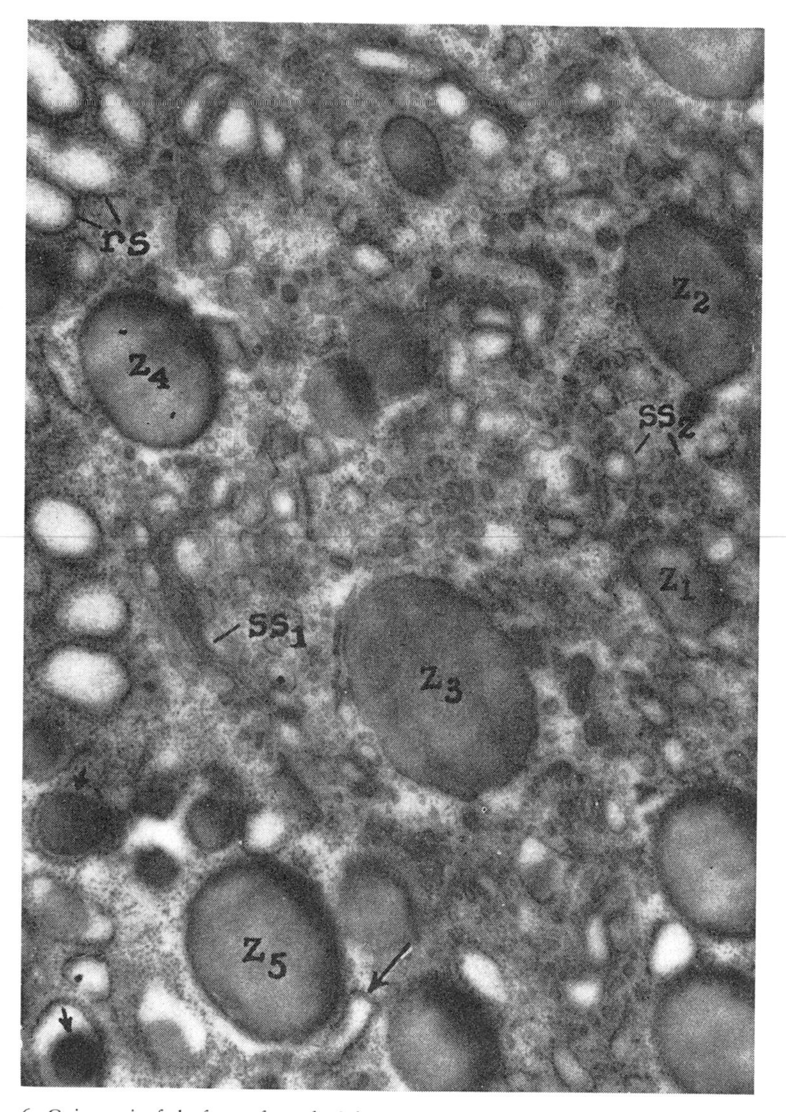

FIG. 6. Guinea pig fed after a fast of 48 hours. Limited field at the periphery of the centrosphere region of an exocrine cell. Profiles of rough-surfaced (*rs*) elements of the endoplasmic reticulum can be seen along the left margin of the figure. Some of them contain intracisternal granules (*short arrows*). The smooth-surfaced elements of the centrosphere region occupy the rest of the field and appear either as arrays of elongated profiles (ss_1) or as scattered circular profiles (ss_2) of various dimensions. An element of intermediate appearance (part rough and part smooth) is marked by a *long arrow*. The large vesicles with a dense, homogeneous content (z^1, z^2, z^3) represent zymogen granules in formation. Almost mature zymogen granules can be seen at z^4 and z^5. $\times$ 32,000.

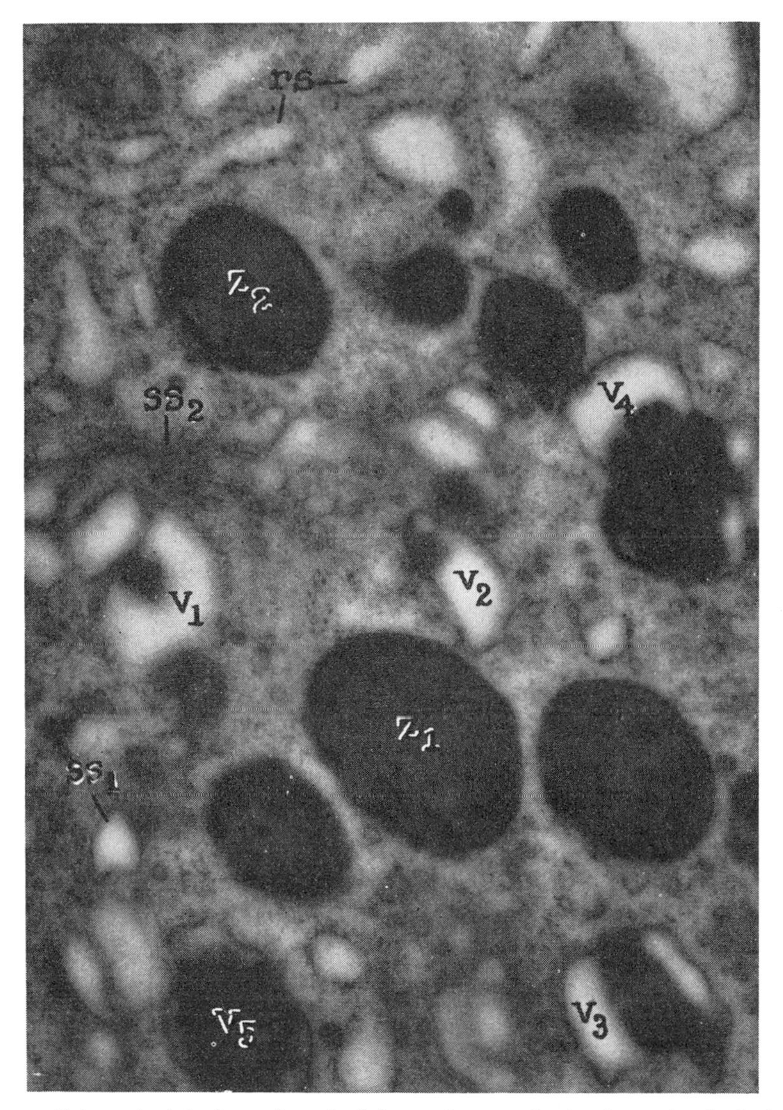

FIG. 7. Guinea pig fed after a fast of 48 hours. Pancreas fixed 1 hour after beginning of meal. The micrograph shows a limited field at the periphery of the centrosphere region. Rough-surfaced elements (*rs*) of the endoplasmic reticulum can be seen along the upper margin of the figure. Smooth-surfaced vesicles (ss_1) and stacked cisternae (ss_2) together with large vacuoles (v_1 — v_5) of irregular shape occupy the centrosphere region. These vacuoles are partially filled with masses of dense material similar in density and texture to the content of the zymogen granules (z_1, z_2). It is assumed that they represent successive stages in a filling process that ends with the formation of mature zymogen granules. $\times$ 37,000

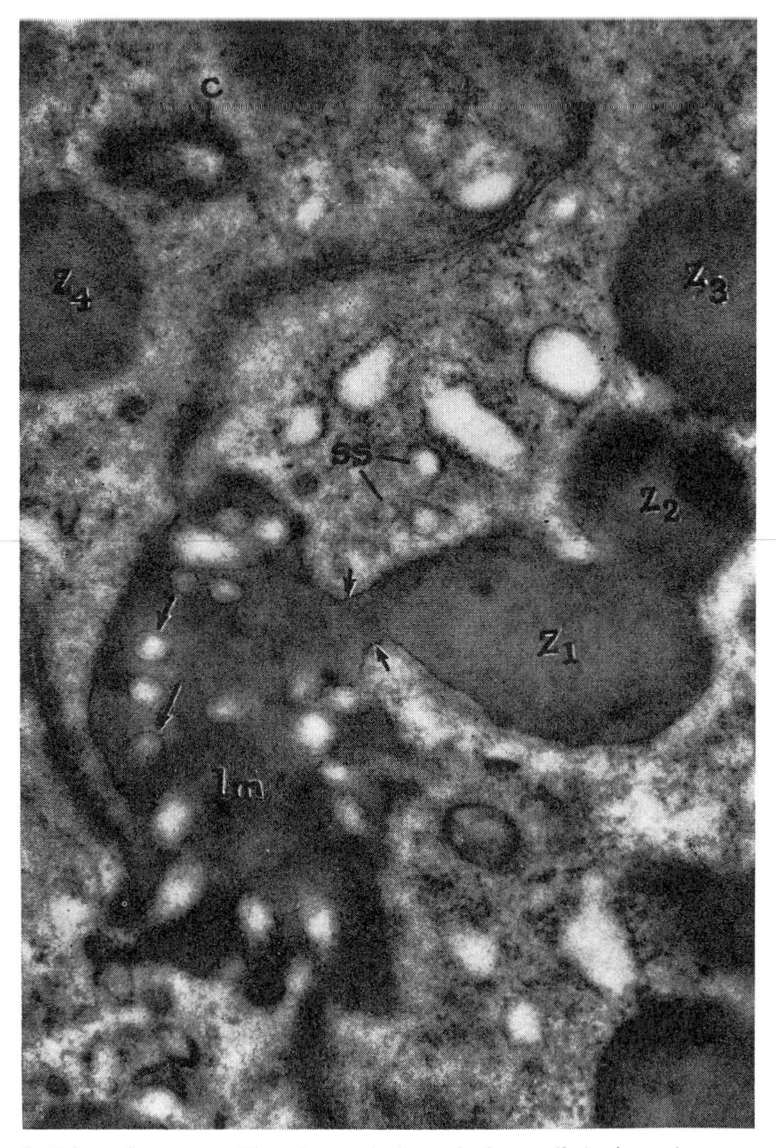

Fig. 8. Guinea pig pancreas. The micrograph shows the lumen (*lm*) of an acinus surrounded by the apical poles of 3 exocrine cells. Microvilli (*long arrows*), in cross or oblique section, appear against the dense background of the discharged zymogen that fills the lumen. The limiting membrane and the content of the zymogen granule marked z_1 appear in continuity with the cell membrane (*short arrows*) and the luminal content respectively. It is assumed that this granule was fixed while emptying its contents into the lumen. Another zymogen granule (z_2) discharges through the intermediary of z_1. Other zymogen granules, still far from the cell membrane, are marked z_3 and z_4. A few 'empty' vesicles, most of them smooth-surfaced (*ss*), can be seen among the zymogen granules. A centriole (*c*) appears close to the luminal surface of one of the cells. × 45,000.

the piles of cisternae in the centrosphere region represent the membrane depot of the cell. Finally we should consider that the two membranes involved in the process, the one at the cell surface and the one in the centrosphere region, are probably related in their chemistry or in their molecular architecture. Evidently all these assumptions should be taken for what they are: mere hypotheses to be tested by future experimentation.

In conclusion, I have presented three examples in which noticeable changes affecting either the relationship, or the structure, or the location of a number of cell components have been detected by electron microscopy. Experimental conditions and complementary biochemical information indicate that the changes described are functional modulations of the structures under consideration.

In my belief, these findings clearly support the thesis that the electron microscope can be a useful tool in physiological research at the cellular or intracellular level.

REFERENCES

1. Babkin, B. P. *Secretory Mechanism of the Digestive Glands* (2nd ed.). New York: Hoeber, 1950.
2. Brachet, J. *Arch. Biol.* 53: 207, 1941–42.
3. Brachet, J. In: *The Nucleic Acids,* edited by E. Chargaff and J. N. Davidson. New York: Acad. Press, 1955, Vol. 2: 475.
4. Brandt, P. W. *Exper. Cell Res.* 15: 300, 1958.
5. Caspersson, T. *Cell Growth and Cell Function.* New York: Norton, 1950.
6. Chapman-Andresen, C. and D. M. Prescott. *Compt. rend. lab. Carlsberg, Ser. chim.* 30: 57, 1956.
7. Claude, A. In: *Fine Structure of Cells.* Groningen: P. Noordhoff, 1955, p. 307.
8. Farquhar, M. G. and S. R. Wellings. *J. Biophys. Biochem. Cytol.* 3: 319, 1957.
9. Gey, G. O. *The Harvey Lect.* 50: 154, 1954–55.
10. Green, D. E. *Biol. Rev.* 29: 330, 1954.
11. Heidenhain, R. *Arch. ges. Physiol.* 10: 557, 1875.
12. Heidenhain, R. In: *Handbuch der Physiologie,* edited by L. Hermann. Vogel Verlag, 5/1: 173, 1883.
13. Hokin, L. E. *Biochim. et biophys. acta* 18: 379, 1955.
14. Holter, H. and J. M. Marshall. *Compt. rend. lab. Carlsberg, Ser. chim.* 29: 7, 1954.
15. Knox, E. W., B. N. Noyce and V. H. Auerbach. *J. Biol. Chem.* 176: 117, 1948.
16. Laird, A. K. and A. D. Barton. *Biochim. et biophys. acta* 27: 12, 1958.
17. Lansing, A. J. *J. Histochem. Cytochem.* 1: 265, 1953.
18. Lehninger, A. L. and E. R. Kennedy. *J. Biol. Chem.* 179: 957, 1949.
19. Lewis, W. H. *Harvey Lect.* 31: 214, 1935–36.
20. Littlefield, J. W., E. B. Keller, J. Gross and P. C. Zamecnik. *J. Biol. Chem.* 217: 111, 1955.
21. Loftfield, R. B. *Prog. Biophys. Biophys. Chem.* 8: 347, 1957.
22. Ma, W. C. *Am. J. Anat.* 36: 215, 1925.
23. Marshall, J. M. *Exper. Cell Res.* 6: 240, 1954.
24. Palade, G. E. *Anat. Rec.* 114: 427, 1952.
25. Palade, G. E. *J. Histochem. Cytochem.* 1: 188, 1953.

26. PALADE, G. E. *J. Biophys. Biochem. Cytol.* 2: 417, 1956.
27. PALADE, G. E. *J. Biophys. Biochem. Cytol.* 2, suppl.: 85, 1956.
28. PALADE, G. E. AND K. R. PORTER. *J. Exper. Med.* 100: 641, 1954.
29. PALADE, G. E. AND G. SCHIDLOWSKY. *Anat. Rec.* 130: 352, 1958.
30. PALADE, G. E. AND P. SIEKEVITZ. *J. Biophys. Biochem. Cytol.* 2: 671, 1956.
31. POMERAT, C. M., C. G. LEFEBER AND D. MCSMITH. *Ann. New York Acad. Sci.* 58: 1311, 1954.
32. PORTER, K. R. *J. Exper. Med.* 97: 727, 1953.
33. SCHNEIDER, W. C. *J. Biol. Chem.* 176. 259, 1948.
34. SCHUCHER, R. AND L. E. HOKIN. *J. Biol. Chem.* 210: 551, 1954.
35. SCOTT, W. J. M. *Am. J. Anat.* 20: 237, 1916.
36. SIEKEVITZ, P. AND G. E. PALADE. *J. Biophys. Biochem. Cytol.* 4: 203, 1958.
37. SIEKEVITZ, P. AND G. E. PALADE. *J. Biophys. Biochem. Cytol.* 4: 309, 1958.
38. SIEKEVITZ, P. AND G. E. PALADE. *J. Biophys. Biochem. Cytol.* 4: 557, 1958.
39. SIEKEVITZ, P. AND G. E. PALADE. *J. Biophys. Biochem. Cytol.* 5: 1, 1959.
40. SJÖSTRAND, F. S. AND V. HANZON. *Exper. Cell Res.* 7: 393, 1954.
41. SJÖSTRAND, F. S. AND V. HANZON. *Exper. Cell Res.* 7: 415, 1954.
42. WATANABE, Y. *J. Electronmicroscopy (Japan)* 3: 43, 1955.
43. WATSON, M. L. AND P. SIEKEVITZ. *J. Biophys. Biochem. Cytol.* 2: 639, 1956.
44. WEISS, J. M. *J. Exper. Med.* 98: 607, 1953.
45. ZIEGLER, D. M., A. W. LINNANE, D. E. GREEN, C. M. S. DASS AND H. RIS. *Biochim. et biophys. acta* 28: 524, 1958.

DISCUSSION

V. R. Potter, G. E. Palade, D. E. Green, Spirtes, R. Weber, A. B. Novikoff, J. W. Littlefield, A. Marshak, C. L. Prosser, A. W. Swift

DR. POTTER: In the case of mitochondria bearing fat droplets, will centrifugation cause the combination to move up or down?

DR. PALADE: I do not know of any systematic work carried out to answer this question, but I presume that 'the combination' would be lighter than usual mitochondria. Some results obtained by Lansing (17) on centrifuged *Arbacia* eggs may have some bearing on this point. He found many mitochondria among the lipid droplets of the 'oil cap' at the centripetal pole of such eggs. These 'light' mitochondria were displaced far away in the centripetal direction from the layer formed by the 'heavy' mitochondria of the cell. In retrospect one may wonder whether Lansing's 'light mitochondria' were not mitochondrial-lipid complexes similar to the ones just described.

DR. GREEN: Suggestion is made that the accumulation of lipid is due largely to the fact that oxidation of fats is limited by the unavailability of citric cycle subtrates during starvation. Synthesis of fat appears to be carried out largely by a nonmitochondrial system. If synthesis were more rapid than oxidation, this accumulation would result. Increased rate of oxidation can hardly explain the fact that fat actually accumulates.

DR. PALADE: To assess the value of Dr. Green's suggestion one should know the concentration levels at which citric cycle substrates become a limiting factor in the oxidation of fatty acids. As far as I know, such information is not yet available. One can assume, however, that the concentrations needed are very low, since citric cycle substrates are required only to initiate or sparkle the oxidation of fatty acids (15). It is unlikely that lipid is synthesized *in situ* in starving cells. The lipid inclusions found in this situation in certain cells (e.g., the muscle fibers of the myocardium and the exocrine cells of the pancreas) are probably derived from the mobilized fat of the adipose tissue of the animal. Therefore, their intracellular accumulation should be interpreted in terms of the relationship between the rate of local lipid oxidation and the rate of lipid transport from the fat depots of the body to the recipient cell.

DR. SPIRTES: How do the following facts fit in with your theory of function of mitochondria around lipid droplets after 48 hours starvation? *1*) fatty acid oxidation little decreased; and *2*) fatty acid synthesis extremely low?

DR. PALADE: They fit in very well, since I believe that the lipid inclusions found in the starving cells are not made up of newly synthesized lipid. They represent mobilized fat, brought in from the depots of the organism, to be oxidized by the mitochondria of the myocardium or the pancreas.

DR. WEBER: I should like to ask Dr. Palade a question concerning the striking association of mitochondria and lipoid droplets. Is this an indication that mitochondria take part in the elaboration of lipoid droplets—as it has been assumed in studies from light microscopy—or is this only a transitional association, needed for a certain functional period?

DR. PALADE: As indicated by Dr. Weber, it has been repeatedly postulated—on the basis of light microscope observations—that mitochondria are involved in the formation of lipid inclusions, the prevalent assumption being that the organelles are bodily transformed into lipid masses (cf. 35, 22). Our experiments on starved animals indicate that the association is transitory and should be considered as an expression of fat removal by oxidation, rather than of fat synthesis. Preliminary observations show that a similar mitochondrion-lipid association is encountered in the glycogen-loaded liver of cortisone-treated rats. In this condition, lipid is probably synthesized from surplus carbohydrate. In both cases, however, the association should be interpreted in terms of close apposition of a tool (the mitochondrial enzymes involved in lipid metabolism) to either raw material (lipid to be oxidized), or product (synthesized lipid). In the light microscope literature, the mitochondrion was usually considered as raw material on its way to be converted into a lipid inclusion. With our present knowledge of mitochondrial chemistry and enzymology, this type of relationship appears very unlikely, at least under normal conditions.

DR. NOVIKOFF: I would like to ask two questions: *1*) Has Dr. Palade studied pathological material? For example, at the edge of a myocardial infarct lipid droplets accumulate in perfectly linear fashion, just like the mitochondria which apparently disappear. This might be good material in which to examine the old notion concerning mitochondrial degeneration into lipid droplets. *2*) Dr. Palade speaks of two outer mitochondrial membranes. Would it not be preferable to speak of *one* external membrane enclosing the mitochondrial body? The latter has 'cristae' and, of course, an outer limit. This outer limit apparently remains quite visible even though the external membrane cannot be resolved at the time mitochondrion and lipid droplet are in close association. As Dr. Palade has indicated, it is likely that the enzymes of oxidative phosphorylation are in the mitochondrial body, but not, as suggested by work from Dr. Green's laboratory, in the external membrane.

DR. PALADE: *1*) The periphery of myocardial infarcts may be a good test material for the old assumption of direct transformation of mitochondria into lipid inclusions but, as far as I know, such material has not yet been studied by electron microscopy. In the ischemic myocardium, however, one would deal with a degenerative process, rather than with a normal physiological event. Even in this case, the relationship between the rate of lipid transport and the rate of lipid oxidation may have some bearing on the accumulation of fat droplets. 2) I believe that there is at present good evidence for the existence of two distinct mitochondrial membranes. The inner one is frequently continuous with the *cristae mitochondriales* (which appear as its infoldings) and corresponds to what Dr. Novikoff calls "the outer limit of the mitochondrial body." The outer membrane—Dr. Novikoff and I agree on its existence—separates the mitochondrion from the cytoplasmic matrix. The hypothesis that the oxidative enzymes are located in the internal membrane and in its cristae is supported by a number of observations (cf. 25). A final answer may be obtained by comparing the concentration of oxidative enzymes with the amount of internal and external membrane per unit volume in a representative series of mitochondria that should include specimens with few and with numerous cristae. Evidence obtained by dismantling isolated mitochondria (cf. 43, 45) cannot solve this problem, because the typical mitochondrial organization is lost in the process, and the derivation of the small, membrane-bound vesicles finally obtained cannot be decidedly ascertained. These 'submitochondrial' vesicles may be derived from both the outer and the inner membrane, but most of them are probably formed at the expense of the latter, since there is more of inner than of outer membrane in all mitochondria.

DR. LITTLEFIELD: You certainly have beautifully correlated evidence on the direction of flow of protein synthesis in the microsomal fractions from your morphologic and *in vivo* labeling experiments. I wonder if you and Dr. Siekevitz have been able to show any movement of labeled protein in homogenates?

DR. PALADE: With our material, i.e., the pancreas of the adult guinea pig, we were not able to obtain a system capable of incorporating amino acids into proteins *in vitro*. Moreover, we have not carried out experiments designed to explore the transfer *in vitro* of proteins labeled *in vivo*.

DR. MARSHAK: Since the intracisternal granules are actually located in the cisternal space, i.e., with their surfaces rather far removed from the RNP granules which presumably synthesize the protein making up the intracisternal granules, is it not necessary also to postulate an additional mechanism aggregating the protein found and removing it from the site of synthesis?

DR. PALADE: It is indeed necessary to postulate a mechanism by which the product is removed from the site of synthesis (presumably the attached RNP particles) and, in addition, transported across the membrane which separates the cytoplasmic matrix from the intracisternal spaces. After being segregated within these spaces, the zymogen molecules probably aggregate into intracisternal granules when a suitable concentration is reached. The biochemical and physiological advantages brought about by the segregation of the newly synthesized zymogens are easily understood, but the mechanisms involved remain, for the moment, entirely unknown

DR. PROSSER: *1*) Have you evidence for localization of amylase and lipase similar to that of proteolytic enzyme? 2) Is the discharge of the zymogen granules altered according to the nature of the meal given after starvation, that is, by high protein, fat or carbohydrate?

DR. PALADE: *1*) No, but evidence answering in part your question has been obtained by Hokin (13) and by Laird and Barton (16). According to their findings, amylase and lipase are present in the zymogen granules although in smaller relative amounts than the proteolytic zymogens. 2) As far as I know, the influence of the nature of the meal upon the zymogen discharge has not been studied by electron microscopy. Earlier work, carried out with the light microscope, has established that there is extensive discharge of zymogen granules when peptones, soaps or carbohydrates are introduced in the duodenum but not when acid is instilled therein (1).

DR. SWIFT: How do you postulate the mechanism of zymogen material ejection? Is this a mechanical event similar to muscular contraction? If fluids are brought back in to replace zymogen material how are they sucked in?

DR. PALADE: At present there is no evidence of contractile structures in the apical region of the acinar cell. It is, however, reasonable to assume that the cell membrane itself (and the membrane limiting the zymogen granules) may be contractile and may thereby help in the ejection of the zymogen. The mechanism by which vesicles move from the centrosphere region to the cell surface and back is entirely unknown. The fusion of the membrane of the zymogen granules with the cell membrane and the subsequent discharge of their content seem to be, however, under chemical control: zymogen discharge is greatly accelerated by acetylcholine and carbamylcholine (1, 34).

Mitochondrial Structure and Function

DAVID E. GREEN

University of Wisconsin
Madison, Wisconsin

THE MITOCHONDRION IS A BIOCHEMICAL MACHINE, universally distributed in all aerobic organisms, which oxidizes pyruvic acid to carbon dioxide and water by way of the citric acid cycle and which links these oxidative reactions involving molecular oxygen to synthesis of adenosinetriphosphate (ATP). In some mitochondria, oxidative reactions other than those of the citric acid cycle may be coupled to synthesis of ATP, but there appears to be no known exception to the rule that all mitochondria carry out the citric acid cycle. Most mitochondria carry out reactions other than those of the citric acid cycle and other than oxidative reactions, but we shall not be concerned with these processes in the context of the present talk.

We may define some of the basic biochemical problems of the mitochondrion in terms of the following broad questions:

1) How are the enzymes arranged? Are they organized in a definite pattern?

2) What is the physical state of the mitochondrion? Can we think of the mitochondrion as a particle in which all the component parts are rigidly positioned with respect to one another and held together in chemical bonding, or are the components in solution within the mitochondrial interior and interacting with one another by thermal collision?

3) How are the enzymes which implement the citric cycle geared to the electron transport chain, and how in turn is electron flow coupled to oxidative phosphorylation?

As you may be aware, our laboratory has been intimately concerned with these problems during the past 12 years, and I would like to summarize for you in capsular form some of our experimental observations and present working hypotheses which bear on the problems I have just defined.

One of the greatest impediments to the biochemical study of the mitochondrion has been the functional instability of isolated mitochondria. Liver suspensions, for example, have a half-life time of several hours at best. About 5 years ago we explored the possibilities of heart mitochondria as a stable source of material for large scale isolation, and this material turned out to be just what the doctor ordered. They can easily be prepared from slaughterhouse material on any desired scale; they are incredibly stable even to freezing and thawing (19), they are readily fragmented into stable particles; and they have made it possible for our

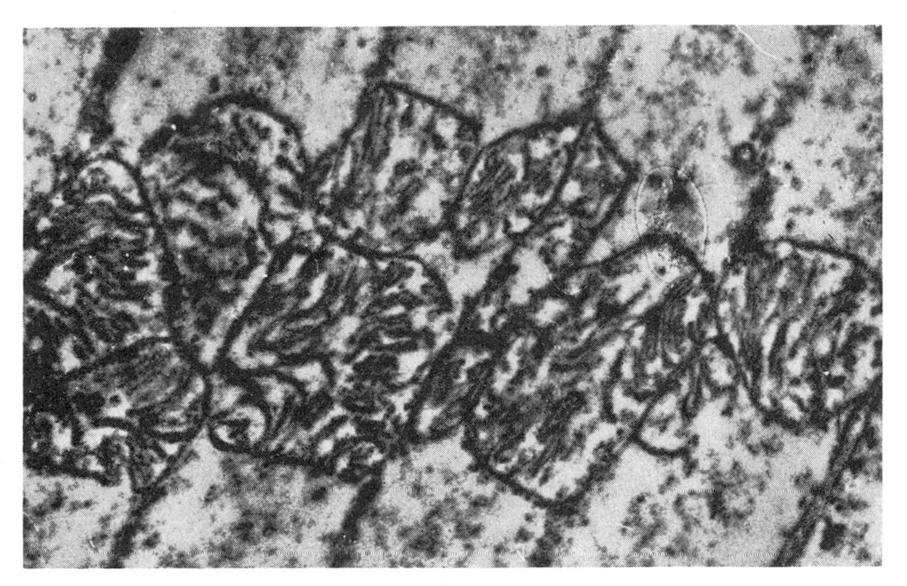

FIG. 1. Section of beef heart muscle. × 28,700.

laboratory to embark on a systematic program of degrading the mitochondrion step by step and then reconstructing mitochondrial function and structure from the composition and properties of the fragments. We can thus work on an adequate scale to study chemically the components of the electron transport system and of the mitochondrion. We have a little factory in our laboratory which produces each day about a liter of thick mitochondrial suspension from beef hearts, and we can draw upon this supply, which is kept in the deep freeze, at our convenience. More and more biochemists have become aware of the virtues of heart mitochondria, and others are now sharing with us the advantages of working with such stable material.

The electron microscope has been developed by Palade, Sjöstrand, and others into a very powerful tool for the study of mitochondrial structure. We have relied heavily on this tool for insight into the nature of the processes by which we have been able to fragment mitochondria into successively less complex fragments. In this enterprise we have enjoyed the collaboration of Professor Hans Ris and, more recently, Professor Paul Kaesberg and Mr. D. L. Filmer of the University of Wisconsin.

The first four figures[1] show the transitional steps from intact heart mitochondria *in situ* to the least common denominator of oxidative phosphorylation, the electron transport particles or ETP (34, 14). The mitochondrion *in situ* (fig. 1) shows a well defined outer envelope and an interior which is crammed

[1] Electron micrographs (figs. 1–4) by D. L. Filmer and P. Kaesberg, University of Wisconsin.

full of tightly packed cristae, stacked in a regular fashion like logs on a pile. The double membrane structure of both the outer envelope and the cristae is clearly seen on close inspection of the electron micrographs. Mitochondria isolated from beef heart muscle can be sharply resolved into two fractions: the heavy or more rapidly sedimenting fraction and the light or more slowly sedimenting fraction (19). For present purposes we shall consider only the more intact particle, viz., the heavy mitochondrial particle, the electron micrograph of which is seen in figure 2. You will note first that the arrangement of the cristae is not as regular as in the mitochondrion *in situ* and also that the distinction between outer envelope and cristae is not quite so sharp. When the particles of the heavy mitochondrial fraction are frozen and thawed they have the appearance shown in figure 3. There has clearly been extensive loss of material. The cristae are relatively few in number and very irregularly arranged, and the outer envelope is rather diffuse. But the double membrane structure of both the envelope and cristae is well defined. When such damaged particles are sonicated, all mitochondrial form disappears, and fragments with double membrane structures are found, as shown in figure 4. These are unmistakably derivatives of the cristae and outer envelope. The heavy mitochondrial particles both before and after freezing carry out oxidative phosphorylation. But only the particles with mitochondrial form carry out the citric acid cycle (34). By appropriate methods mitochondria can be comminuted into smaller and smaller fragments which still retain a well defined outer membrane surrounding the internal cristae. Such particles can carry out the citric acid cycle. It is only when the outer envelope is completely stripped that the capacity for citric cycle oxidations is abolished.

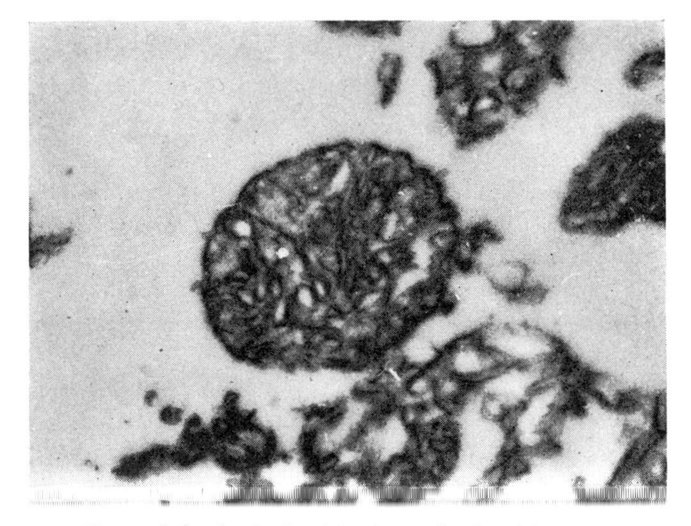

FIG. 2. Isolated mitochondria—heavy fraction. × 40,000.

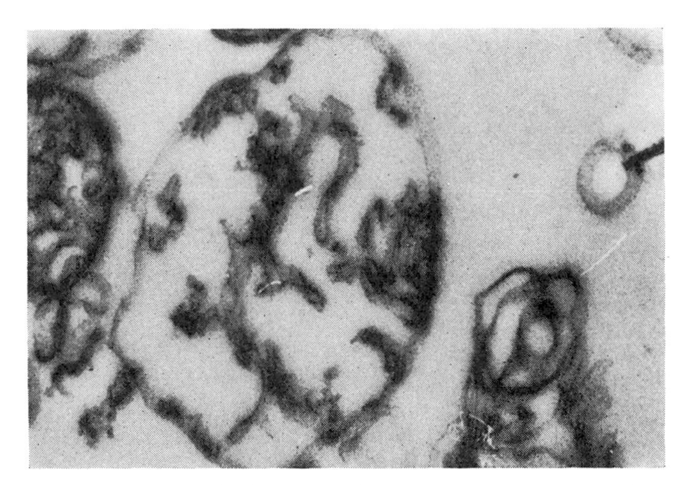

FIG. 3. Heavy mitochondrial fraction after freezing and thawing. × 40,000.

The electron transport particle couples the oxidation of DPNH or succinate to synthesis of ATP but has lost the capacity for carrying out all the oxidative steps of the citric acid cycle. This loss can be correlated with the release of pyridinoproteins and bound diphosphopyridine nucleotide (DPN) during fragmentation by sonication (25).

To enable you to visualize a little better just which part of the enzymatic machinery is lost in the transition from mitochondria to ETP, I have made a schematic representation of the electron transfer chain of the two respective particles (fig. 5). Electrons in the mitochondrion originate from the citric cycle sub-

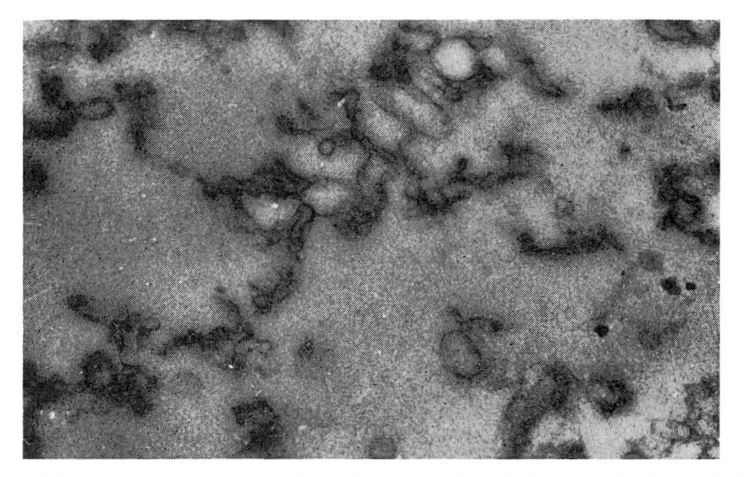

FIG. 4. Phosphorylating particles derived from sonicated heavy mitochondrial fraction (ETP_H). × 38,000.

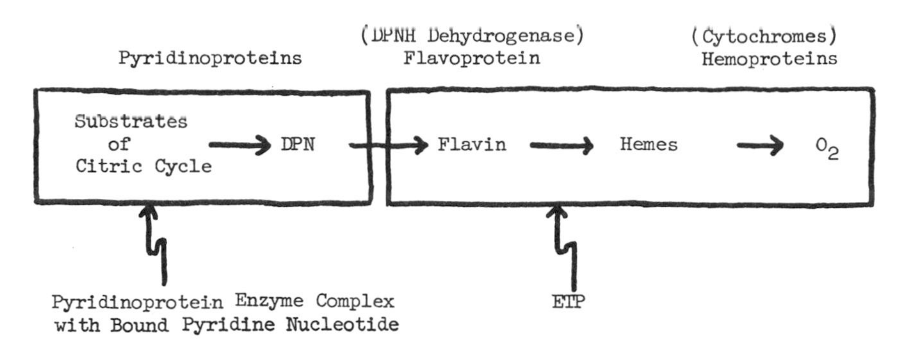

FIG. 5. Schematic representation of electron transfer chain.

strates and, leaving succinate out of the picture, all these electrons are funneled through the electron transfer chain by way of bound DPN. In the electron transport particle electrons can only enter the chain by way of externally added DPNH or succinate. These particles have no bound pyridine nucleotide and lack most of the pyridinoprotein enzymes of the citric acid cycle.

Now why the pyridinoprotein enzymes and bound DPN are lost during fragmentation of mitchondria by sonication is an extremely intriguing problem, in which we have been deeply interested. There is a good deal of information now available on this point, but I fear that this is not the appropriate occasion to do more than raise the problem.

When the fragmentation of mitochondria is carried out under other conditions, an electron transport particle can be obtained which can oxidize both succinate and DPNH, but these oxidations are no longer coupled to phosphorylation (10). From the standpoint of chemical composition and the components of the electron transfer chain the phosphorylating and nonphosphorylating electron transport particles are indistinguishable. The electron microscope has shed light on the basic difference between phosphorylating and nonphosphorylating forms of the electron transport particle (figs. 4 and 6). The nonphosphorylating particle has a vesicular structure, whereas the phosphorylating particle has the double membrane structure characteristic of cristae and envelope. There is thus a very precise relation between double membrane structure and the capacity for oxidative phosphorylation. In our laboratory Dr. A. W. Linnane has discovered a component which determines whether a particular particle will phosphorylate or not (24). When the component is made available, the particles are coupled; when it is absent the particles are uncoupled.

Our studies on mitochondrial fragmentation have led us to the conclusion that the mitochondrion is a polymer, as it were, of a repeating unit which we believe to be the electron transport particle. There are probably many thousand such units in a single mitochondrion. This hypothesis is represented diagrammatically in figure 7.

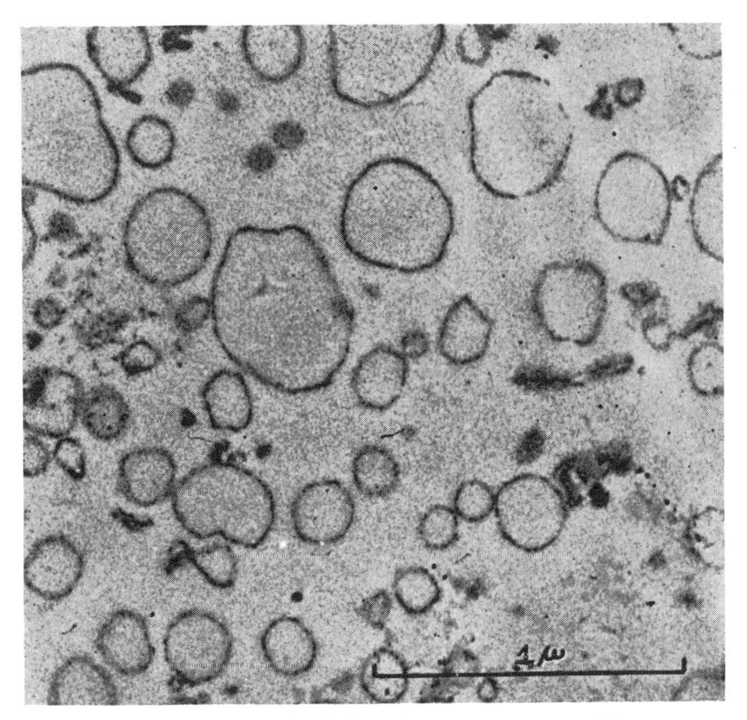

FIG. 6. Non-phosphorylating electron transport particle.

It should be pointed out that the electron transport particle is a submitochondrial unit of somewhat variable size which, however, is minute compared to the dimensions of a mitochondrion. Each particle may well be an aggregate of many repeating units. Only the fully disaggregated electron transport particle would correspond to the individual repeating unit. Prolonged sonication of mitochondria does indeed lead to smaller and smaller particles which in the limit could approach the dimensions of the repeating unit. But the chemical composition of the repeating unit as well as its enzymatic activity should be indistinguishable from any aggregate thereof such as the electron transport particle. The particle or molecular weight of the repeating unit would be from 3.3 to 5×10^6 based on the assumption of one molecule of DPNH dehydrogenase per repeating unit.

How the mitochondrion as a polymer is built up from the repeating units, the nature of the structural principles which underlie the stacking of the cristae, the exact relationship of the outer envelope to the cristae, and the role of the outer envelope to the problem of permeability or accessibility, are fascinating problems, but at present our information is too meager to do more than state them.

It is highly significant that the isolated mitochondrion which is morpho-

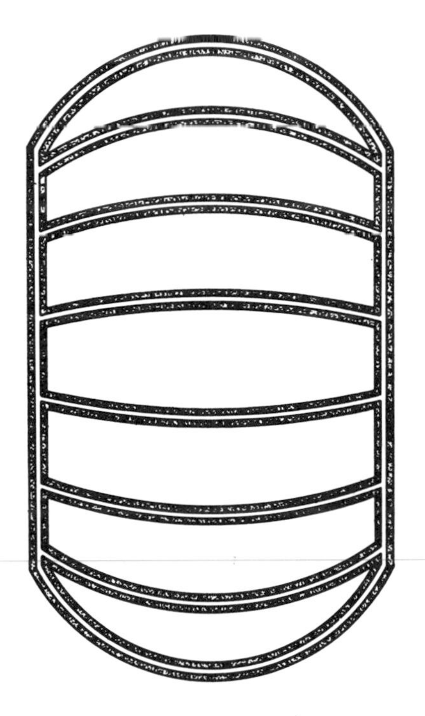

FIG. 7. Diagrammatic representation of the subunits of the mitochondrion.

logically intact shows only a very restricted number of enzymatic activities. It does not oxidize citrate or isocitrate; it does not reduce externally added cytochrome *c* or DPN; and it does not oxidize DPNH. Only when the mitochondrion is damaged morphologically do these activities emerge (33). This is the well known opening phenomenon which underlies some basic features of mitochondrial structure. The neglect of this phenomenon has led Hogeboom and Schneider (21, 30) to their conclusion, which has had wide currency among biochemists, that the mitochondrion does not carry out the complete citric acid cycle and that some of the key enzymes of the cycle are localized outside the mitochondrion. It has taken almost 10 years to correct this erroneous conclusion, and it will probably take many more years to clear up the confusion which has been created.

In our laboratory we have taken the approach that an understanding of electron transport is the key to oxidative phosphorylation and, in turn, that an understanding of oxidative phosphorylation is the key to mitochondrial structure and function. Our main efforts, therefore, have been concentrated on the chemical structure and components of the electron transfer chain as a necessary preliminary to an attack on oxidative phosphorylation. The point of departure for these studies has been the electron transfer particle which according to our evidence is the smallest common denominator of the complete electron [illegible] the transfer of electrons from a substrate to molecular oxygen.

All the available evidence suggests and is in harmony with the concept that the electron transfer particle is made up of limited numbers of protein components which are linked to one another in a very precise manner by chemical bonds which are strong enough to preserve the particle as a unit under physiological conditions. The various components occur in stoichiometric proportions which are as invariant as is the ratio of heme to globin in hemoglobin. The logical consequences of this picture of the electron transfer particle lead us to some very difficult problems which have yet to be fully resolved. If the component proteins of the electron transfer chain are bonded to one another, then thermal collision has to be excluded as a mechanism of electron transfer. What alternative mechanism can account for the properties of the chain? There appears to be a way out of this dilemma, but I shall take the point up again when I have had the opportunity of providing some background information.

Perhaps the best way of explaining how we have set about acquiring information on the structure of the electron transfer chain would be by way of the following schematic device. Let us represent the electron transfer chain as a linear aggregate of proteins—A, B, C, D, E—linked together in the form A-B-C-D-E. This would be the complete chain. By the application of appropriate reagents the chain can be fragmented into smaller units such as A-B-C-D, A-B-C, and A-B. The loss of any one component is accompanied by the loss of some enzymatic property. From the composition and properties of the fragments one can deduce the structure of the complete chain just as the structure of insulin has been deduced from the structure of the many peptides obtained by proteolytic or chemical degradation of the parent protein.

Nature has not obliged the biochemist with a simple linear chain. On the contrary, it appears to be one of bewildering complexity. But the argument still holds —the difficulty is one of experimental execution, not of principle. Ways and means have to be found to degrade the electron transport particle in a step-wise manner without destroying activity. This has not been an easy assignment, and while we have had a satisfying measure of success along these lines a vast area still remains to be explored.

It would not be easy for me to explain in a few words the many technical difficulties which have for more than three decades frustrated efforts to deduce the structure of the electron transport system. Suffice it to say that the technology for the preparation and isolation of enzymatically active particles and the methodology for the rapid assay, isolation and identification of particle-bound lipids had to be developed before any substantial progress could be achieved. I might say parenthetically that lipid reagents such as higher alcohols, bile salts, and detergents are the only reagents which have proved of value for the fragmentation of the electron transport particle.

The conversion of mitochondria to subunits such as the electron transport particle requires relatively mild methods such as sonication or other devices for comminution. However, the degradation of subunits into the constituent protein components is an entirely different kettle of fish. For this purpose physical methods are valueless, and only chemical methods rather brutal in nature can do the trick. Clearly the forces which hold repeating units together are entirely different from the forces which bind together the components of any one repeating unit.

Before we can consider in detail the various fragmentation products of the electron transfer particle it would be appropriate to list the known components of the electron transfer chain (table 1). There are two flavoproteins—the succinic and DPNH dehydrogenases. The flavin prosthetic group which is flavin adenine dinucleotide is readily detached from the DPNH dehydrogenase by acid, but not from the succinic dehydrogenase. Tryptic digestion is required for the release of flavin from the succinic dehydrogenase. This difference in the extractability of the flavins has made it possible to estimate accurately the amount of each flavoprotein in a given particle.

There are four known hemoproteins in the electron transfer particle of beef heart mitochondria; viz., cytochromes a, b, c_1, and c. They are readily distinguishable by spectroscopic and other properties, and they have vastly different enzymatic properties, which is what would be expected in view of their different positions and roles in the electron transfer chain. There are chemical as well as spectroscopic methods of analysis available which make it possible to determine the exact amount of any cytochrome in a given particle.

The lipoproteins represent the third category of protein components of the electron transfer chain. They are relatively new entities. The first to be isolated and characterized as a definite entity we have called the Q lipoprotein (1). It is too early to say exactly how many lipoproteins are present in the electron transfer particle. At present three have been isolated: one associated with coenzyme Q, the second with cytochrome c_1 and the third with the DPNH dehydrogenase.

The lipoproteins are complexes of lipid and protein which behave as *bona fide* molecules. The Q lipoprotein we have recently described has about 96 per cent lipid and 4 per cent protein. The ratio of lipid to protein will probably vary from one lipoprotein to the next.

Associated with the flavoproteins, hemoproteins and lipoproteins are certain

TABLE 1. KNOWN COMPONENTS OF ELECTRON TRANSPORT PARTICLE

Flavoproteins	Lipoproteins
Succinic (f_S)	Q, c_1-lipoprotein complex
DPNH (f_D)	Small molecules
	Coenzyme Q, carotenoids, α-tocopherol, f_D
Hemoproteins	Metals
Cytochromes a, b, c_1, c	Iron (non-heme), copper

TABLE 2. MITOCHONDRIAL LIPIDS

A. Phosphatidyl ethanolamine and serine	*C.* Neutral fats
Inositol phosphatides	Cholesterol
Lecithin, cephalin	Waxes
Sphingolipids	α-tocopherol
B. Lysophosphatides	Fatty acids
Plasmalogens	Coenzyme Q
Lipid cytochrome *c*	Carotene 451 mμ
	Carotene 447 mμ
	Carotene 441 mμ

metals which occur in definite proportions in the electron transfer chain. Iron, in a form other than that of heme iron, is found to be present in all components of the chain, and there are some hints that iron is concerned in the links which bind the different components together in the particle. Copper is also present in the particle, but it is associated exclusively with cytochrome *a*. Other metals such as Mg^{++} are always present, but there is as yet no evidence that the bound Mg^{++} is not adventitious metal.

The electron transport particle contains a bewildering variety of lipids, a partial list of which is given in table 2. The bulk, if not all, the lipid is part of lipoprotein lipid, though some lipids may be associated directly with the flavoprotein or hemoprotein components.

The succinic and DPNH flavoproteins have both been isolated from the electron transport particle or derivative particles and brought to a state of ultracentrifugal and electrophoretic homogeneity (31, 4, 26, 13). Cytochromes *c* and c_1 have been isolated as pure components, but *b* and *a* have yet to be brought to heel. The work on lipoproteins is in its infancy and the study of the lipid components of the lipoprotein is far from complete. Thus our knowledge of the components of the electron transfer chain is still fragmentary to a degree.

The electron transfer particle contains the complete respiratory chain for the oxidation of succinate and DPNH by molecular oxygen. Succinate is oxidized to fumarate and DPNH to DPN^+. The composition of the electron transport particle from beef heart mitochondria is shown in table 3. For each mole of flavin there are approximately 3 moles of heme, 30 atoms of non-heme iron, and 4 atoms of

TABLE 3. COMPOSITION OF ETP

COMPONENT	μM OR μM AT. × 10^3	MOL. OR AT. RATIO*
Flavin	0.64	1
Heme $(a + b + c_1)$	2.11	3.3
Non-heme iron	20.3	32
Copper	2.5	3.9
Lipid	34.5†	

* Flavin is taken as 1. † Per cent.

TABLE 4. MOLECULAR RATIOS OF OXIDATION-REDUCTION COMPONENTS IN ETP

Component	Ratio	Component	Ratio
Succinic dehydrog. flavoprotein	1	Cytochrome *b*	2
DPNH dehydrog. flavoprotein	1	Cytochrome $c + c_1$	2
		Copper	8
Cytochrome *a*	2	Coenzyme Q	8

copper. The lipid content is 35 per cent by weight. The electron transport particle can be isolated in a variety of ways, and regardless of the method of isolation the composition of the particles in terms of the basic components is remarkably constant.

The stoichiometry of the components in the electron transport particle is summarized in table 4. The two flavoproteins are present in equal amounts. For each 2 moles of flavoprotein there are 2 moles each of cytochromes *b* and *a* and approximately 1 mole each of cytochromes c_1 and *c*. It is of interest that the electron transport particle of *Azotobacter vinelandii* which Dr. Bruemmer in the Department of Bacteriology under Professor Perry Wilson has isolated (7) shows great similarities in enzymatic activity and stoichiometry to the corresponding particle of beef heart (table 5). There is thus some experimental support for the concept of the electron transport particle as a fundamental unit of mitochondrial function.

By a variety of procedures, all of which involve reagents which react with lipid, the electron transport particle can be fragmented into derivative particles. A summary of the components in a few such particles is given in figure 8. The succinic dehydrogenase complex (16, 3) contains cytochromes *b* and c_1 but no cytochrome *a*. This is a red particle. The flavoprotein present in the succinic dehydrogenase complex is predominantly succinic dehydrogenase. An analogous particle called the succinic-DPNH dehydrogenase complex has much the same composition except that the two flavoproteins, the succinic and DPNH dehydrogenases, are both present in equal amounts as in ETP (29). A green particle has been prepared by Crane and Glenn (9) which has the complete respiratory chain for DPNH but has essentially no capacity for oxidation of succinate. There

TABLE 5. COMPARISON OF ETP FROM BEEF HEART AND A. VINELANDII

	BEEF HEART	AZOTOBACTER
Succinic-oxygen	2.0*	2.4
DPNH-oxygen	5.7	6.8
Succinic-ferricyanide	2.0	1.6
DPNH-ferricyanide	5.0	3.5
Succinic-cytochrome *c*	0.1	0.3
DPNH-cytochrome *c*	0.2	0.2
Hemes	a, b, $c_1 + c$	$a_2, b_1, c_4 + c_5$
Flavin:Heme:Fe:Cu	1:3.3:30:3.7	1:5:16:2
Lipid	30†	20†

* In μmoles substrate/min/mg protein at 38°C. † Per cent.

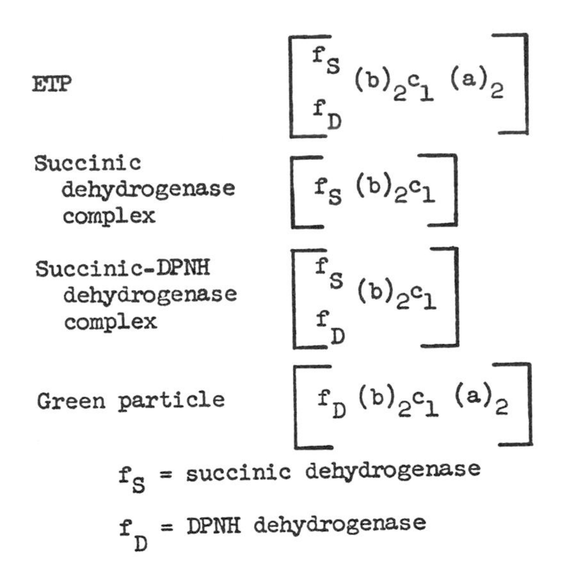

FIG. 8. Elementary composition of ETP and derivative particles.

is, correspondingly, only DPNH flavoprotein and no succinic flavoprotein in this particle. Particles which lack cytochrome *a* no longer are capable of reacting with molecular oxygen. However, red particles appropriately prepared will react readily with cytochrome *c*, and the bound cytochromes of these particles are rapidly reducible by succinate or DPNH.

At present there is insufficient knowledge to permit writing a definitive formula for the electron transfer chain. We still do not know all the components of the chain and, in fact, it is still impossible to say with confidence which two components of the chain react directly with one another. But at least we are now in a much better position to state the problems to be resolved even if the solution still eludes us.

When succinate or DPNH is added to the electron transfer particle, all the hemes, cytochromes *b*, c_1, *c* and *a*, are rapidly reduced. Thus regardless of the way by which electrons flow into the chain—whether by way of succinate of DPNH—all the cytochromes in the particle become reduced. Taken at face value this observation would suggest one respiratory chain with two entry points. However, ETP can be fragmented into daughter particles which contain either a succinic or DPNH chain, and this fragmentation cannot be accounted for in terms of the liberation of free flavoprotein.

This type of evidence suggests separate chains for oxidation of succinate and DPNH. When ETP is treated in a variety of ways the requirements for oxidation of succinate and DPNH are often entirely different. The oxidation of DPNH may depend upon the addition of cytochrome *c* whereas that of succinate does not, or vice versa. The oxidation of succinate requires the addition of coenzyme Q whereas that of DPNH does not (12). These observations clearly point to basic differences in the succinic and DPNH chains, but they do not necessarily exclude a part of the chain which is common to both. Thus several formulations have to be considered, of which two obvious ones are shown below:

I $\begin{array}{ccccc} f_S & - & bc^* & - & a \\ | & & | & & | \\ f_D & - & bc^* & - & a \end{array}$, two separate intercommunicating chains, where c^* is either c or c_1, or

II $\begin{array}{l} f_S \searrow \\ \quad\quad (b)_2\ (c_1 + c) - (a)_2 \\ f_D \nearrow \end{array}$, a single chain into which both flavoproteins funnel electrons. The weakness of the second formulation is that all the differences between the two chains would have to be localized between the two flavoproteins and the bc_1 cytochromes. One of the weaknesses of the first formulation is that there is insufficient c_1 for two chains and c and c_1 are not equivalent. The other weakness is that electronic intercommunication of two separate chains would require implementation by a special set of components, and no components are as yet known which fulfill that function.

In mitochondria both cytochromes *b* and c_1 are rapidly reducible by either succinate or DPNH, according to the measurements of Chance and Williams (8). In nonphosphorylating ETP the reduction of cytochrome c_1 is far more rapid than that of cytochrome *b*, and in several derivative particles prepared by fragmentation of ETP the disparity in the two rates of reduction is so great that for practical purposes cytochrome *b* can be considered no longer capable of reduction (29). Whatever the position of cytochrome *b* in the chain, it cannot be the electron donor for cytochrome c_1. The reduction of cytochrome c_1 is antimycin-sensitive, whereas that of cytochrome *b* is not. Thus cytochrome c_1 cannot be the electron donor for cytochrome *b*. These observations appear to exclude a common chain for cytochromes *b* and c_1 and they suggest that electrons from succinate or DPNH reach cytochrome *a* either by way of cytochrome *b* or by way of cytochrome c_1. The path by way of cytochrome *b* is more labile than that by way of cytochrome c_1, and it is only in the intact mitochondrion of ETP, with phosphorylating potentialities preserved, that the two pathways are equivalent. Thus *formula I* for the respiratory chain of ETP has to be modified as shown below:

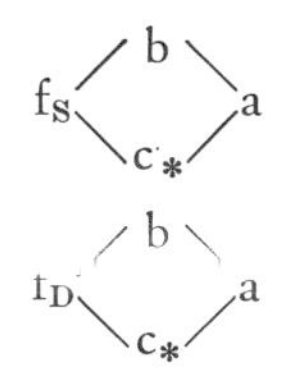

and *formula II* correspondingly,

IIa

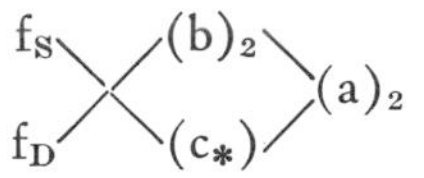

$$\begin{matrix} f_S \\ f_D \end{matrix} \times \begin{matrix} (b)_2 \\ (c_*) \end{matrix} > (a)_2 \qquad \text{where } c_* = c_1 \text{ or } c.$$

The most recent information suggests an arrangement quite different from that of *I* and *II*. As shown in *formula III* below, coenzyme Q is localized in the succinic chain while a new component which we shall call dithiolipoic dehydrogenase (D_t) is part of the DPNH chain:

III

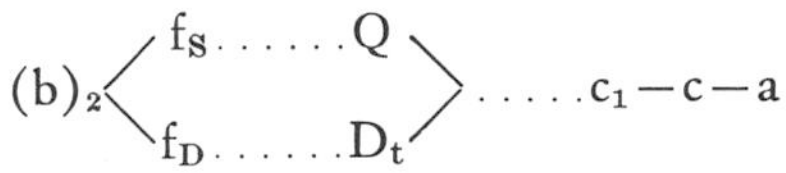

$$(b)_2 < \begin{matrix} f_S \ldots\ldots Q \\ f_D \ldots\ldots D_t \end{matrix} > \ldots\ldots c_1 - c - a$$

The position of *b* is still indeterminate, and it is not excluded that it may be the link between f_S and Q. The dotted lines indicate that additional components may be implicated.

The oxidation-reduction components of the electron transfer chain may be classified into two categories: *1*) the fixed components, which are usually relatively high-molecular weight proteins from 100,000 upwards; and *2*) the mobile components, which are relatively small molecules of molecular weight 500–13,000. The fixed components include the two flavoproteins, cytochromes *b*, c_1 and *a*, whereas the mobile components include cytochrome *c*, coenzyme Q and α-tocopherol. The available evidence suggests that the isolated fixed components cannot react with one another. For example, the isolated succinic or DPNH dehydrogenases cannot react with isolated cytochrome c_1 with any measurable speed. Though information is still far from adequate, the indications are that the fixed components react with one another through small molecules which shuttle electrons from one to the other, and that these small molecules operate within lipoproteins which bridge together pairs of fixed components. Thus there are at least four sites in the succinic and DPNH chains where mobile components and lipoproteins could be anticipated and there could be additional sites where electrons would flow from one chain to the other, assuming separate succinic and DPNH chains and the intercommunication of these two chains.

This picture of the interaction of the fixed oxidation-reduction components through shuttling small molecules housed in bridging lipoproteins is at present an unabashed extrapolation from limited experimental evidence. But the auguries are good that this picture represents the true state of affairs and I shall bring to your attention some of the observations which give us this sense of confidence, so that you can judge for yourselves.

My colleague, F. L. Crane, discovered in mitochondria a fat-soluble quinone which was capable of undergoing oxidation and reduction in the electron transfer chain. This discovery was the starting point for an extensive series of studies by R. Lester, Y. Hatefi and F. L. Crane on the chemistry (23) and enzymatic (12, 20, 17) function of this new quinone, which has been named coenzyme Q. Some of the pertinent chemical and enzymatic properties of coenzyme Q or Q_{275}, as it was first called, are summarized in tables 6 and 7.

The definitive structure of coenzyme Q was established first by Karl Folkers and his group at the Merck Sharpe and Dohme Research Laboratories (32a), and this was later confirmed by R. A. Morton of Liverpool in collaboration with a group of the Hoffmann-La Roche Company in Basel (27a). The formula shown below represents the structure of the coenzyme present in higher animals, viz., coenzyme Q_{10}.

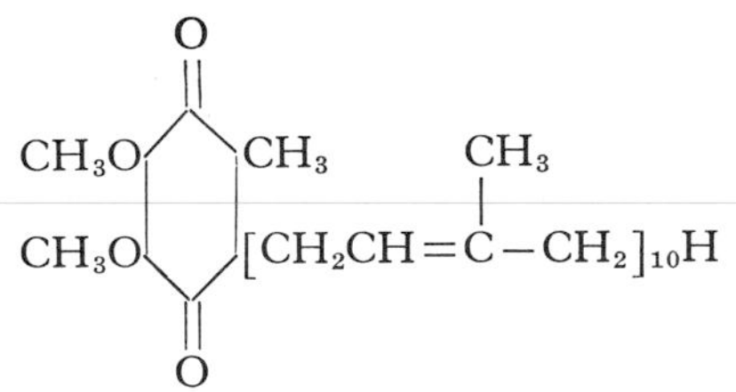

Bacteria and microorganisms contain variants with 6, 7, 8 and 9 isoprenoid units in the side chain, and these are called coenzyme Q_6, coenzyme Q_7, etc. (23).

The available evidence points to the position of coenzyme Q in the electron transfer chain between cytochrome *b* on the electron donor side and cytochrome *a* on the electron acceptor side. Whether coenzyme Q accepts electrons from reduced cytochrome *b* is unknown. But it can be stated unambiguously that reduced coenzyme Q does not donate electrons directly to cytochrome *a*.

TABLE 6. CHEMICAL PROFILE OF COENZYME Q

1) Orange yellow crystals, m.p. 49.9°
2) $C_{58}H_{88}O_4$
3) Molecular weight 850
4) Ultraviolet and infrared confirm quinone structure
5) Quinone ring system—side chain with approximately 10 isoprenoid units
6) Isolated from mitochondria and particles with electron transport activity
7) Analogs of coenzyme Q are widely distributed in all aerobic organisms

TABLE 7. EVIDENCE FOR ROLE OF COENZYME Q IN ELECTRON TRANSPORT

1) > Respiratory rate of tissue > concentration (*Azotobacter* > heart > liver)
2) Internal coenzyme Q reducible by succinate and DPNH in ETP and mitochondria
3) Restores succinoxidase activity of heptane extracted particles
4) Phosphate freezes coenzyme Q in reduced form, ADP in oxidized form
5) Oxidoreduction of coenzyme Q inhibited by antimycin and other respiratory inhibitors

TABLE 8. PROPERTIES OF Q LIPOPROTEIN

1) Soluble in H_2O
2) Lipid 96%, 4% protein
3) Homogeneous in ultracentrifuge and electrophoresis
4) Molecular weight about 5×10^6
5) Binds cytochrome *c*, vitamins A, E, and K_1, indophenol, coenzyme Q and phenazine
6) Accounts for bulk of mitochondrial lipid, coenzyme Q and carotenoids
7) Denatured by successive freezing and thawing
8) Disaggregated by cholate and deoxycholate

My colleagues, J. Järnefelt, R. Basford and Howard Tisdale, and I (22, 2) have isolated a lipoprotein from the electron transport particle which has the properties summarized in table 8 and which has been called the Q lipoprotein. There are many fascinating properties of this lipoprotein which I should like to discuss with you, but I shall have to restrict myself to one particular property which is germane to our previous discussion. This lipoprotein contains coenzyme Q in sufficiently high concentration that the possibility cannot be excluded that the bulk, if not all, of the coenzyme Q of the electron transport particle is concentrated in the lipoprotein. Whatever uncertainty there is as to how much of the total coenzyme Q is concentrated in this lipoprotein, there are no reasons to doubt that a part at least of coenzyme Q normally resides within the lipid core of the lipoprotein and there undergoes cyclical oxidation and reduction. My colleague, Y. Hatefi, has recently shown that the oxidation of reduced coenzyme Q by molecular oxygen catalyzed by a purified cytochrome oxidase preparation (table 9) requires, in addition to cytochrome *c*, the Q lipoprotein (18). This is a most significant series of observations because it demonstrates that the lipoprotein is essential for the catalytic effect of coenzyme Q and it provides the clearest evidence for the concept of small molecules operating in a shuttle capacity within lipoproteins. What is still indeterminate is exactly which pair of oxidation-reduction components is linked through coenzyme Q.

Cytochrome *c* was one of the first oxidation-reduction components of the electron transfer chain to be isolated. Keilin in the late 1920's succeeded in isolating

TABLE 9. REQUIREMENT FOR LIPOPROTEIN IN OXIDATION OF REDUCED COENZYME Q BY CYTOCHROME OXIDASE SYSTEM

	mμM RED. CO Q*		mμM RED. CO Q*
Complete system	97	No cytochrome *c* (1.5 mμmoles)	5
No lipoprotein (20γ protein)	6	No cytochrome oxidase (0.5 mg)	0

Cytochrome oxidase is a purified preparation which contains *a* heme. The externally added coenzyme Q in this experiment represents > 50 times the coenzyme Q content of the added lipoprotein. Reaction mixture contains 170 mμmoles reduced coenzyme Q in a final volume of 1 ml.

* Oxidized/45 sec. at 38°C.

this cytochrome from both yeast and heart muscle. The isolated cytochrome is a water-soluble molecule of molecular weight 13,000. It is only very recently that we have come to appreciate that the least complex water-soluble forms in which the cytochromes and the flavoproteins can be isolated bear the same relation to their physiological forms as does nicotinamide to diphosphopyridine nucleotide. For that reason the properties of these simple forms are highly deceptive, and two generations of biochemists have understandably fallen into a trap.

To the best of our knowledge, cytochrome *c* in its classical form does not exist as such in mitochondria or in the electron transport particle. Widmer and Crane in our laboratory have discovered that cytochrome *c* exists in the form of one or more lipid-soluble complexes in the electron transport particle (32). One such complex can be isolated by treating ETP with deoxycholate; another can be prepared by mixing cytochrome *c* and the Q lipoprotein. These complexes are insoluble in water and soluble in various organic solvents including hydrocarbons. The lipid-complexes of cytochrome *c* still retain enzymatic activity and can substitute for the water-soluble form in restoring enzymatic activity. There may well be a family of lipid-cytochrome *c*'s which function at different parts of the chain and which may be peculiar to either the succinic or DPNH chain. One locus of action is certainly between coenzyme Q and cytochrome *a* in the succinic chain, but other loci are not excluded.

The particular point I want to stress is that cytochrome *c* functionally resembles coenzyme Q more closely than the fixed oxidation-reduction components. It is a relatively small molecule. It is readily taken up by the Q lipoprotein. It is readily extracted from the electron transfer particle by lipid-splitting reagents such as isobutyl and butyl alcohols and deoxycholate, and it can be reinserted into the particles from which it was extracted. The fact that the water-soluble form has catalytic properties is not surprising in view of the ease with which the lipid-complex is formed by interaction of cytochrome *c* with the phosphatides of various lipoproteins.

The exact chemical composition of the various lipid complexes of cytochrome *c* has yet to be clarified and this problem is now under active investigation by F. L. Crane and K. Ambe.

My colleagues, J. Järnefelt, and H. Tisdale, and I have isolated cytochrome c_1 for the first time in our laboratory as a water-soluble molecule in homogeneous state with a molecular weight of about 380,000 (15). It can readily be shown that this form is derived from a complex of cytochrome c_1 and a specific lipoprotein which contains 66 per cent by weight of lipid. When this complex is exposed to the action of sodium lauryl sulfate or Duponol, the cytochrome is released from the complex, and the lipoprotein and cytochrome c_1 can then be isolated separately. Again we find evidence of lipid, in the form of a lipoprotein, being closely associated with the oxidation-reduction components of the electron transfer chain.

More recently my colleagues, Daniel Ziegler and Howard Tisdale, and I have been able to isolate DPNH dehydrogenase in the form of a lipid complex which is at least ten times more active in enzymatic assays than the classical lipid-free dehydrogenase. The lipid-free DPNH dehydrogenase was previously shown by Mahler and co-workers in our laboratory to react with cytochrome *c* and to contain as prosthetic group a flavin dinucleotide other than flavin adenine dinucleotide. It has been possible to show quite unambiguously that flavin adenine dinucleotide is indeed the prosthetic group of the DPNH dehydrogenase. In the course of isolation by the older method the flavin prosthetic group becomes modified, and coincident with this modification of the flavin the capacity to interact with cytochrome *c* emerges. Apparently both of these properties are artifacts of preparation. More important, the physiological form of the dehydrogenase which contains FAD as prosthetic group is linked to lipid—one of the components of which may well be the physiological electron acceptor for reduced flavin.

I hope that my account so far has at least acquainted you with the broad strategy of our efforts to deduce the structural pattern of the electron transfer chain. Vitamin K, vitamin E, and carotenoids are other lipid components which may eventually find a place in the electron transport system, though we ourselves have made relatively little contribution in that area. Vitamin E has been shown by Nason (28) and Slater (5) to be present in mitochondria, and a requirement for the vitamin in the oxidation of DPNH by cytochrome *c* can be shown with isooctane-extracted particles according to Nason. A role for vitamin K in the electron transfer chain of *Mycobacterium phlei* has been indicated by the work of Brodie *et al.* (6).

Martius was first to claim a role for vitamin K in oxidative phosphorylation reactions of animal mitochondria. However, it should be stressed that the occurrence of vitamin K *as such* in animal mitochondria has not been established. An intriguing possibility is that coenzyme Q is either the functional form of vitamin K which is operative in mitochondrial reactions, or that coenzyme Q plays a role analogous to the role of vitamin K in microorganisms.

Finally, I would like to remind you that it is no longer possible to entertain seriously the classical picture of the electron transfer chain as a series of free-moving cytochromes interacting with one another serially by thermal collisions. The cytochromes, with the possible exception of cytochrome *c*, are rigidly positioned in the particle. They do not react directly with other cytochromes or flavoproteins, and they are separated from one another by lipoproteins or lipid components. It is presumably only the small molecules which react by thermal collision and even this degree of freedom is limited by the spatial restrictions imposed by the lipid core of the lipoproteins in which they are located.

REFERENCES

1. Basford, R. E. and D. E. Green. In preparation.
2. Basford, R. E. and D. E. Green. *Biochim. et biophys. acta.* In press.
3. Basford, R. E., H. D. Tisdale, J. L. Glenn and D. E. Green. *Biochim. et biophys. acta* 24: 107, 1957.
4. Basford, R. E., H. D. Tisdale and D. E. Green. *Biochim et biophys. acta* 24: 290, 1957.
5. Bouman, J. and E. C. Slater. *Biochim. et biophys. acta* 26: 624, 1957.
6. Brodie, A. F., M. M. Weber and C. T. Gray. *Biochim. et biophys. acta* 25: 448, 1957.
7. Bruemmer, J. H., P. W. Wilson, J. L. Glenn and F. L. Crane. *J. Bact.* 73: 113, 1957.
8. Chance, B. and G. R. Williams. *J. Biol. Chem.* 217: 383, 1955.
9. Crane, F. L. and J. L. Glenn. *Biochem. et biophys. acta* 24: 100, 1957.
10. Crane, F. L., J. L. Glenn and D. E. Green. *Biochim. et biophys. acta* 22: 475, 1956.
11. Crane, F. L., Y. Hatefi, R. L. Lester and C. Widmer. *Biochim. et biophys. acta* 25: 220, 1957.
12. Crane, F. L., C. Widmer, R. L. Lester and Y. Hatefi. *Biochim. et biophys, acta* 31: 476, 1959.
13. de Bernard, B. *Biochim. et biophys. acta* 29: 510, 1957.
14. Filmer, D. L., P. J. Kaesberg, A. W. Linnane and D. E. Green. Unpublished observations.
15. Green, D. E., J. Järnefelt and H. Tisdale. *Biochim. et biophys. acta* 31: 34, 1959.
16. Green, D. E., S. Mii and P. M. Kohout. *J. Biol. Chem.* 217: 551, 1955.
17. Hatefi, Y. *Biochem. et biophys. acta.* In press.
18. Hatefi, Y. Unpublished observations.
19. Hatefi, Y. and R. L. Lester. *Biochem. et biophys. acta* 27: 83, 1958.
20. Hatefi, Y., R. L. Lester, F. L. Crane and C. Widmer. *Biochim. et biophys. acta* 31: 490, 1959.
21. Hogeboom, G. H. and W. C. Schneider. *J. Biol. Chem.* 186: 417, 1950.
22. Järnefelt, J., R. E. Basford, H. Tisdale and D. E. Green. *Biochim. et biophys. acta* 29: 123, 1958.
23. Lester, R. L., F. L. Crane and Y. Hatefi. *J. Am. Chem. Soc.* 80: 4751, 1958.
24. Linnane, A. W. *Biochim. et biophys. acta* 30: 221, 1958.
25. Linnane, A. W. and D. M. Ziegler. *Biochim. et biophys. acta* 29: 630, 1958.
26. Mahler, H. R., N. K. Sarkar and L. P. Vernon. *J. Biol. Chem.* 199: 585, 1952.
27. Martius, C. *Biochem. Ztschr.* 326: 26, 1954.

27a. Morton, R. A., U. Gloor, O. Schindler, G. M. Wilson, L. H. Chopart-dit-Jean, F. W. Hemming, O. Isler, W. M. F. Leat, J. F. Pennock, R. Riegg, O. Schwieter and O. Wiss. *Helvet. chim. acta* 41: 2343, 1958.

28. Nason, A., B. C. Averbach and A. J. Terrell. *Biochim. et biophys. acta* 19: 395, 1956.
29. Rabinowitz, M. and B. de Bernard. *Biochim. et biophys. acta* 26: 22, 1957.
30. Schneider, W. C. and G. H. Hogeboom. *Ann. Rev. Biochem.* 25: 201, 1956.
31. Singer, T. P., E. B. Kearney and P. Bernath. *J. Biol. Chem.* 223: 599, 1956.
32. Widmer, C. and J. L. Crane. *Biochim. et biophys. acta* 27: 203, 1958.

32a. Wolf, D. E., C. H. Hoffman, N. R. Trenner, B. H. Arison, C. H. Shunk, B. O. Linn, J. F. McPherson and K. Folkers. *J. Am. Chem. Soc.* 80: 4752, 1958.

33. Ziegler, D. M. and A. W. Linnane. *Biochim et biophys. acta* 30: 53, 1958.
34. Ziegler, D. M., A. W. Linnane, D. E. Green, C. M. S. Dass and H. Ris. *Biochim. et biophys. acta* 28: 524, 1958.

DISCUSSION

L. V. Heilbrunn

DR. HEILBRUNN: I want to thank Dr. Green for the liberal education he has given us. Also, I am happy to note that lipids are now given an important place in the oxidative machinery of a cell. Back in 1943, in the second edition of *Outline of General Physiology,* I predicted that something of the sort would happen.

Particles in Photosynthetic Phosphorylation[1]

MARTIN D. KAMEN AND JACK W. NEWTON

Brandeis University
Waltham, Massachusetts

THE DIVERSITY OF PHOTOSYNTHETIC TISSUES, ranging from anaerobic photosynthetic bacteria to the aerobic higher green plants, may be correlated with a hierarchy of photo-active subcellular particles. These particles range in size from those encountered in bacteria and some blue-green algae—so-called 'chromatophores' in bacteria and 'grana' in the algae—to relatively enormous chloroplasts in some green plants. Chromatophores are spherical or semispherical bodies which can be as small as 20–40 millimicrons in diameter, while chloroplasts are variegated and often up to two orders of magnitude greater in linear dimensions. Grana are usually disc-shaped and intermediate in size between chromatophores and chloroplasts. They can occur as components or as individual entities.

Considerable work has been done on the structure of chloroplasts and grana (28). Chloroplasts in higher plants are generally ellipsoidal, typical dimensions in unicellular algae being 4–6 microns in diameter and 0.5–1 micron thick. They can exhibit a variety of forms. Usually a laminar pattern is seen in grana, indicating a structure consisting of 20–30 thin disc-shaped plates in a stack. These platelets are probably protein discs about 10 millimicrons thick which can carry one or more complete layers of chlorophyll intermixed with other components of the photo-active system such as carotenoids, pyridine nucleotides, heme proteins, etc. Generally, the grana are embedded in unpigmented lipoproteins—so-called 'stroma'—which are probably the locus for enzymes involved in secondary functions such as CO_2 assimilation, phosphate transfer, protein and lipid synthesis, etc.

Nothing is known about the fine structure of bacterial chromatophores but it is reasonable to suppose they are similar to small grana such as those found in blue-green algae. In fact, if we neglect the specification of a nucleus, a cell like the anaerobic sulfur bacterium ***Chromatium*** can be considered as analogous to a chloroplast, the chromatophores filling the role of grana and the extrachromatophore material that of the stroma. Recently, electron microscope pictures of

[1] Publication No. 21, Graduate Department of Biochemistry, Brandeis University. Many of the researches described in this paper were made possible by financial support from the National Science Foundation, the C. F. Kettering Foundation and the National Institutes of Health.

Chromatium have been published which suggest strongly that this analogy is not far-fetched (30).

These considerations lead to the expectation that a varied pattern of enzymatic composition should be found in all of these subcellular photo-active particles, depending on their degree of fragmentation. 'Whole' chloroplasts such as those isolated from *Spirogyra* (29) or spinach (4) appear to contain a great number of enzymes, sufficient in fact to enable the chloroplast to function as a complete photosynthetic unit (1). Fragmented chloroplasts, grana and chromatophores show fewer enzymatic activities, a number of soluble enzymes being recovered in the supernatant fluid from broken particles (11, 12, 2, 20). However, all of these particles, fragmented or not, exhibit a general reaction initiated by light absorption and presumably intimately connected with the photochemical act. This reaction is the light-activated esterification of adenosine diphosphate (ADP) by inorganic phosphate (P_i) to form adenosine triphosphate (ATP); *e.g.*, $ADP + P_i + light \rightarrow ATP$. The characteristics of this reaction, called 'photophosphorylation,' are quite similar in all the different particles encountered, regardless of structural complexity, and can be described adequately by considering any one of the many systems which have been studied. This report will be based on results obtained using bacterial chromatophores.

HISTORY

The hypothesis which is favored at present for the general mechanism of photophosphorylation pictures the process as a phosphorylation coupled to electron transport in an oxidative system, analogous to the coupled oxidative phosphorylation seen in mitochondria of plant and animal cells. The notion of an oxidation coupled with the photochemical act is quite old. R. Hill was probably the first to formulate such a process specifically in biochemical terms (14). Many others have considered it since, particularly in connection with phosphorylations. An example is the mechanism proposed by Ruben, who formulated a scheme in 1943 whereby the eventual carbon dioxide acceptor—an aldehyde—was activated for carboxylation by an enzymic phosphorylation reaction (25). The energy for this reaction was supplied in his scheme by coupled oxido-reduction reactions utilizing a portion of the reductant and oxidant generated photochemically. As models he proposed the well-known phosphorylation mechanisms operative in the oxidation of triosephosphate to 1, 3-diphosphoglycerate (33) and in the generation of acetyl phosphate during pyruvic acid oxidation (17). Lipmann and Tuttle (18) formulated a similar scheme based on stepwise reduction of acylphosphate bonds. Davenport and Hill (9) postulated dismutation reactions between heme protein components to be involved in the energy storage reactions.

In 1953, Vernon and Kamen noted an enzymic cytochrome *c* photo-oxidase system in chromatophores of photosynthetic bacteria (31), a system later found also by Nieman and Vennesland in green plant chloroplasts (23). This reaction required oxygen and did not occur anaerobically when exogenous hydrogen acceptors other than oxygen were added. From evidence gathered in studies on simultaneous photo-oxidation of ethanol and ascorbate by both plant chloroplast preparations and bacterial chromatophores, it was adduced that the photo-oxidation of the cytochrome *c*, or of any cytochrome *c* substitute such as 2,6-dichlorophenolindophenol, was the resultant of two simultaneous photo-oxidations (32). One of these involved the action of oxygen as a Hill reagent, the other involved utilization of the photochemical oxidant itself. Thus, if we denote by [H] the photo-reductant and by [OH] the photo-oxidant, then a series of reactions of the following type could be visualized:

1) $2HOH \xrightarrow{h\nu} 2[H] + 2[OH]$
2) $2[H] + O_2 \longrightarrow `H_2O_2'$
3) $`H_2O_2' + 2H^+ + 2Fe^{+2}\ Cyt \longrightarrow 2Fe^{+3}\ Cyt + 2H_2O$
4) $2[OH] + 2H^+ + 2Fe^{+2}\ Cyt \longrightarrow 2Fe^{+3}\ Cyt + 2H_2O$

The over-all reaction would be:

$$4Fe^{+2}\ Cyt + 4H^+ + O_2 \longrightarrow 4Fe^{+3}\ Cyt + 2H_2O$$

as required by the stoichiometry established experimentally (32).

This scheme was based on the specific requirement for oxygen as a Hill reagent for trapping [H], and the experimental failure to separate [H] and [OH] under anaerobic conditions. In 1954, however, Frenkel, using the same experimental system (*R. rubrum* chromatophores), showed that a light-activated phosphorylation occurred under strictly anaerobic conditions (10). A similar observation was made by Arnon and co-workers at about the same time, using green plant chloroplast preparations (4). These results could be interpreted to indicate sufficient separation of photo-oxidant and photo-reductant to support anaerobic oxidative electron transport reactions in which coupled phosphorylation could occur. A similar photo-activated phosphorylation was demonstrated somewhat later using the chromatophores from the strict anaerobes *Chromatium* and *Chlorobium* (19, 20).

Earlier, Gest and Kamen (13) had demonstrated that illumination greatly accelerated the uptake of inorganic phosphate (P^{32}-labeled) by intact cells of *R. rubrum,* incubated anaerobically, and also the turnover of phosphorus between soluble and insoluble cellular fractions. These effects of illumination were no doubt the result of the photo-activated phosphorylation later observed by Frenkel and others in chromatophore preparations. It appears that photophosphorylation is the experimental realization in cell-free systems of the process of coupled phosphorylation postulated in the schemes of Ruben, Lipmann, and others. If we add that the phosphorylated acceptor of carbon dioxide is considered to be ribulose diphosphate (7) formed by reaction of this light-generated ATP with ribulose phosphate (15, 24), we have the formulation for the biochemical process of carbon dioxide fixation assumed at present to be operative in photosynthesis.

CHARACTERISTICS OF PHOTOPHOSPHORYLATION IN CHROMATOPHORE PREPARATIONS

Properties of Chromatophores. The photo-active subcellular particles in which coupled phosphorylation occurs, from any given species of the photosynthetic bacteria, appear to be very similar or identical to those obtained from any other species, at least as regards gross morphology and chemical composition. Those from *R. rubrum,* first noted by Schachman, Pardee and Stanier (27), have been described as spherical bodies ranging in size from 50 to 200 millimicrons (3, 11, 12). They may be obtained in a variety of ways; e.g., extraction of cells disrupted by grinding with alumina, sonication, etc., followed usually by differential centrifugation. With increasing fragmentation of the cells, the percentage of lipid in the chromatophores rises to over 50 per cent of the dry weight, the remainder being mainly protein.

Similar results are obtained using *Chromatium.* When sonication is prolonged, fragmentation of the *Chromatium* chromatophores results, accompanied by the loss of polysaccharide and small quantities of protein. The chromatophore fragments appear to be uniform in size, in the range 20–40 millimicrons in diameter, and are essentially phospholipoprotein in nature; they contain all the chlorophyll and most of the carotenoid and cytochrome components of the original intact cell. Thus, per milligram of protein, Newton and Newton (21) find in the chromatophore fragments, in millimicromoles each: 40 chlorophyll, 17 carotenoid, 2.75 cytochrome (lumped and determined as pyridine hemochromogen), 0.5 flavin and 0.9 pyridine nucleotide (21). The corresponding values for intact chromatophores are 20, 11, 1.48, 1.0, and 1.2.

It is seen that the chlorophyll and cytochrome remain bound tenaciously to the particles, while other components are lost to a certain extent. Co-factors for the photophosphorylation reaction are apparently also lost, because the fragments exhibit only 5–10% of the specific reaction rate given by intact chromatophores (20). Similar findings have been reported with washed *R. rubrum* chromatophores (11) and spinach chloroplasts (2, 6).

An interesting finding with the *Chromatium* chromatophore fragments is that all the basic moiety of the phospholipid is accounted for as ethanolamine. This, taken with the finding of equimolar amounts of ethanolamine, phosphate and glycerol indicates the presence of a considerable amount of ethanolamine phosphatidic acid (21).

The action spectrum for photophosphorylation coincides with the absorption spectrum of the bacteriochlorophyll (12, 16).

Requirements for Photophosphorylation. Photophosphorylation is an anaerobic process and is inhibited by oxygen (12, 19, 34). In addition to ADP and inorganic phosphate, magnesium ion is required (32, 11, 2). To activate the washed chromatophores of *R. rubrum,* small or catalytic amounts of succinate or DPNH (but not DPN) are needed. Arnon, Whatley and Allen (5) have shown that TPN rather than DPN is a specific catalyst in chloroplast photophosphorylation. A soluble TPNH-linked dehydrogenase is present in chloroplast supernatant extracts which is required to demonstrate the TPN requirement (26). San Pietro and Lang have described recently a light-catalyzed pyridine nucleotide reductase in spinach chloroplast extracts which is more active with TPN than DPN (26). Extension of these studies to the bacterial systems is indicated.

In *Chromatium* chromatophore fragments, succinate is ineffectual, while other reducing agents, such as thiol compounds and DPNH, work well. The most dramatic effects are noted with compounds of intermediate electrochemical potential, such as phenazine methosulfate and ascorbate (12, 20). Detailed studies with both *R. rubrum* and *Chromatium* preparations are in accord, generally, in ascribing the effect of either of these agents to an interaction with some component of the electron transport chain, whereby the component is brought to an optimal value of electrochemical potential (20).

Interactions With Inhibitors. The effect of various inhibitors, other than oxygen, are generally similar whether using preparations from bacteria or green plants. Thus, all observers are agreed on the failure of the well-known respiratory inhibitors (cyanide, azide and carbon monoxide) to affect photophosphorylation when present in concentrations usually almost 100 per cent effective in stopping oxygen uptake. Responses to other inhibitors, especially those blocking electron transport in oxidative phosphorylation, depend on the nature of the preparation. In *R. rubrum,* for instance, the succinate- or DPNH-catalyzed photophosphorylation is inhibited by antimycin at levels which are effective in blocking electron transport, but the phenazine methosulfate-catalyzed reaction is not (12).

Inhibitors of oxidative phosphorylation, like dinitrophenol, the butyl ester of 3,5-hydroxybenzoic acid, dicumarol and various dyes (2,6-dichlorophenolindophenol, methylene blue, brilliant cresyl blue, pyocyanine, etc.) are all effective as inhibitors of photophosphorylation (12), although in some cases the concentration required for inhibition may be an order of magnitude greater than that observed with oxidative phosphorylation (20). One notable difference between *Chromatium* and *R. rubrum* preparations is that 2,6-dichlorophenolindophenol in trace amounts is an activator rather than an inhibitor for the former.

Arsenite fails to affect photophosphorylation, indicating strongly that participation of lipoic acid is unlikely (12). Chelating agents, such as *o*-phenanthroline or 8-hydroxyquinoline, are only effective at rather high concentrations (12, 20).

An interesting finding is that phenazine methosulfate, or ascorbate, when present with an excess of reducing agent, or in the presence of each other, fail to activate photophosphorylation, and in fact become inhibitory (2). Likewise, a catalytic amount of 2,6-dichlorophenolindophenol, ordinarily an activator, profoundly diminishes the activating effect of phenazine methosulfate (20).

IMMUNOCHEMICAL STUDIES

Recently, Newton and Levine (22) have begun a series of researches based on an immunochemical approach. They have shown that antisera directed specifically against different immunologically active sites in the chromatophores, chromatophore fragments, cell walls of *Chromatium,* and intracellular proteins can be obtained in the usual manner by injection of suspensions of these cellular derivatives, or of whole cells, into rabbits. Cross-reactions between antisera directed against the chromatophore fragments and a number of cellular macromolecules, including wall polysaccharide, intracellular lipoprotein and polysaccharide from chromatophore fragments, have been studied, using such procedures as precipitin reactions, single and double diffusion in agar, complement fixation and immunoelectrophoresis. All of the tests confirm the identity of the chromatophore fragment antigen and the various fractions cited. From these results it can be concluded that the chromatophores are derived, at least in part, from material structurally similar to that making up the cell wall, and that soluble intracellular protein is structurally similar to the surface protein of chromatophores. A unique feature of this technique as applied to a photo-active system is that the antigen is colored, thereby simplifying application of the method.

These studies indicate that immunochemical techniques can be extended as a promising method for identifying active sites on the lipoprotein complex. In addition, the nature of the binding sites for chlorophyll and carotenoid can be inferred by correlation of observations of changes in chlorophyll spectrum and degree of antigenic activity as a function of proteolytic digestion by agents such as trypsin, subtilin, etc. There are many other applications too numerous to mention in this limited space.

SIGNIFICANCE OF PHOTOPHOSPHORYLATION REACTION

The similarities which exist between the bacterial chromatophores and the green plant chloroplasts are such as to indicate that the same general mechanism is operative in photometabolism in both types of systems. It appears that the only essential difference between green plant and bacterial photosynthesis—namely, the lack of an oxygen evolution system in the latter case—is also the only essential difference found between bacterial chromatophores and green plant chloroplasts. It is likely that both systems function identically, or very similarly, in effecting photophosphorylation.

We may discuss briefly the mechanisms which may be operative on the basis of the facts presented and the comparative biochemistry of photosynthesis. The various observations recorded can be fitted into a scheme in which it is supposed that the phosphorylating particles contain a system of electron transport carriers comprising a 'chain' of interacting oxidation-reduction (redox) systems. It seems reasonable to suppose that an optimal steady-state relation exists between oxidized and reduced forms of the interacting electron carriers (8). Upon illumination of the chromatophores, both electron donors and acceptors are made available to this system because it is coupled so closely to the photo-active pigments (19). The resultant recombination reaction, or back-oxidation, is mediated by this electron transport chain, resulting in accumulation of ATP. In green plants, only a small fraction of the electron transport possible is required for the ATP needed to activate the biosyntheses ascribed to the photochemical apparatus; accordingly, most of the photo-oxidant can be dispensed with as oxygen, while the unreacted photo-reductant is utilized for reductive assimilation of carbon dioxide. In the bacteria, no oxygen-evolving system is present. It seems possible that one of the several important functions of the added accessory hydrogen donor is to prevent destructive peroxidation reactions, which, as a corollary, may inhibit metabolism by over-oxidizing components of the photo-activated electron transport chain.

It is not certain that the electrochemical potential difference generated by the light reaction between photo-reductant and oxidant is the same in green plants and photosynthetic bacteria. That is, there may be oxidants of different electrochemical potentials produced. In plants the terminal oxidant certainly has a potential close to that of the oxygen electrode at physiological pH ($E'_0 = +0.8$ v) so that the full potential difference between the hydrogen and oxygen electrode potentials (approximately 1.2 v) may be available. The electron transport chain coupled to the chloroplast system may span this whole range so that photophosphorylation efficiency is maximal for each electron transferred. On the other hand, the bacterial photo-oxidant may be generated at a considerably lower electrochemical potential, particularly in the strict anaerobes, so that a much smaller potential span is available in bacterial photosynthesis. Hence, the photophosphorylation efficiency in the bacteria may be significantly less. This may be correlated with the fact that although green plants dissipate most of their photo-oxidant as molecular oxygen, they still make enough ATP by photophosphorylation to satisfy all requirements for carbon dioxide assimilation. On the other hand, the bacteria with a less efficient system may require all their photo-oxidant to be reduced through the electron transport system.

We have remarked that the electron transport chain couples maximally when each of the component redox systems is at an optimal oxidation level. We may suppose that alteration of the steady-state condition for optimal coupling will result in a certain amount of inactivation of the system. In the extreme cases of complete oxidation or reduction of all components, there would be minimal photophosphorylation. It is reasonable to assume that isolation of the chromatophores from the cell upsets one or more of the redox systems in its relation to the others so that suboptimal conditions for coupling arise. Compounds which can enter into redox equilibrium with the chain can activate by 'pushing' or 'pulling' the affected redox systems back to a better electrochemical range for coupling, that is, a range in which the redox system operates during chromatophore function in the intact cell. The dramatic repression of activation by phenazine methosulfate, or ascorbate, when excess reducing agent is added (20), could be explained on the basis of this mechanism; i.e., if phenazine methosulfate is converted to a more reduced state, it may no longer be effective in restoring the electrochemical potential of the redox system postulated to be altered by the isolation procedure.

Excessive oxidation of the phenazine methosulfate should also create a suboptimal redox state. This, in fact, is noted when phenazine methosulfate is photo-oxidized; i.e., the products formed are inhibitory (20). Geller (12) has observed that a slight reduction of phenazine methosulfate is required for optimal activation.

The remarkable effect of 2,6-dichlorophenolindophenol in inhibiting photophosphorylation activation by ascorbate or phenazine methosulfate in *Chromatium* preparations (12) cannot be ascribed to direct reactions with the activators because the indophenol dye exerts an effect when added in catalytic concentrations. A possible explanation is that a redox couple between the activator and the dye is set up which effectively bypasses a portion of the natural chain; if the potential drop left along the chain is insufficient to supply the requisite energy for formation of ATP when one electron is transferred, phosphorylation would not occur. This 'bypass' mechanism has also been proposed to account for the fact that while antimycin inhibits succinate-catalyzed photophosphorylation, it does not affect the phenazine methosulfate-activated system (12). It is remarkable that the condition—presence of a redox couple such as ascorbate + 2,6-dichlorophenolindophenol—which is optimal for photo-oxidation in air (31) is also the same condition which under anaerobic conditions leads to inhibition of photophosphorylation. This suggests that the redox couple is setting up a competitive interaction with the portion of the electron transport chain involved in photophosphorylation and effectively bypassing a part of the chain. The involvement of vitamin K in the chloroplast photophosphorylation, inferred from effects of addition of vitamin K and ascorbate (1), may possibly be explained as owing to a bypass mechanism of this type. Vitamin K, as well as its analogs, however, does not appear to be involved in the bacterial system.

In conclusion, it appears that further study of bacterial photophosphorylation, while of interest per se, should also reveal many of the salient features of oxidative phosphorylation which may not be directly amenable to study in mitochondria and mitochondrial fragments. This expectation derives from the stability of the bacterial chromatophores, together with the absence of a number of complications associated with the obligatory use of oxygen or oxidants of relatively high electrochemical potential as hydrogen acceptors.

REFERENCES

1. Allen, M. B., D. I. Arnon, J. B. Capindale, F. R. Whatley and L. J. Durham. *J. Am. Chem. Soc.* 77: 4149, 1955.
2. Allen, M. B., F. R. Whatley, L. L. Rosenberg, J. B. Capindale and D. I. Arnon. In: *Research in Photosynthesis,* edited by H. Gaffron *et al.* New York: Interscience, 1957, p. 288.
3. Anderson, I. and R. C. Fuller. Personal communication.
4. Arnon, D. I., M. B. Allen and F. R. Whatley. *Nature* 174: 394, 1954.
5. Arnon, D. I., F. R. Whatley and M. B. Allen. *Nature* 180: 182, 1957.
6. Avron, M., A. T. Jagendorf and M. Evans. *Biochem. et biophys. acta* 26: 262, 1957.
7. Calvin, M. *Proc. 3rd Internat. Congr. Biochem. Brussels,* 1955, p. 221.
8. Chance, B. and G. R. Williams. *Advances Enzymol.* 17: 65, 1956.
9. Davenport, H. E. and R. Hill. *Proc. Roy. Soc. London, ser. B* 139: 327, 1952.
10. Frenkel, A. *J. Am. Chem. Soc.* 76: 5568, 1954.
11. Frenkel, A. J. *Biol. Chem.* 222: 823, 1956.
12. Geller, D. W. PhD. Dissert. Harvard Univ., 1957.
13. Gest, H. and M. D. Kamen. *J. Biol. Chem.* 176: 299, 1948.
14. Hill, R. *Proc. Roy. Soc. London, ser. B* 127: 192, 1939.
15. Hurwitz, J., A. Weissbach, B. C. Horecker and P. Z. Smyrniotis. *J. Biol. Chem.* 218: 769, 1956.
16. Jagendorf, A. T., S. B. Hendricks, M. Avron and M. B. Evans. *Plant Physiol.* 33: 72, 1958.
17. Lipmann, F. *Advances Enzymol.* 1: 99, 1941.
18. Lipmann, F. and L. C. Tuttle. *J. Biol. Chem.* 158: 505, 1945.
19. Newton, J. W. and M. D. Kamen. *Bacteriol. Proc.* 1956, p. 115.
20. Newton, J. W. and M. D. Kamen. *Biochim. et biophys. acta* 25: 462, 1957.
21. Newton, J. W. and G. A. Newton. *Arch. Biochem. Biophys.* 71: 250, 1957.
22. Newton, J. W. and L. Levine. Personal communication.
23. Nieman, R. H. and B. Vennesland. *Science* 125: 353, 1957.
24. Racker, E. *Nature* 175: 249, 1955.
25. Ruben, S. *J. Am. Chem. Soc.* 65: 279, 1943.
26. San Pietro, A. and H. M. Lang. *J. Biol. Chem.* 231: 210, 1958.
27. Schachman, H. K., A. B. Pardee and R. Y. Stanier. *Arch. Biochem. Biophys.* 38: 245, 1952.
28. Thomas, J. B. *Progr. Biophys. Biophys. Chem.* 5: 109, 1955.
29. Thomas, J. B. and A. M. J. Haans. *Biochim. et biophys. acta* 18: 287, 1955.

30. VATTER, A. E. AND R. S. WOLFE. *J. Bact.* 75: 480, 1958.
31. VERNON, L. P. AND M. D. KAMEN. *Arch. Biochem. Biophys.* 44: 298, 1953.
32. VERNON, L. P. AND M. D. KAMEN. *Arch. Biochem. Biophys.* 51: 122, 1954.
33. WARBURG, D. AND W. CHRISTIAN. *Biochem. Ztschr.* 303: 40, 1939.
34. WILLIAMS, A. M. *Biochim. et biophys. acta* 19: 570, 1956.

DISCUSSION

L. Ernster, M. D. Kamen

DR. ERNSTER: Do these particles exhibit phosphate-ATP exchange or ATPase activities, and, if so, are these dependent on light or dark?

DR. KAMEN: The ATP-P_i exchange is negligible. Practically all the incorporation of inorganic P is associated with net synthesis of ATP. There is no light-dependent ATPase activity.

Biochemical Studies of Isolated Golgi Membranes

EDWARD L. KUFF AND ALBERT J. DALTON

National Cancer Institute
Bethesda, Maryland

UNLIKE THE OTHER SUBCELLULAR COMPONENTS discussed in this symposium, structures encompassed by the terms 'Golgi system' or 'Golgi complex' must still be described essentially in morphological terms (21). At the level of light microscopy, Golgi structures have been defined primarily by their capacity to react with osmium tetroxide or silver salts under controlled conditions of post-fixation impregnation (10). The greater resolving power of the electron microscope has revealed that a complex and rather characteristic ultrastructure underlies the visual images thus produced (4, 5, 25, 11, 24). For example, in the case of the epithelial cells of the epididymis, we know that the Golgi image observed with the light microscope after application of the classical osmium impregnation techniques results from the deposition of metal upon the complex system of membranes and vacuoles shown in figure 1 (4). In a number of other instances, similar correlations between light and electron microscopy have been made (6, 14); and we are now accustomed to speak of such ordered arrays of smooth-surfaced membranes, presumably consisting of flattened sacs and appearing generally in association with small vesicles and vacuoles of varying size, as systems of Golgi membranes. It is not known whether these morphologically similar systems have identical biochemical composition or function wherever they are found or even whether they constitute entities entirely separate from the other cytoplasmic membranes. Indeed, these are the major problems with which we are concerned.

The results to be presented deal only with rat epididymis. The virtue of this tissue for purposes of the present study rests in the very extensive development of the Golgi system in the cells that line the highly convoluted epididymal duct (figs. 1 and 2). It has the disadvantage that we know very little about the specific cellular functions of the epididymis (16). As will be shown, it has been possible to isolate Golgi membranes that retain many of the structural details that are seen in the intact cells. Furthermore, there appear to be certain biochemical respects in which the isolated Golgi material differs from the other particulate structures of intracellular origin.

Several years ago, it was reported that a characteristic positive image could be observed with the phase contrast microscope in the supranuclear or Golgi

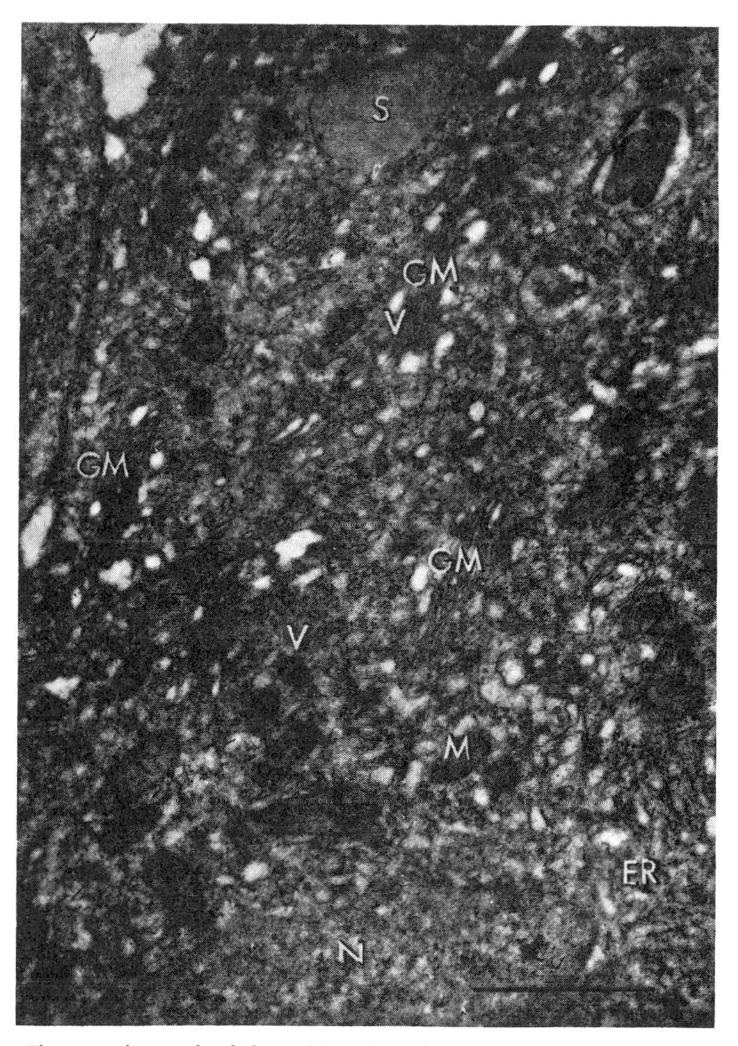

FIG. 1. Electron micrograph of the Golgi region of an epithelial cell in the rat epididymis. A portion of the nucleus (N) appears at the bottom. A pair of cell membranes runs obliquely across the upper left corner. The free surface of the cell is not shown but is toward the top. Parallel arrays of Golgi membranes (GM) are interspersed throughout the central part of the field and may be continuous in places outside the plane of section. Numerous small vesicles (v) as well as larger vacuoles with electron-lucent interiors (v) appear in association with the regularly arranged membranes. Towards the lower right and outside of the main Golgi zone appear ergastoplasmic membranes (ER) studded with small dense ribonucleoprotein particles, as well as many mitochondria (M). S denotes a large granule that is possibly secretory in nature. Fixative, 1 per cent osmium tetroxide. In this figure the bar at the lower right represents 1 micron. $\times$ 23,850.

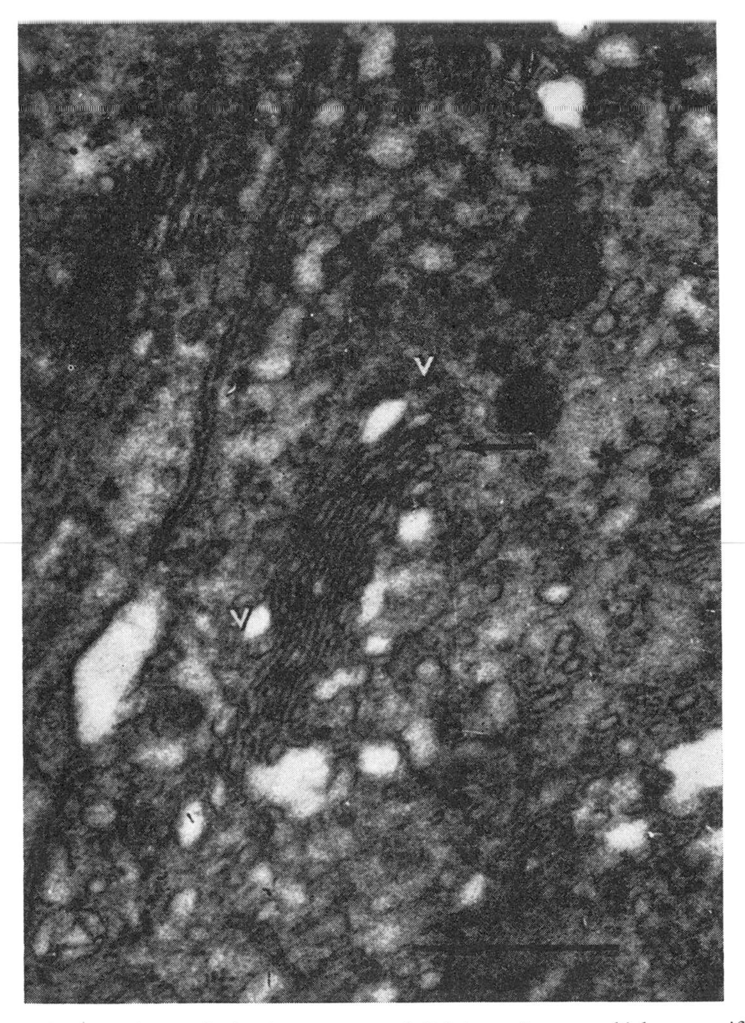

FIG. 2. Electron micrograph showing an array of Golgi membranes at higher magnification. Pairs of membranes are joined at the ends (*arrow*) indicating that the membranes bound flattened sacs of considerable extent. Expansion of an intramembranous space forms a large vacuole at V. Smaller vesicles are also present (v). The bar represents 0.5 micron. × 55,000.

region of the epididymal cells in the unfixed state (4). Upon disruption of the cells in salt-containing media, structures were released which retained for several hours the configuration and optical properties peculiar to the *in situ* formations (4). In collaboration with Dr. Walter C. Schneider, it was found that this particulate material, which we referred to as Golgi material or Golgi substance, could be isolated by centrifugation in a sucrose density gradient (22, 23).

Figure 3 illustrates both the method of fractionation and some of the biochemical results that we obtained in our first study (23). The homogenates were prepared with a loosely fitting plastic homogenizer of the Potter-Elvehjem type in a medium consisting of 0.25 M sucrose containing 0.34 M sodium chloride, The high salt concentration was employed because it provided optimum preservation of the Golgi structures as judged by phase microscopy. After centrifugation of the gradient tubes, bands of light-scattering material were present at each interface between solutions of differing density (fig. 3). Phase microscopic examination of the material in the bands revealed that characteristic Golgi structures were concentrated at the interface between densities of 1.09 and 1.13 grams per centimeter [3] (referred to as interface 1.09/1.13). The light band at interface 1.05/1.09 appeared to be optically empty under phase and was collected with the supernatant fluid. The band at interface 1.13/1.15 consisted almost entirely of very small particulate material, generally below the resolving power of the phase microscope. Sperm, nuclei, mitochondria and residual whole cells were found in the sediment.

The results of the biochemical analyses of the various fractions are presented in figure 3 in a manner introduced by de Duve and co-workers (8). Without

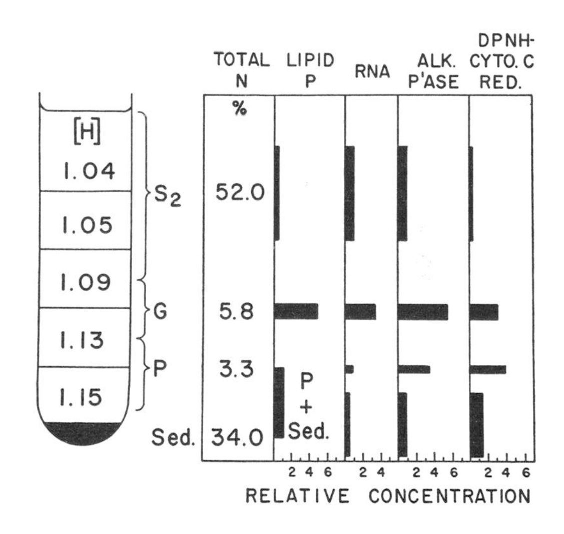

FIG. 3. Density gradient fractionation of rat epididymis. Left, diagram of a lusteroid centrifuge tube with actual dimensions of 1.5 × 4.8 cm, volume about 5.2 ml. A homogenate of epididymis (H, see text) was placed above a discontinuous sucrose gradient freshly prepared by layering solutions of the densities indicated. All solutions contained 0.34 M sodium chloride. Centrifugation at 35,600 rpm (145,000 *g*, max.) was carried out in the SW-39 rotor of a Spinco Model E ultracentrifuge for 1 hour at 0–4°, after which the fluid column was sampled to give the fractions indicated to the right of the tube. The results of the biochemical analyses are presented in the graph, the left hand column of which indicates the percentage of the total nitrogen of the homogenate that was found in each fraction. The vertical dimensions of the bars in the other columns are proportional to these nitrogen values, while the horizontal dimensions indicate the specific activities or concentrations of the biochemical components in the fractions relative to those in the whole homogenate. *Abbreviations:* N, nitrogen; P, phosphorus; Alk. Pase, alkaline phosphatase; RNA, ribonucleic acid; DPNH-cyto.*c* red., DPNH-cytochrome *c* reductase. All data, except those relating to the latter enzyme, were taken from Schneider and Kuff (23).

going into great detail, we may note that the G fraction, i.e., the fraction containing recognizable Golgi material, accounted for approximately 6 per cent of the total nitrogen of the homogenate. Lipid phosphorus was concentrated in this fraction nearly five-fold compared to the homogenate, in agreement with histochemical studies that have indicated a concentration of lipid material in the Golgi structures of intact cells (see discussions by Bourne (2) and Baker (1)). Alkaline phosphatase activity (measured by the release of inorganic phosphorus from β-glycerophosphate at pH 9) was studied because of histochemical evidence that this activity was associated with the Golgi regions of the epithelial cells of the small intestine (9, 7, 18). Again we noted a five-fold concentration of activity in the G fraction, and also a three-fold concentration of the P, or small particle, fraction. Additional data (23), not presented here, indicated that the Golgi fraction was very active in hydrolyzing several other phosphate esters, such as adenosine triphosphate (ATP) and adenylic acid; and in general the evidence suggested that high phosphatase activity was one of the outstanding characteristics of the isolated Golgi material.

Diphosphopyridine nucleotide-cytochrome *c* reductase (DPNH-cyto. *c* reductase) activity, which we shall see later is a component of the microsomes of epididymis as well as those of liver (12), was also present in the Golgi fraction. Perhaps the most surprising observation was related to the ribonucleic acid (RNA); nearly 20 per cent of the entire amount in the homogenate was recovered in the Golgi fraction, at a relative concentration of about 3.5-fold. There had been no previous evidence, either from stained preparations or ultraviolet microscopy, that RNA was associated with the Golgi system in intact cells.

It was recognized at the time that the Golgi fractions may well have been contaminated by submicroscopic material of differing intracellular origin (23). In connection with this question, and also because it was desirable to study the morphology of the isolated Golgi material with the electron microscope when reliable techniques for doing so became available, we took up the problem again after a period of several years. It soon became evident that the high RNA content of the Golgi fraction was probably the result of contamination with small ribonucleoprotein particles (19) that had been released from their original attachment to the microsomal membranes through the action of the high salt concentration employed in the gradient fractionation. For example, figure 4 presents the results of an experiment in which the layer (O) just above the Golgi fraction was examined separately and found to be extremely rich in RNA. Electron microscopy showed that this fraction consisted chiefly of small, electron-dense particles, probably subunits of the original Palade granules.

It seemed desirable, then, to modify the fractionation procedure so as to achieve a better spatial separation of the large, light Golgi material from the much smaller, but more dense (20), ribonucleoprotein particles. The technique

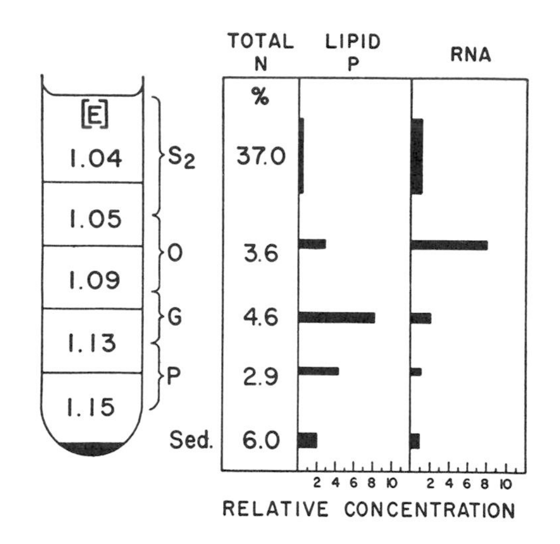

FIG. 4. Density gradient fractionation of rat epididymis (for explanation, see legend for fig. 3). In this instance, the homogenate was subjected to a prior low speed centrifugation to remove the sperm, nuclei and whole cells, and the resultant extract (E) was layered in the position indicated. Centrifugation was for 1 hour at 35,600 rpm.

employed is illustrated in figure 5. The tissue was homogenized in three volumes of 1.45 M (50%) sucrose containing 0.34 M sodium chloride, the final density of the homogenate being about 1.15 grams per centimeter[3]. Sperm and neutral fat were removed by a preliminary low-speed centrifugation, and the resultant extract (E) placed at the bottom of a centrifuge tube. The usual density gradient was then formed above the extract and centrifugation carried out as before. It was

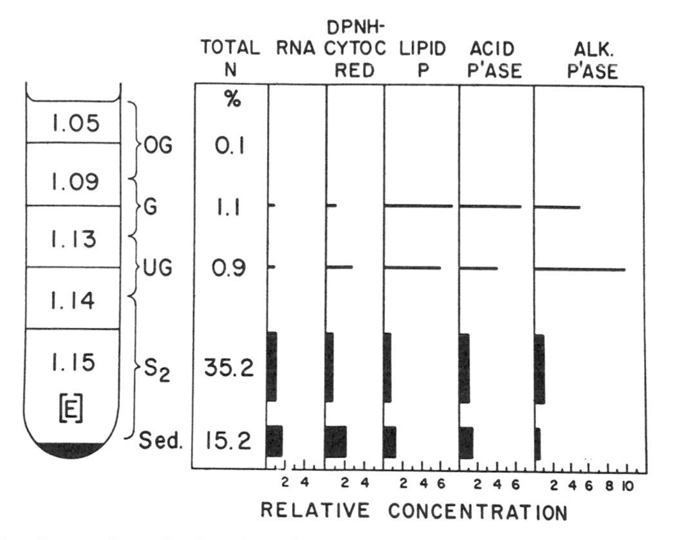

FIG. 5. Density gradient fractionation of rat epididymis (for explanation, see legends for figs. 3 and 4). The initial position of the extract, E, was at the bottom of the centrifuge tube. Centrifugation was for 1 hour at 35,600 rpm.

hoped that under these conditions, the Golgi material would rise to the appropriate density interface, while the free ribonucleoprotein particles would remain at or near the bottom of the tube.

After centrifugation, a very marked band (G) consisting almost entirely of recognizable Golgi material was present at density interface 1.09/1.13. A much less dense band (UG) containing a few Golgi structures but mainly composed of very small particulate material, was present at interface 1.13/1.14. A band at interface 1.14/1.15 could not be separated from the bulk of the material remaining in the original position of the extract.

Only 1 per cent of the total nitrogen of the homogenate was recovered in the Golgi fraction under these conditions. This figure appears in perspective when it is realized that the entire cytoplasmic particulate fraction of epididymis, as isolated by differential centrifugation, accounts for but 16 per cent of the tissue nitrogen. Another 1 per cent of the nitrogen appeared in the UG fraction, and an almost immeasurably small quantity in O. Very small amounts of both RNA and DPNH-cyto.*c* reductase activity were associated with the Golgi fraction. Lipid phosphorus content and β-glycerophosphatase activity at pH 5 (acid phosphatase), on the other hand, were very high in this fraction, and to a lesser extent in UG. Alkaline phosphatase activity was still concentrated five-fold in G; but it is seen that the relative specific activity was even greater in the UG fraction.

When G fractions were isolated by centrifugation for times ranging from 15 to 70 minutes (fig. 6), the amount of each constituent in the fraction increased progressively. However, it may be noted that the lipid phosphorus content and acid phosphatase activity, as well as their relative concentrations, were appreciable even at the shortest time of centrifugation, whereas alkaline phosphatase activity of appreciable intensity appeared only after 30 minutes. The specific activity of alkaline phosphatase in the UG layer (not shown) at 15 minutes and at all subsequent times was higher than the value attained by the G fraction at 70 minutes. The results suggest that acid phosphatase activity was associated with the large Golgi structures (see fig. 1), which might be expected to reach equilibrium position quickly, while alkaline phosphatase was associated primarily with smaller particles that entered the Golgi fraction more slowly.

The electron microscopic appearance of a Golgi fraction isolated at 30 minutes centrifugation is shown in figures 7 and 8. The material retains many of the structural details peculiar to the Golgi membranes observed within the intact cells: for example, the regular linear array of smooth-surfaced membranes and the expansion of the intramembrane spaces to form large vacuoles. One also observes numerous small vesicles that appear to have been formed by the pinching off or fragmentation of membrane pairs.

Figure 9 illustrates the contrasting appearance of the UG fraction, the com-

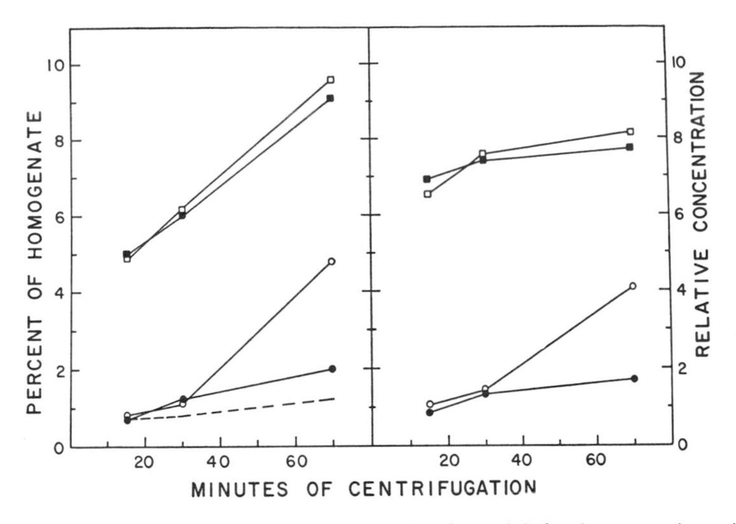

FIG. 6. Appearance of biochemical components in the Golgi fraction at various times of centrifugation. The arrangement for gradient fractionation was the same as that shown in figure 5. Centrifugation was at 35,600 rpm for the times indicated on the abscissa. *Open squares* denote lipid P; *closed squares,* acid phosphatase; *open circles,* alkaline phosphatase; *closed circles,* DPNH-cyto.*c* reductase; *broken line,* total N.

ponents of which are in general smaller than those seen in figures 7 and 8. The profiles of some of the individual large vesicles are indistinguishable from those seen in association with the organized Golgi structures (or, it may be noted, from the numerous smooth-surfaced vesicles seen in microsome fractions of epididymis as well as liver (13)). This fraction may contain some Golgi material that had been extensively comminuted during homogenization. As yet, we cannot identify morphologically the elements with which the alkaline phosphatase activity was associated.

We thought it desirable to compare the biochemical properties of Golgi fractions isolated by a relatively short centrifugation and consisting principally of recognizable Golgi membranes, with the properties of other cytoplasmic material. A mitochondrial and two microsomal fractions (fig. 10) were isolated from epididymis by differential centrifugation in 0.88 M sucrose and washed in sucrose containing 0.34 M sodium chloride. Golgi structures were very poorly preserved in fractions isolated in the absence of added salt. Possibly some Golgi material was present in the mitochondrial fraction; none was seen, even with the electron microscope, in the microsomal fractions. Of the biochemical components under consideration, only RNA was found to be preferentially extracted upon washing with 0.34 M sodium chloride. Accordingly, the RNA values presented in figure 10 were derived from fractions isolated either in sucrose-0.08 M sodium

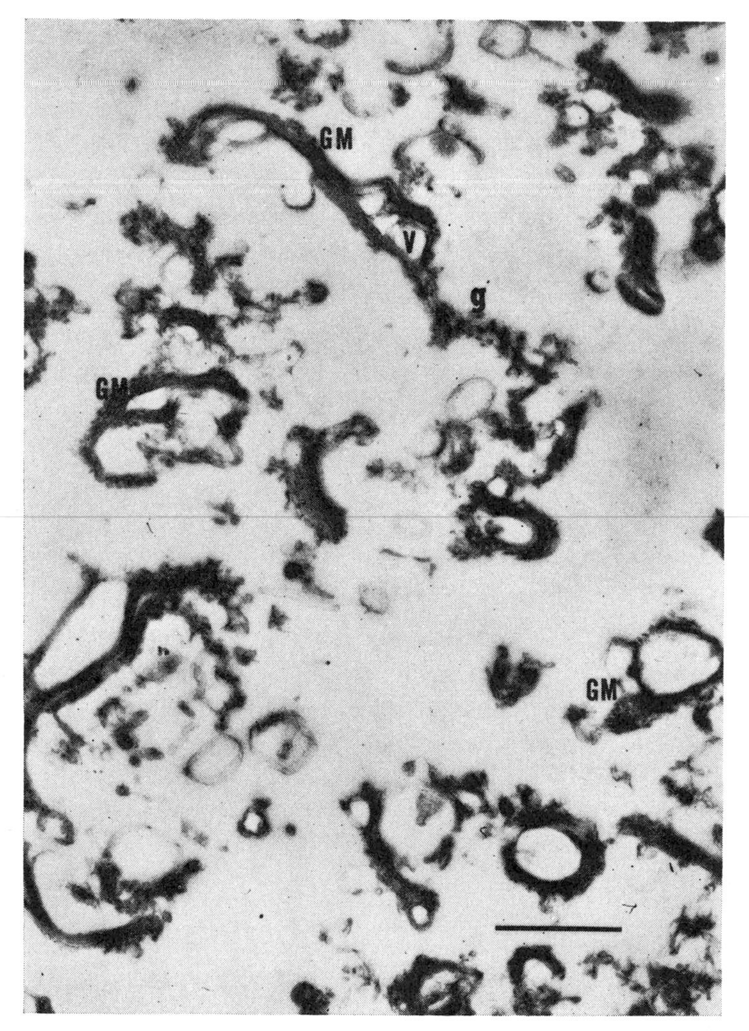

FIG. 7. Electron micrograph of isolated Golgi material. The G fraction, obtained as indicated in the text, was fixed in cold 1 per cent osmium tetroxide containing appropriate concentrations of sucrose and sodium chloride, and centrifuged at high speed. The resultant pellet was washed, dehydrated, embedded in plastic, and sectioned (13). Characteristic arrays of Golgi membranes are seen (GM). Expansion of the intramembranous spaces to form large vacuoles (V) is a frequent occurrence, as is fragmentation of the membranes to form small granules (g) reminiscent of the vesicles (v) seen in the intact cell (figs. 1 and 2). To a large extent, the impression of heterogeneity results from variations in the plane at which the Golgi material was sectioned. The bar represents 0.5 micron. $\times$ 33,000.

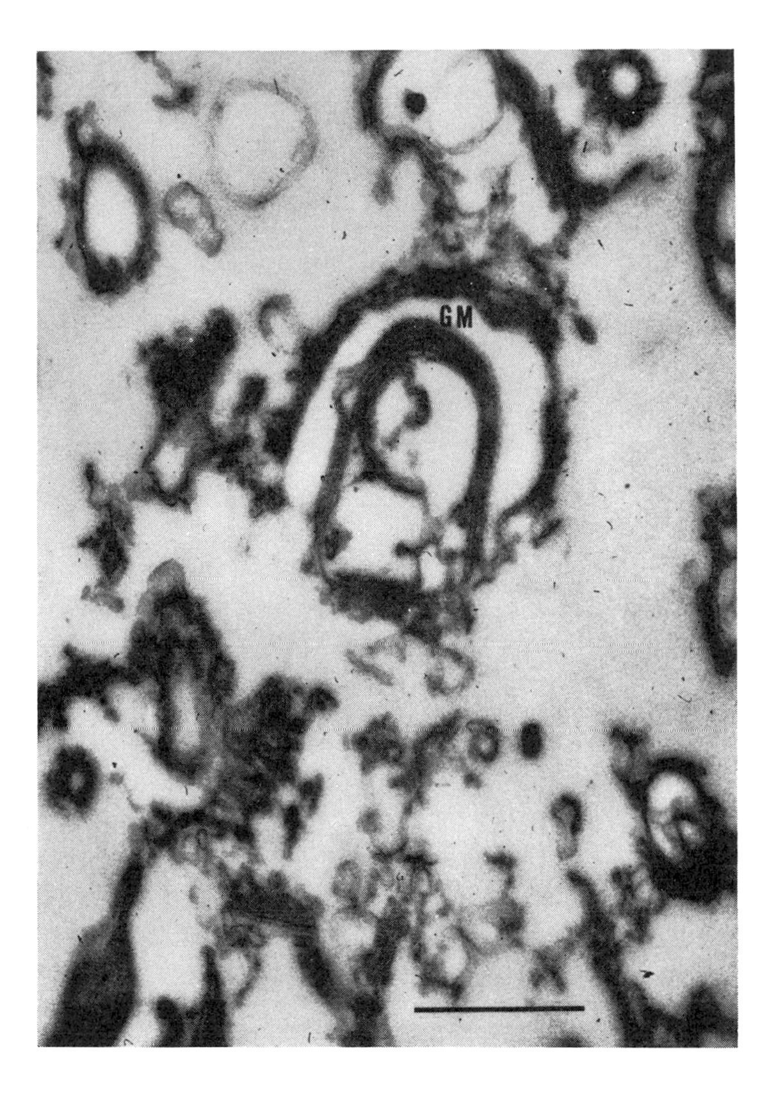

FIG. 8. Electron micrograph of isolated Golgi material. This is a higher magnification of the same fraction pictured in figure 7 to show that the regular spacing of the membranes is retained over considerable distances even in the isolated state. The bar represents 0.5 micron. × 44,000.

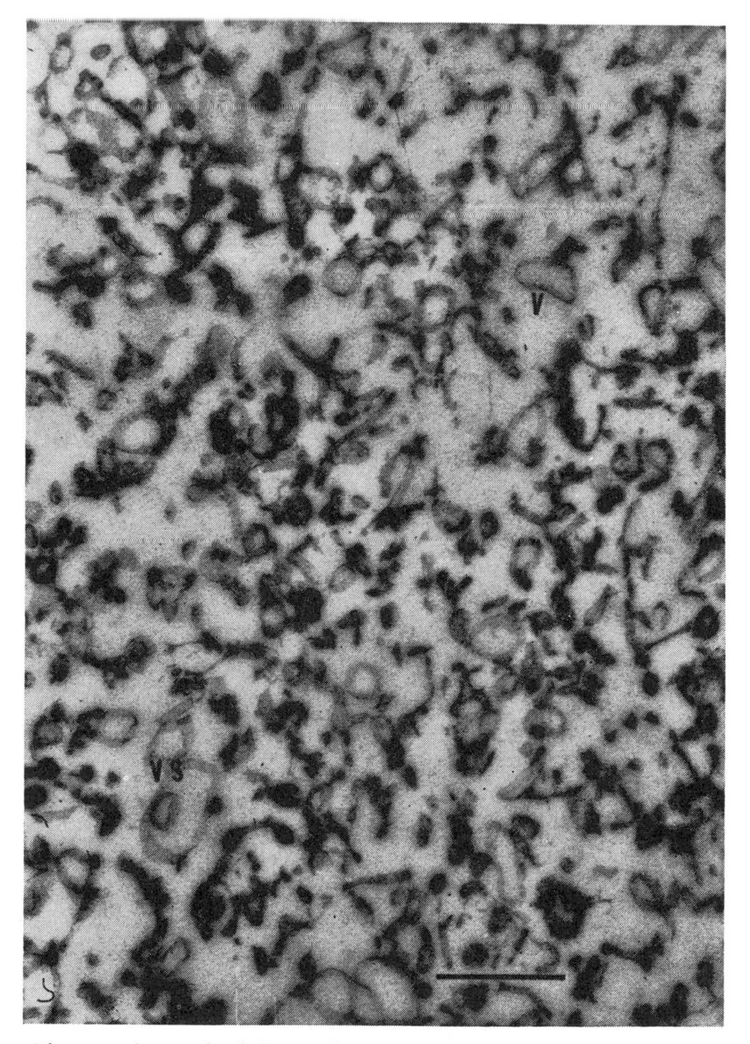

FIG. 9. Electron micrograph of the UG fraction obtained as indicated in the text and treated as described in the legend for figure 7. Organized arrays of membranes do not appear in this fraction. The profiles of many thin-walled vesicular structures, usually cut somewhat tangentially, are seen (VS). The intracellular sites of origin of the material in this fraction cannot be determined with certainty (see text). The bar represents 0.5 micron. × 33,000.

chloride (Golgi and Under-Golgi[1]) or in 0.88 M sucrose alone (mitochondria and microsomes). All other values refer to fractions exposed to 0.34 M salt.

[1] Golgi [illegible] remarkably good preservation of structural details. However, the fractions are contaminated with mitochondria and with rough-surfaced membranes derived from the ergastoplasmic elements of the intact cell (fig. 1).

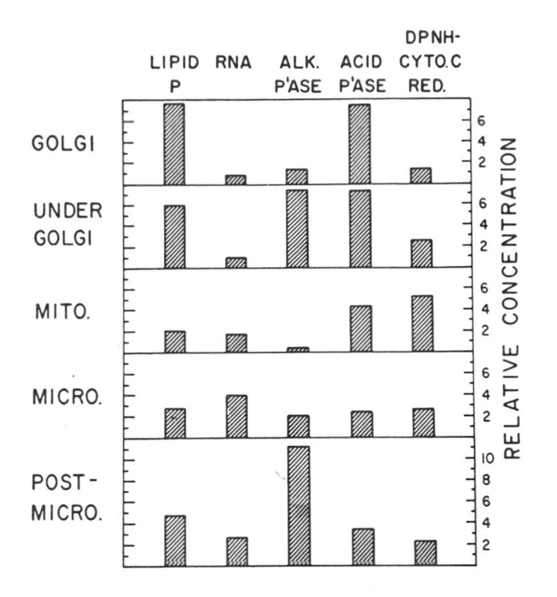

Fig. 10. Comparison of cytoplasmic fractions of rat epididymis. The fractions are indicated on the left: Golgi and Under-Golgi were obtained by centrifugation for 30 minutes at 35,600 rpm of a gradient tube prepared as shown in figure 5; mitochondrial (Mito.), microsomal (Micro.), and post-microsomal (Post-micro.) fractions by differential centrifugation of an epididymal homogenate prepared in 0.88 M sucrose. The width of the bars is without significance. For further details, see text.

Only lipid phosphorus and acid phosphatase activity were concentrated in the Golgi fraction. The results are in agreement with recent histochemical studies that have demonstrated a high concentration of acid phosphatase activity (17, 3) but no alkaline phosphatase activity (17, 3, 15) in the Golgi region of epididymal cells. Assuming that no other nitrogen-containing compounds were present, it may be calculated that the Golgi material contained approximately equal amounts of phospholipid and protein. The relative proportions of lipid phosphorus, alkaline phosphatase and DPNH-cyto.*c* reductase would appear to differentiate the Golgi material from the other subcellular fractions. RNA was not concentrated in the Golgi fraction, nor were a number of enzymatic activities that might be briefly listed: cytochrome oxidase (23), deoxyribonuclease (23), β-glucuronidase, esterase, and ATPase (release of inorganic phosphorus from ATP in the presence of magnesium ion).

It is evident, therefore, that we have not as yet uncovered any distinctive biochemical property of the isolated Golgi structures. Actually, the rather negative picture that has emerged with regard to enzymatic activity might be significant in itself, since the possibility must be kept in mind that the Golgi membranes may carry out their roles in secretion and absorption in some chiefly non-enzymatic fashion. Of course, it would be highly desirable to study material isolated from other sources where we have a better conception of cellular function. This is being attempted at the present time. Meanwhile, we have, in this instance at least, a preparation that appears to consist mainly of morphologically identifiable Golgi material. It is hoped that an analytic and dynamic study of the lipid components of the Golgi membranes may help to clarify their relationship to the other membranous elements of the cytoplasm.

REFERENCES

1. BAKER, J. R. *Symp. Soc. Exper. Biol.* 10: 1, 1957.
2. BOURNE, G. H. In: *Cytology and Cell Physiology* (2nd ed.), edited by G. H. BOURNE. Oxford: Clarendon, 1951, p. 232.
3. BURSTONE, M. S. *J. Nat. Cancer Inst.* 21: 523, 1958.
4. DALTON, A. J. AND M. D. FELIX. *Am. J. Anat.* 94: 171, 1954.
5. DALTON, A. J. AND M. D. FELIX. In: *Fine Structure of Cells* (Symp. VIIIth Internat. Congr. Cell Biol.). Groningen: Noordhoff, 1954, p. 274.
6. DALTON, A. J. AND M. D. FELIX. *Symp. Soc. Exper. Biol.* 10: 148, 1957.
7. DEANE, H. W. AND E. W. DEMPSEY. *Anat. Rec.* 93: 401, 1945.
8. DE DUVE, C., B. C. PRESSMAN, R. GIANETTO, R. WATTIAUX AND F. APPELMANS. *Biochem. J.* 60: 604, 1955.
9. EMMEL, V. M. *Anat. Rec.* 91: 31, 1945.
10. GATENBY, J. B. *Am. J. Anat.* 48: 421, 1931.
11. HAGUENAU, F. AND W. BERNHARD. *Arch. anat. et morphol. exper.* 44: 27, 1955.
12. HOGEBOOM, G. H. *J. Biol. Chem.* 177: 847, 1949.
13. KUFF, E. L., G. H. HOGEBOOM AND A. J. DALTON. *J. Biophys. Biochem. Cytol.* 2: 33, 1956.
14. LACY, D. AND C. E. CHALLICE. *Symp. Soc. Exper. Biol.* 10: 62, 1957.
15. MANEELY, R. B. *Acta anat.* 24: 314, 1955.
16. MANN, T. *Advances Enzymol* 9: 329, 1949.
17. MONTAGNA, W. *Ann. New York Acad. Sci.* 55: 629, 1952.
18. NOVIKOFF, A. B., L. KORSON AND H. W. SPATER. *Exper. Cell Res.* 3: 617, 1952.
19. PALADE, G. E. *J. Biophys. Biochem. Cytol.* 1: 59, 1955.
20. PETERMANN, M. L. AND M. G. HAMILTON. *J. Biol. Chem.* 224: 725, 1957.
21. POLLISTER, A. W. AND P. F. POLLISTER. *Internat. Rev. Cytol.* 6: 85, 1957.
22. SCHNEIDER, W. C., A. J. DALTON, E. L. KUFF AND M. D. FELIX. *Nature* 172: 161, 1953.
23. SCHNEIDER, W. C. AND E. L. KUFF. *Am. J. Anat.* 94: 209, 1954.
24. SJÖSTRAND, F. S. *Internat. Rev. Cytol.* 5: 456, 1956.
25. SJÖSTRAND, F. S. AND V. HANZON. *Exper. Cell Res.* 7: 415, 1954.

DISCUSSION

R. E. Beyer, E. L. Kuff, D. E. Green, G. Rumney

DR. BEYER: Do you see any continuity between the Golgi vesicles and the membrane of the endoplasmic reticulum? If so, do you have any idea of a functional role for the Golgi apparatus in relation to the synthesis of cellular products?

DR. KUFF: Yes, continuities between the Golgi membranes and the rough-surfaced membranes of the endoplasmic reticulum (ergastoplasm) have been observed in a number of cell types. Dr. Palade has illustrated this in the case of the pancreas. In our present state of knowledge, there is no convincing evidence that the Golgi membranes are involved in the actual synthesis of cellular products. It would appear more likely that they function in relation to transport of secretory products to and across the cell membranes.

DR. GREEN: Non-localization of components or activities bespeaks incomplete separation. Paucity of assays may make assignment of enzymatic specificity more difficult.

DR. KUFF: Of course, it is most difficult to decide whether the presence in a fraction of some biochemical component at low concentration represents a true association of that component with the particle in question or merely reflects an incomplete separation of biochemically distinct entities. It would appear that complete separations of cytoplasmic particulates are rather rare. With regard to the number of enzymes assayed, admittedly it is small, since the work is in a fairly early stage.

DR. RUMNEY: Could you define the post-microsomal fraction in terms of method of preparation? Is this fraction derived from the microsomes?

DR. KUFF: In the fractionation of epididymal homogenates in 0.88 M sucrose, a main microsomal fraction was obtained by centrifugation of the mitochondrial supernatant fluid for 30 minutes at 40,000 rpm in the no. 40 rotor of the Spinco Model L ultracentrifuge. The supernatant fluid from this run was diluted with water to a sucrose concentration of 0.25 M and centrifuged for 60 minutes at the same speed. The sediments thus obtained constituted the so-called 'post-microsomal' fraction. Electron microscopy showed that the main microsome fraction consisted of vesicular elements, many of which carried ribonucleoprotein particles on their surfaces. The post-microsomal fraction contained a great preponderance of smooth-surfaced vesicles. Certain biochemical differences were also observed (fig. 10). However, from the operational point of view, both fractions would be thought of as microsomal in nature, in that they consist of submicroscopic particulate material.

Lysosomes, a New Group of Cytoplasmic Particles

C. DE DUVE

University of Louvain
Louvain, Belgium

THE CONCEPT THAT THE HEPATIC CELL contains a special group of lytic particles has emerged from studies on the unspecific acid phosphatase of rat liver, which were later extended with similar results to a number of other hydrolases. The subsequent recognition that droplets isolated from kidney tissue are analogous to the hepatic lysosomes, together with recent observations indicating the presence of similar particles in several other tissues as well as in some lower organisms, has opened the possibility that lysosomes may represent organelles of fairly wide significance. Speculations as to their physiological function have been stimulated by various morphological and biochemical studies suggesting a possible involvement of lysosomes in intracellular digestion, in connection with phenomena of phagocytosis, athrocytosis and pinocytosis. Other experiments indicate that they may play a significant role in autolysis and necrosis.

Although adequate documentation is still lacking on many of these points, enough data have already been gathered to warrant a survey covering the present status of the problem. In particular, a precise definition of the lysosome concept, together with a critical discussion of its experimental basis, has been deemed necessary in view of the loose manner in which these particles are sometimes referred to, considered as mitochondria, or confounded with the fractions in which they are concentrated.

LIVER LYSOSOMES

Definition and Main Properties. The name 'lysosomes' designates a special class of particles present in suitably prepared rat liver homogenates (29). The term has this peculiarity, that it refers to what is believed to be a morphologically distinct entity, defined on the basis of purely biochemical data. As will be shown below, a tentative morphological identification of lysosomes has been made, but definite proof of its correctness is still lacking and it seems preferable to retain the name in its original connotation, at least provisionally.

The simplest (though not the only possible one; see the discussion in INDIVIDUALITY AND HOMOGENEITY) schematic representation of lysosomes, embodying most of the biochemical evidence available at the present time, is shown in figure 1. The diagram, which is largely self-explanatory, stresses the following properties of the particles: *1*) dimensions corresponding, in 0.25 M sucrose and on the assumption of a spherical shape, to a mean diameter of 0.4 micron and an average density of 1.15, both properties showing a fairly wide dispersion around these mean values; *2*) an enzymic equipment lacking several key enzymes of oxidative metabolism, but comprising a number of easily soluble hydrolases (hence the name lysosomes) having further in common an acid pH optimum; *3*) a surrounding membrane of lipoprotein nature which effectively prevents the enzymes from escaping from, as well as their respective substrates from penetrating into, the particles; *4*) the simultaneous release of all internal enzymes in soluble and fully active form, following injuries to the membrane, as caused by the various treatments listed in the diagram.

As represented in figure 1, our picture of lysosomes is bound to be incomplete. Moreover, it is partly interpretative with regard to the experimental facts on which it rests, stripping the latter of various complicating artifacts to the extent perhaps of oversimplifying reality. Although lengthily discussed in our original publications, these points are not always clearly appreciated and will be briefly examined again here.

Structure-linked Latency and Activation of Lysosomal Enzymes. First observed with acid phosphatase, latency and release were studied in great detail in the case of this enzyme and adequate evidence was, we believe, brought forward in support of the concept that the sole factor involved in these phenomena is the integrity of a membrane-like barrier, as depicted in figure 1 (26, 14, 13, 2). Extending the concept to the other enzymes which were found to exhibit similar properties was admittedly an extrapolation, since elaborate proof of the membrane hypothesis was neither provided nor looked for in their case. It could however be shown that the graded release of these enzymes, as produced by several different means, occurred in an almost perfectly parallel fashion with that of acid phosphatase (27, 38, 29, 101) and this was further confirmed when other means of releasing the lysosomal enzymes were uncovered (103, 5). Obviously, the more numerous the enzymes which are released simultaneously, as well as the means which bring about this release, the greater the probability that the linkage which maintains the enzymes in bound and inactive form is an unspecific one.

Proof that the membrane is of lipoprotein composition was given by the nature of several of the releasing agents, in particular of the enzymic ones (62, 5). We have been unable to confirm the claim of Allard, de Lamirande and Cantero (1) that ribonuclease can cause the release of acid phosphatase; lysozyme also proved inactive in our hands.

In figure 1, the enzymes present within intact particles have been represented as being entirely inactive on external substrates. This has clearly been shown to be the case for acid phosphatase at pH 5, but may not be strictly true at higher pH values, where evidence of a slight penetration of the substrate has been obtained

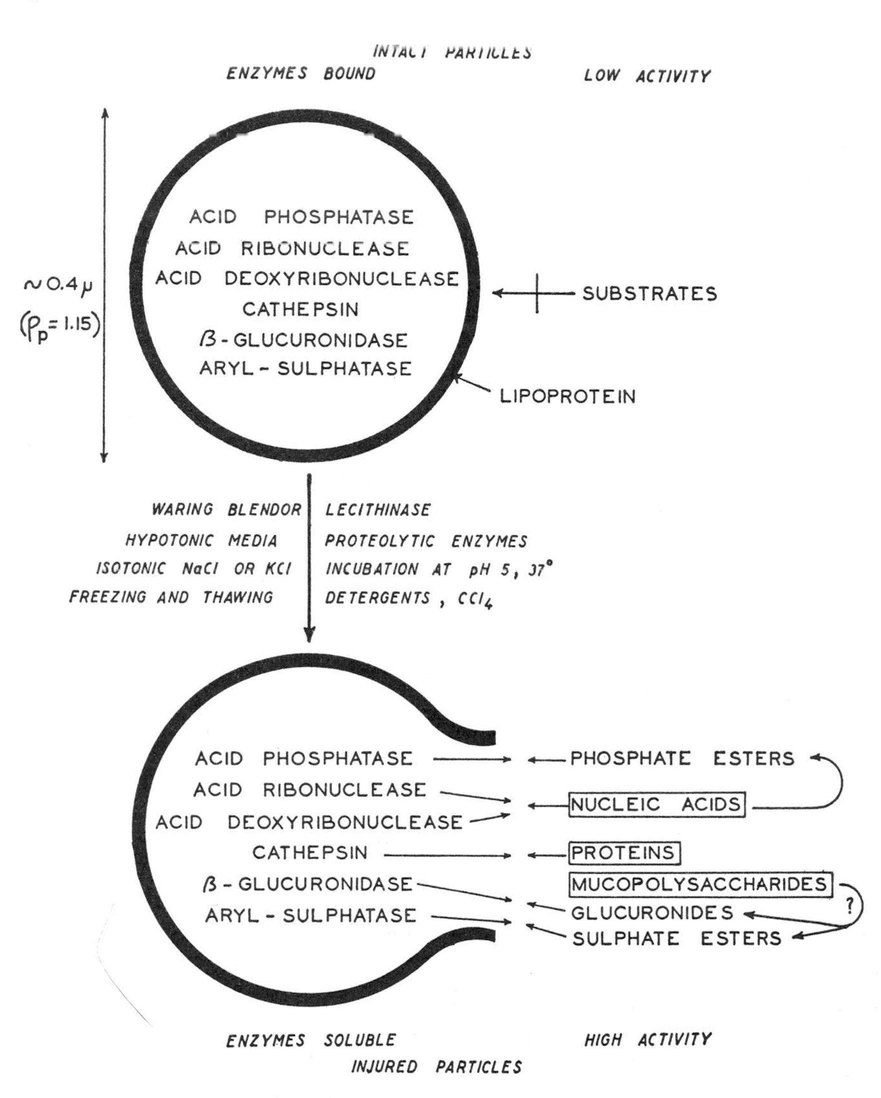

FIG. 1. Schematic representation of the lysosome concept.

(2). For the other enzymes, total lack of activity has not been demonstrated directly but has been deduced from the fact that they show the same proportion of latent activity as acid phosphatase.

An obvious corollary of the enzymic inertia of intact particles is that the activities actually observed in a preparation must be due to free enzymes, and should therefore be recovered quantitatively in a high-speed supernatant of the preparation. Such ideal behavior is never seen. In the first place, the assay conditions favor the autolysis of the particles, so that additional enzyme molecules may become free to participate in the reaction as the incubation proceeds. In the second place, part of the free enzyme molecules present in the original preparation undergo secondary adsorption onto the surface of mitochondria, microsomes or other particles, or remain trapped within injured lysosomes, thus appearing in the sediment after high-speed centrifugation. With acid phosphatase, some 50–60 per cent of the free activity has been found to suffer this fate in sucrose solutions, about half this amount in media of higher ionic strength (13).

Assay of Lysosomal Enzymes. In view of the above considerations, it is necessary to distinguish clearly between various assay measurements of lysosomal enzymes.

Total activities are measured after quantitative release by one of the treatments listed in figure 1. The most convenient method is to run the assay in the presence of 0.1 per cent Triton X-100, taking a few precautions to guard against some artifacts caused by the detergent (103).

Free activities are determined similarly but without activating treatment and under conditions which preserve the integrity of the particles as much as possible; i.e., by incubating at 37° for no longer than 10 minutes in a medium containing 0.25 M sucrose and at a pH no lower than 5. These conditions are essential to keep the autolysis of intact particles at a minimum, but often furnish values representing only a small relative rise above the blanks. Since, in addition, there is always some uncertainty in such assays as to what is the true blank value, determinations of free activity are frequently inaccurate and may in some cases be almost impracticable.

Unsedimentable activities are measured under the same conditions as the total activities, and thus with the same degree of accuracy, on the supernatant obtained after centrifuging for 30 minutes at 100,000 *g*. For the reasons mentioned above, these values are lower than the free activities, but may serve to estimate the latter, to which they are approximately proportional.

Latent activities (termed 'bound' in our early publications) are obtained by subtracting the free from the total activities. They represent an estimate of the amount of intact particles present.

Individuality and Homogeneity of Lysosomes. The existence of lysosomes as an individual group, distinct from mitochondria and from microsomes, has been deduced entirely from centrifugation experiments. These have also provided the information on which is based our estimate of the dimensions of the particles. Here again, acid phosphatase has acted as our tracer enzyme.

As shown in figure 2*A*, the distribution of bound acid phosphatase, as studied by means of conventional fractionation techniques (14), was found to differ significantly from those found by Schneider and Hogeboom (86) for the mitochondrial cytochrome oxidase and by Hers, Berthet, Berthet and de Duve (44) for the microsomal glucose-6-phosphatase. Subsequent investigations, performed independently by Novikoff, Podber, Ryan and Noe (67, 68), and in this laboratory (22, 27, 3), showed that the dissociation between bound acid phosphatase and cytochrome oxidase or succinoxidase could be magnified by centrifuging and washing under suitably chosen conditions. While the former authors interpreted their results in terms of the heterogeneity of the particles, our experiments led us to the conclusion that acid phosphatase is probably attached to a special group of particles entirely distinct from the oxidizing mitochondria. This interpretation has also been favored by Kuff, Hogeboom and Dalton (58), by Thomson and Moss (99), and by Thomson and Klipfel (97), who have confirmed the above results by means of density-gradient centrifugation, and it has now been adopted by Novikoff (65).

As a result of the investigations on acid phosphatase, a modified fractionation scheme with greater discriminating power (fig. 2*B*) was worked out (3). In experiments performed according to this scheme, cathepsin, acid ribonuclease, acid deoxyribonuclease (DNA-ase II) and a large part of β-glucuronidase were

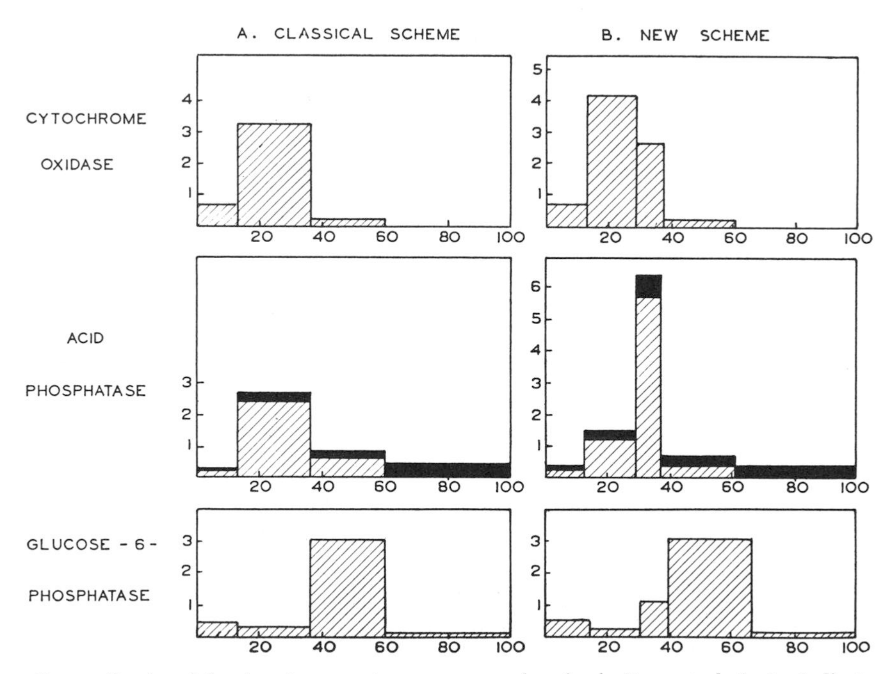

FIG. 2. Results of fractionation experiments, expressed as in de Duve *et al.* (29). *Ordinate:* relative specific activity = activity per mg N of fraction/activity per mg N of homogenate. *Abscissa:* percentage of total N in fraction. Filled-in areas represent free activities. *A*, conventional fractionation scheme; *order of fractions:* nuclei, mitochondria, microsomes, supernatant. *B*, scheme of de Duve *et al.* (29); *order of fractions:* nuclei, heavy and light mitochondria, microsomes, supernatant.

found to show a distribution similar to that of acid phosphatase. This fact, together with the close similarities in structure-linked latency and activation mentioned above, led to the conclusion that all five enzymes belong to the same special class of cytoplasmic particles, which were termed lysosomes as a reminder of their manifold hydrolytic activities (29).

The inclusion of aryl-sulphatases A and B amongst the lysosomal enzymes (see fig. 1) rests on the fractionation experiments of Roy (84, 85) and of Dodgson, Spencer and Thomas (30) and on the comparative investigation by Viala and Gianetto (101) of the activation of these enzymes and of acid phosphatase. According to recent observations by Paigen and Griffiths (personal communication), the group, as defined by the above criteria, may also include a phosphoprotein phosphatase.

In recent years, our efforts have been directed towards a better dissociation between lysosomes and mitochondria, taking advantage of the new possibilities provided by density-gradient centrifugation. Figures 3–6 illustrate some results which have been obtained by Beaufay, Baudhuin and Bendall (6). These graphs may serve to delineate the precise experimental basis as well as the actual limitations of our concept of lysosomes.

The frequency curves of figure 4 indicate a mean sedimentation constant (in 0.25 M sucrose and at 0°) of about 5,000 Svedberg units for acid phosphatase and of 10,000 S for cytochrome oxidase. The respective mean densities (in 0.25 M sucrose) of the particles bearing these enzymes have recently been estimated by density-equilibration experiments in gradients of colloidal thorium oxide (Thorotrast) at 1.13–1.15 for acid phosphatase and 1.10–1.11 for cytochrome oxidase (Beaufay, unpublished). From these values, average diameters of 0.4 and 0.8 micron can be calculated. The shape of the two curves suggests strongly the presence of two distinct populations, which cannot be separated quantitatively from each other by centrifugation owing to the fairly wide overlapping of their sedimentation constants. All that can be done is to cut in somewhere between the two curves and to separate two fractions differing in their relative content of the two enzymes. That is actually what we believe has been done to some extent with the classical fractionation scheme (fig. 2*A*), and in a more clearcut fashion with the new scheme (fig. 2*B*).

Our thesis, therefore, which has been set forth more elaborately in previous reviews (24, 21), is that results such as those of figure 2 indicate that the isolated *fractions* are heterogeneous and contain mixtures of at least two distinct populations of particles in different proportion. Implicit in this interpretation are the rejection of the alternative hypothesis that the results may be due to the heterogeneity of the *particles* themselves within a single group, and therefore the acceptance of the postulate that "granules of a given population are enzymically homogeneous or at least cannot be separated by centrifuging into subgroups differing significantly in relative enzymic content" (29).

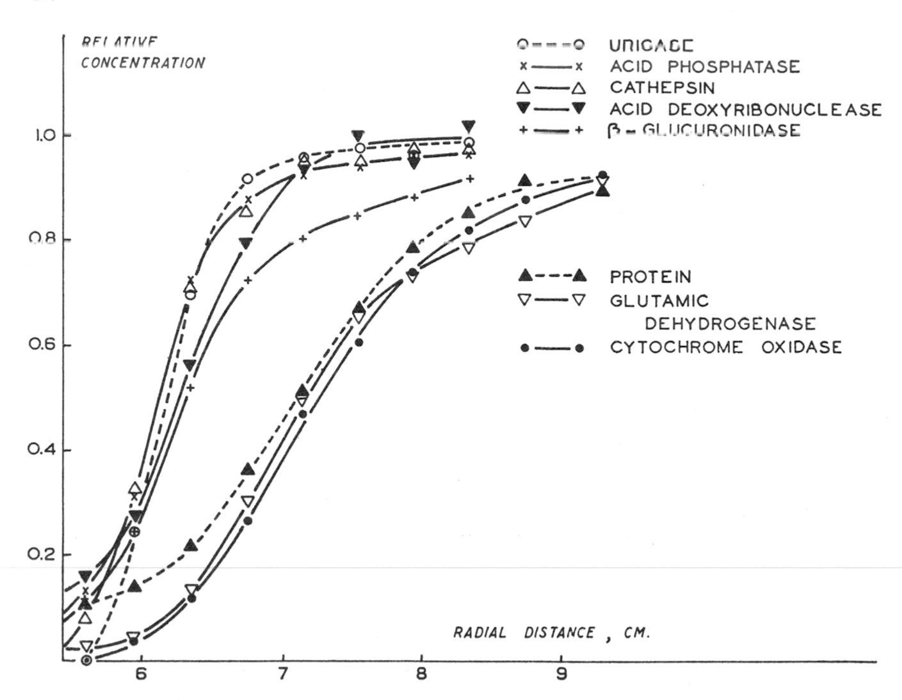

FIG. 3. Sedimentation diagrams in sucrose gradient. Washed total mitochondrial fraction centrifuged according to the technique of Kuff *et al.* (58), but in a linear gradient of sucrose ranging from 0.25 to 0.5 M over a radial distance from 5.4 to 9.6 cm. As demonstrated by de Duve, Berthet and Beaufay (25), the sedimentation velocity of mitochondria is practically independent of the radial distance in this gradient. Time-integral of squared angular velocity $= 2.6 \times 10^8$ rad^2 sec^{-1}.

We were able to back up this postulate by a limited number of correlations between cytochrome oxidase, succinic dehydrogenase, rhodanese and the antimycin-sensitive cytochrome *c* reductases, and between glucose-6-phosphatase and the antimycin-insensitive cytochrome *c* reductases. To the list of enzymes obeying the postulate of homogeneity we may now add glutamic dehydrogenase, malic dehydrogenase and alkaline deoxyribonuclease (DNA-ase I) in the mitochondrial group (6; see figs. 3–6) and in the microsomal group aryl-sulphatase C (39) and esterase (100). In addition, two more facts may be marshalled in support of the distinction between the particles bearing acid phosphatase and the oxidizing mitochondria; namely, the results of figures 5 and 6, showing that the two groups can also be largely dissociated on the basis of their density in solutions of sucrose in heavy water (6); and those of figures 7 and 8, indicating that the release of a soluble mitochondrial enzyme does not follow that of acid phosphatase, when brought about by a decrease in tonicity or repeated freezing and thawing (9). Apparently arguing against our interpretation is the fact that the

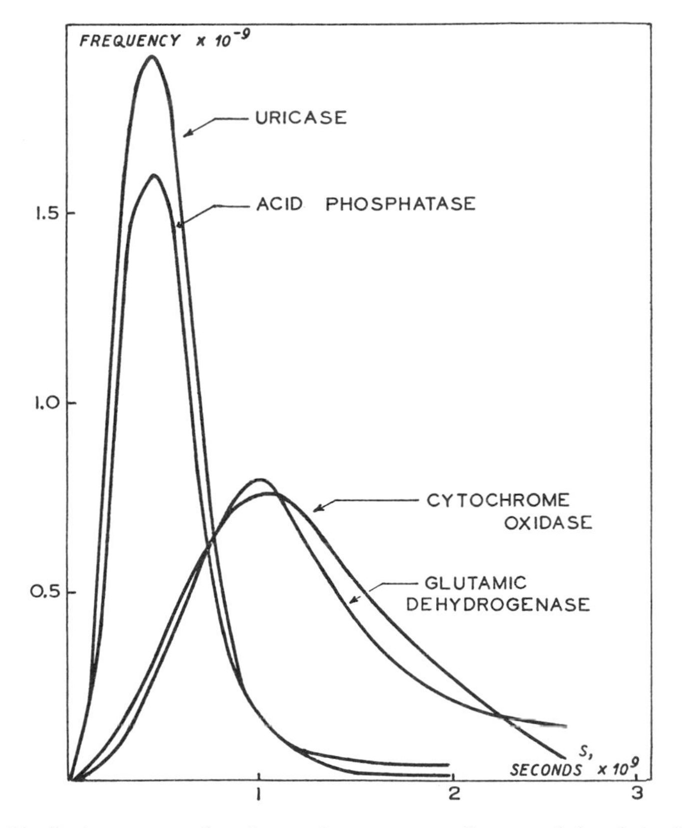

FIG. 4. Distribution curves of sedimentation constants. Constructed by derivation of the sedimentation diagrams of figure 3, according to de Duve *et al.* (25). The sedimentation constant s applies to 0.25 M sucrose at 0°.

sedimentation diagram of protein (fig. 3) shows no sign of being bimodal. This, however, we believe to signify that the phosphatase particles are associated with a very small proportion of the total protein of the preparation; in other words, that they are much less numerous than mitochondria.

The association of acid phosphatase with a special group of particles thus rests on a firm experimental basis. That the other hydrolases belong to the same general group is made obvious by our previous results and by those of figures 3 and 6. However, these results also make it clear that the lysosomal enzymes do not obey the postulate of homogeneity as closely as do the mitochondrial or microsomal enzymes which have been similarly studied. At present, the situation may be summed up as follows: the release of all lysosomal enzymes occurs in an almost perfectly parallel fashion; but their distributions, whether determined on the basis of sedimentation rate or of density, are not identical. Either, there-

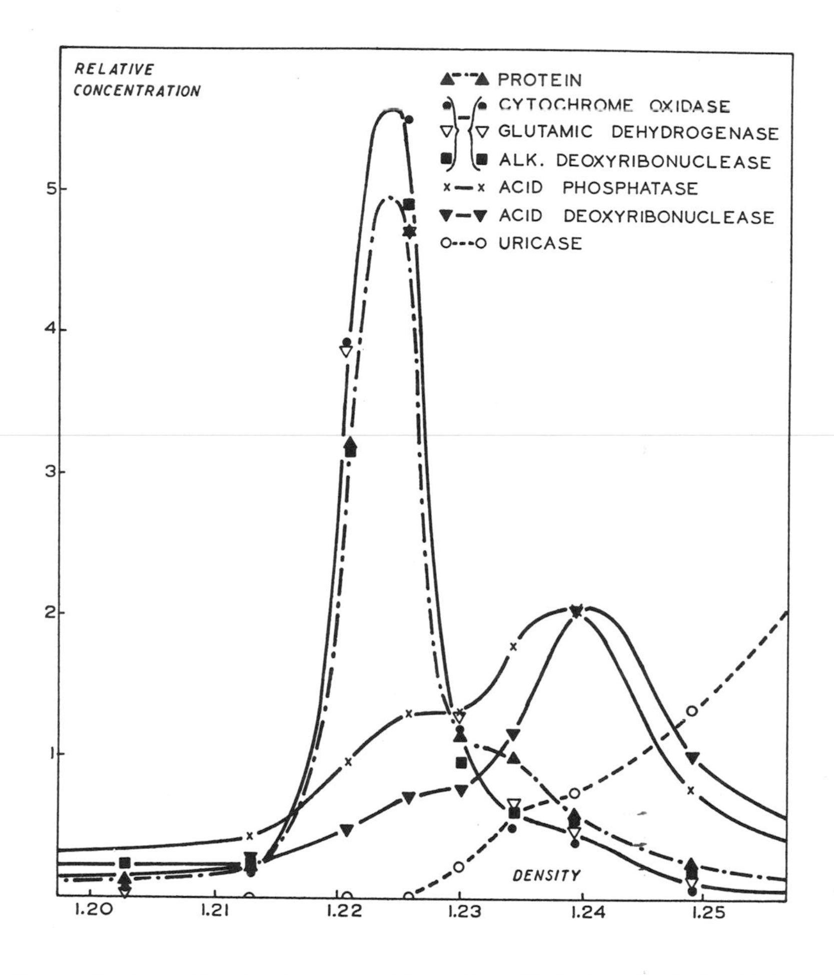

FIG. 5. Density-equilibration in sucrose-D_2O gradient. Washed total mitochondrial fraction evenly distributed in a gradient of sucrose in D_2O and centrifuged for $2\frac{1}{2}$ hr. at 39,000 rpm in SW-39 rotor of Spinco Model L centrifuge. For technical details, see de Duve *et al.* (25). It should be noted that a negligible separation between mitochondria, lysosomes and uricase particles obtains in similar experiments performed in H_2O-sucrose solutions.

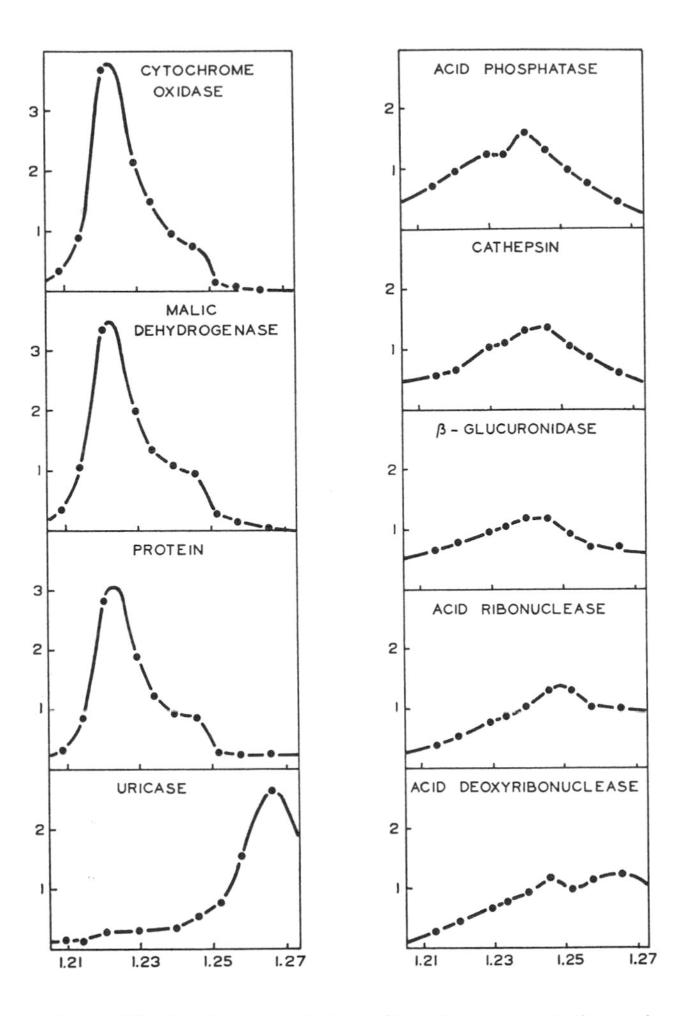

FIG. 6. Density-equilibration in sucrose-D_2O gradient. Experiment similar to that of figure 5, but with a different gradient. Note third uricase peak. The low degree of resolution, as compared with figure 5, is due to an unexplained complicating factor. *Ordinate:* relative concentration; *abscissa:* density.

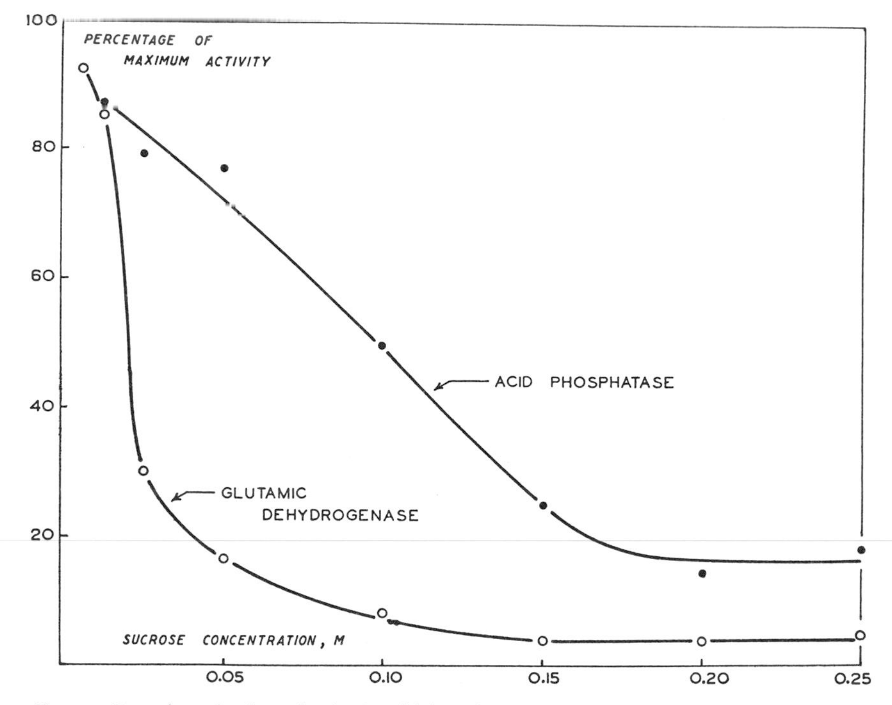

FIG. 7. Osmotic activation of mitochondrial and lysosomal enzymes. Washed mitochondrial fraction exposed for 15 min. to sucrose concentrations indicated in abscissa and then brought back in 0.25 M sucrose. Free acid phosphatase activities measured as in Gianetto and de Duve (38). Free dehydrogenase activity determined spectrophotometrically at 550 mμ in the presence of DPN, purified DPN-cytochrome *c* reductase and cytochrome *c*, according to original technique of Bendall (9).

fore, one is dealing with a single population of particles, within which variations in enzymic content, correlated with size and density but not with sensitivity to rupturing agents, may occur; or there are two or more populations, up to one per enzyme, differing slightly in size and density, but not in sensitivity to rupturing agents. The biochemical evidence at present available does not enable us to distinguish between these possibilities. Neither do the physiopathological data. As will be shown below, these indicate that the levels of lysosomal enzymes in the liver are not controlled in bulk and may suffer considerable independent variations, but that their release occurs simultaneously *in vivo* as it does *in vitro*.

Particularly delicate in connection with these problems is the case of uricase. Novikoff *et al.* (67, 68) were the first to point out the similarity in distribution between this enzyme and acid phosphatase. Their results have been confirmed by a number of authors (98, [illegible], 29, [illegible], 99, 97), and it is generally assumed that the two enzymes belong to the same particles (47). However, uricase is fully active

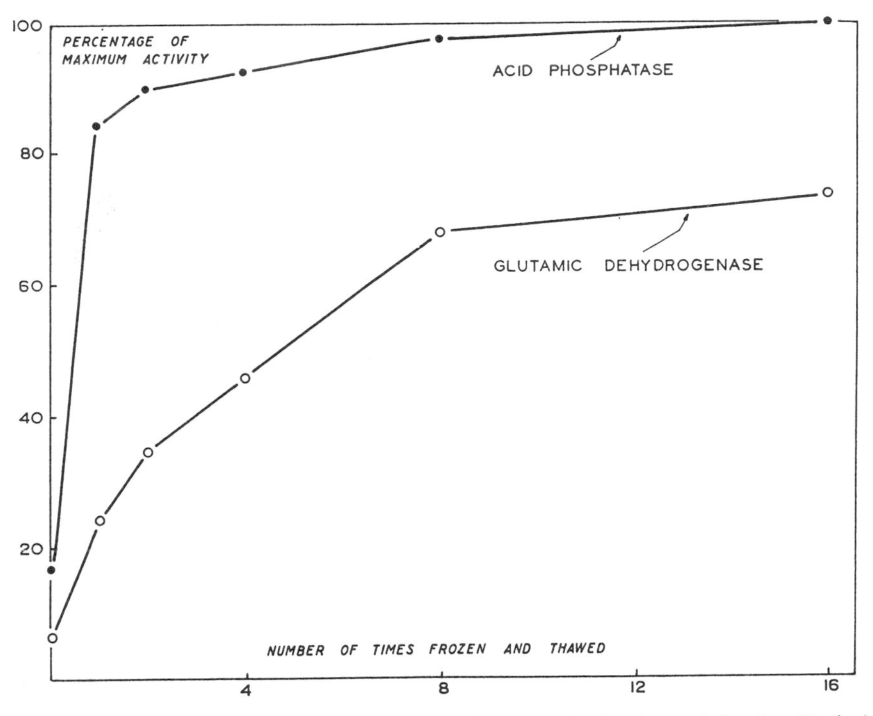

FIG. 8. Activation of mitochondrial and lysosomal enzymes by freezing and thawing. Washed mitochondrial fraction frozen in dry ice-acetone mixture and thawed number of times indicated in abscissa. Analytical techniques as in figure 7.

in preparations of intact particles and is not solubilized by most of the treatments which release the lysosomal hydrolases. In our experiments, its distribution pattern differed significantly from those of the hydrolases and we were led to conclude that uricase is ". . . attached either to the insoluble framework of lysosomes or to a fourth distinct group of granules with the properties of large microsomes" (29). The difficulty involved is illustrated by a comparison of figures 3–4 and 5–6. According to the former, the frequency curve of sedimentation constants is practically the same for uricase and for acid phosphatase. On the other hand, their density distribution curves in sucrose-heavy water solutions (figs. 5 and 6) differ to a remarkable extent and suggest the existence of a special group of uricase-containing particles. Of interest in this respect are the recent findings by Thomson and Klipfel (97) that the distribution of catalase is very similar to that of uricase.

To conclude this lengthy discussion, an additional word must be said concerning the postulate of homogeneity. This postulate has been used as a working hypothesis, and even when verified experimentally, can obviously be true only in first approximation. It would indeed be very astonishing if all the mitochondria from all the liver cells had exactly the same ratio of, let us say, glutamic dehydrogenase to cytochrome oxidase. In fact, such a possibility seems almost incompatible, at least for some enzymes, with the histochemical demonstration of zonal differences within hepatic lobules, as with the existence of several types of cells within the liver. The homogeneity is therefore a statistical one, and the crux of the matter is to appreciate at what stage our techniques become sensitive enough to show up the heterogeneity which undoubtedly exists. Another point is that true heterogeneity can never be entirely disproved. In the case of mitochondria and lysosomes, for example, the evidence is compatible not only with the possibility that the two populations are entirely independent of one another, but also with the eventuality that they may be related genetically and linked by transition forms containing enzymes of both groups. This problem concerns the life cycle of the particles and must be settled on other grounds. Even if a relation between the two types of particles should one day be shown to exist, this would not invalidate the distinction which has been made between mitochondria and lysosomes, since the transition would obviously be a drastic one and involve a complete change in biochemical and even structural properties.

Morphological Identification of Lysosomes. Fractions which had been enriched 10- to 14-fold in acid phosphatase have been examined in the electron microscope by Novikoff, Beaufay and de Duve (66). They were found to contain, besides a fair amount of mitochondria and a few microsomal fragments, to be expected from their cytochrome oxidase and glucose-6-phosphatase activities, a large number of distinctive particles which were practically absent in fractions with a low content in lysosomes. These particles, representatives of which can be seen in figures 9 and 10, could be identified with the dense peribiliary bodies described by Rouiller (82) and by Palade and Siekevitz (73) or with the microbodies of Rouiller and Bernhard (83). Their relationship with the newly described siderosomes of Richter (80) is not clear.

Since no other type of particle was recognized in these lysosome-rich fractions, it is tempting to conclude that the biochemical concept of lysosome and the morphological one of dense peribiliary body refer to the same entity. But this can by no means be regarded as proved, especially since both concepts are still somewhat imprecise. As mentioned above, the relationship between uricase and the lysosomes is still uncertain and the latter do themselves form a complex group. On the other hand, the dense peribiliary bodies are characteristically polymorphic and the term could therefore cover several distinct types. A direct link between the two entities is apparently provided by the histochemical observations of Holt (48), who has found acid phosphatase to be concentrated around the bile canaliculi in rat liver. However, this author has observed an almost identical localization for esterase, which sediments quantitatively with the microsomes (100).

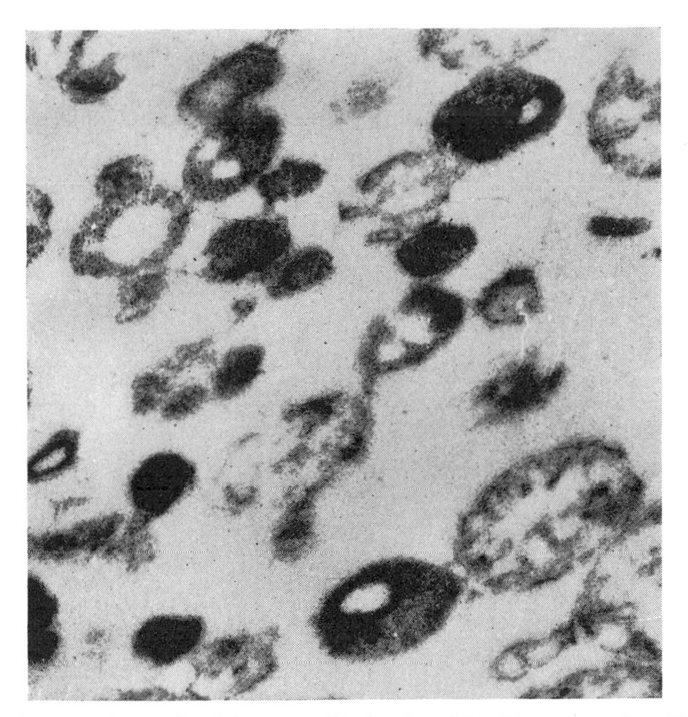

FIG. 9. Electron micrograph of lysosome-rich fraction. Ultrathin section of purified pellet. [From (66).] × 36,300.

The final morphological identification of lysosomes must therefore await a better purification of the particles. The following account of a recent experiment performed by Beaufay may serve to illustrate the difficulties which attend this problem. A mitochondrial fraction containing about 75 per cent of the total lysosomal enzymes and of uricase and 25 per cent of the total proteins of the homogenate was subjected to a fractionation in a gradient of sucrose in heavy water, analogous to that of figure 6. From one gram of liver a minute dark-brown pellet was obtained, which contained essentially no cytochrome oxidase, 10–15 per cent of the lysosomal enzymes, 35 per cent of the uricase and about 0.5 per cent of the proteins of the fraction. In this pellet, therefore, the lysosomal enzymes were purified 60- to 90-fold with respect to the homogenate, with a yield of about 10 per cent; and uricase more than 200-fold with a yield of 25 per cent. The material was fixed in osmium tetroxide, at which stage it became almost invisible to the naked eye; attempts to embed and section it proved unsuccessful. We are obviously dealing here with what might be called 'trace organelles,' and their purification for the purpose of identification may prove quite arduous.

The dense bodies found in our fractions or seen around bile canaliculi in liver preparations are fairly polymorphic. The simplest ones appear to be solid and

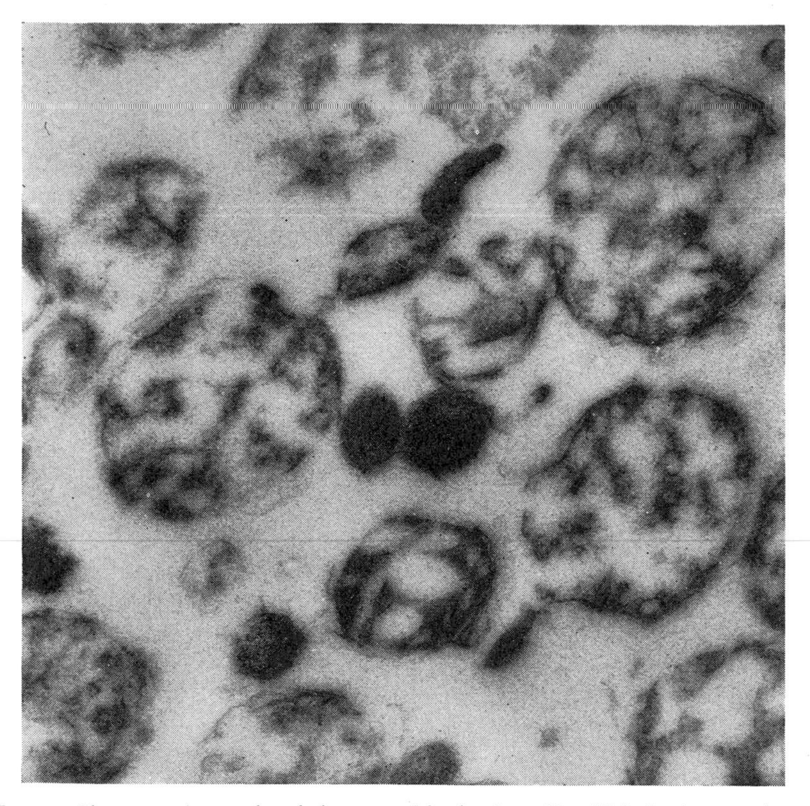

FIG. 10. Electron micrograph of lysosome-rich fraction. Unpublished picture taken by Dr. Novikoff in collaboration with Dr. Claude. Preparation similar to that of figure 9. × 37,500.

are surrounded by a single membrane; others show one or more internal cavities, sometimes lined with a broad layer of denser material, or contain clumps of such material. Most of them have in common a fine granular texture, made of small granules of high electron density, reminiscent of the iron micelles described by Farrant (32) in crystalline ferritin. It has indeed been established that lysosome-rich fractions contain more easily detachable iron (ferritin?) than the other particulate fractions (23). The results of these determinations suggest that up to 10 per cent of the cell ferritin may be associated with lysosomes or related particles, most of the remainder being in the final supernatant. They are therefore not in conflict with the recent observations of Kuff and Dalton (57), who have identified ferritin in the cytoplasmic ground substance and recovered it to a large extent in the soluble fraction. It should finally be noted that dense bodies lacking the ferritin-like granules were also occasionally found in our fractions (fig. 10). These appear to correspond to the microbodies described by Rouiller and Bernhard (83).

LYSOSOME-LIKE PARTICLES IN OTHER TISSUES

Kidney. It has long been known that the parenteral administration of some proteins, as of a number of colloidal dyes, causes the appearance of characteristic droplets in the brush-border cells of the convoluted tubules. Early work on these droplets has been reviewed by Gerard and Cordier (37) and more recently by Rather (74). They have been extensively studied by Zollinger (106) and by Oliver and his co-workers (70, 71, 61), and with the aid of electron microscopy by Rhodin (79) and by Gansler and Rouiller (36), who have also demonstrated the presence of smaller bodies of a similar type (big granules and microbodies) in the kidneys of untreated animals. Most authors believe that the droplets originate from mitochondria and are involved in the reabsorption of proteins and other substances from the lumen of the tubules.

According to Kretchmer and Dickerman (56), kidney droplets retain their characteristic shape after disruption of the cells and are recovered with the nuclear and mitochondrial fractions after differential centrifugation. Straus (92) has succeeded in purifying these bodies by a combination of filtration and centrifugation procedures; he has also shown that droplets of smaller size could be isolated from normal rat kidneys. His purified preparations had low cytochrome oxidase and succinic dehydrogenase activities (easily accounted for by a contamination with mitochondria) and a high content in acid phosphatase as well as significant autolytic (catheptic?) activity (92). After publication of the work on the hepatic lysosomes, Straus (93) was able to show that in addition to acid phosphatase, the droplet fractions contain the acid nucleases, β-glucuronidase and cathepsin, all concentrated 10- to 15-fold with respect to the original homogenates. He also found that these enzymes are not fully active in fresh preparations and are activated by exposure to hypotonic media (94). A close kinship between the kidney droplets and the hepatic lysosomes was thus clearly established.

The droplets isolated by Straus vary enormously in size, from 0.1 to 5 microns. Some therefore are smaller, others larger, than mitochondria, and this indicates that a size intermediate between those of mitochondria and microsomes may not be a necessary characteristic of lysosomes in other tissues. Like the liver particles, the droplets appear to be denser than mitochondria and of a darker color. Although purified preparations have not been examined in the electron microscope, it is possible that the three size-groups distinguished by Straus correspond approximately to the microbodies, big granules and hyaline droplets observed by the electron microscopists (89, 79, 36). Like the dense bodies in liver, these formations appear to be surrounded by a single membrane and have a dense interior. On the few pictures available in the literature, they seem to be less polymorphic, to show an internal cavity only exceptionally, and to be devoid of the ferritin-like granules seen in most hepatic bodies. Thus these granules may not be a constant feature of lysosomes. This may also be true in liver, since particles resembling the microbodies are also found in lysosome-rich fractions (see fig. 10). It would be interesting in this respect to know whether the droplets found in kidney after the injection of hemoglobin contain such granules, since iron deposits are seen histochemically under those conditions (70). Iron-containing particles (siderosomes) have been described in kidney by Richter (80).

Brain. In rat brain homogenates, acid phosphatase, acid ribonuclease, acid deoxyribonuclease, cathepsin and β-glucuronidase are all present in low but significant concentrations. All five enzymes are largely sedimentable and show structure-linked phenomena of latency and activation, as they do in liver preparations (7). Similar observations have been made on cat brain, which, however, appears to be devoid of acid deoxyribonuclease activity. In neither preparation could the lysosomal enzymes be clearly separated from cytochrome oxidase or glutamic dehydrogenase, presumably owing to the cellular heterogeneity of the material. Very complex diagrams were indeed given by density equilibration experiments. These results make it probable that lysosome-like particles exist in brain tissue, but the exact properties of these particles and their relationship with mitochondria remain to be established. In a few preliminary trials, they appeared to be more resistant to disruptive treatment than the hepatic lysosomes.

Other Mammalian Tissues. A few preliminary investigations have been made in our laboratory on spleen and thyroid tissues, with results which are not entirely negative. In rat spleen, which is a particularly rich source of the acid hydrolases which characterize lysosomes, Mrs. Deckers-Passau has found free activities of the order of 60 per cent for acid phosphatase and β-glucuronidase, and unsedimentable activities of 35–40 per cent for acid phosphatase and cathepsin. Thus these enzymes appear to be partly sedimentable and inactive, though to a smaller extent than in liver. It is interesting that Doyle (31) has located most of the acid phosphatase of spleen in the macrophages and that these cells contain an exceptionally large number of particles resembling the dense peribiliary bodies in several respects (including the ferritin-like granules) and described by Palade (72) under the name of residual bodies.

In a number of experiments on beef thyroid, Neil was able to isolate particulate fractions containing the lysosomal enzymes in partially inactive form. The yields were low and measurements made on the homogenates indicated that only 20–30 per cent of the activities were present in bound form. Thyroid tissue is extremely difficult to homogenize and it is possible that a greater percentage of the enzymes are particle-bound in the intact cells.

It should finally be recalled that particles having some morphological features in common with the dense peribiliary bodies or the kidney droplets have been described in several tissues. To the siderosomes (liver, kidney) of Richter (80) and the residual bodies (macrophages) of Palade (72), which have already been mentioned, one may add the dense bodies of mesothelial cells (69), the osmiophilic corpuscules of alveolar epithelium and Kupffer cells (87), the lipid bodies of pigeon breast muscle (53), the globoid bodies of HeLa cells (43) and the iron particles of erythroblasts and erythrocytes (15). However, since the common structural characters of lysosomes—if they have any—are not yet known, the significance of these observations cannot be assessed at the present time.

Lower Organisms. In a series of investigations on the giant amoeba *Chaos chaos,* Holter (49, 50) has found that acid phosphatase and cathepsin, like succinic dehydrogenase, accumulate in the centrifugal pole when the intact cell is centrifuged, but, unlike the latter enzyme, become unsedimentable in homogenates. He concludes that the hydrolytic enzymes may be attached to a special group of particles analogous to the hepatic lysosomes.

Conclusion. The fragmentary results obtained so far make it clear that lysosome-like particles are not confined to liver. They certainly occur in kidney, possibly also in brain, spleen and other tissues, as well as in some lower organisms. In addition, it must be remembered that lysosomal enzymes are widely distributed and that their appearance in free form in some homogenates does not necessarily disprove the existence of lysosomes in the intact cell, since the particles may be disrupted by the homogenizing process, as appears to be the case with amoeba. It is however much too early to decide whether lysosomes represent a cell organelle of general significance or are restricted to some kinds of cells only.

PHYSIOPATHOLOGICAL ROLE OF LYSOSOMES

General Considerations. Obviously, the possible biochemical functions of the lysosomes are circumscribed by the activities of their enzymes. These include at least six and probably more soluble acid hydrolases capable of acting on the most important cell constituents (see fig. 1), a fact which is rendered all the more significant by the absence of numerous metabolically active enzymes and of several neutral and alkaline hydrolases. The next step in our reasoning is a little more delicate, since the identified hydrolases can catalyze synthetic processes and transfer reactions, as well as hydrolytic splittings. In our opinion, an essentially hydrolytic function of the lysosomal enzymes is supported by the following arguments:

1) Very special conditions are needed for the spontaneous reversal of a hydrolytic reaction, especially in an aqueous medium. That such conditions could be realized simultaneously for numerous compounds appears improbable and most recent developments concur in showing that the cell does not rely on such reversals for its syntheses, but makes use of special activating mechanisms. This is now known to be true for most of the substrates which are split by the lysosomal enzymes.

2) Transfer reactions, although not subjected to such thermodynamic barriers, do in fact require conditions very similar to those which favor the synthetic processes in order to compete successfully with the hydrolytic splitting. This at least is what has generally been found *in vitro* (see, for instance, 4, 64, 35 and 34). Admittedly, as is believed to be the case for some ATPases, the situation may be different in an intact system.

3) The location of the lysosomal enzymes does not correspond with the sites of maximum synthesis, as evidenced by isotope experiments.

Our working hypothesis will therefore be that lysosomes are involved in processes of acid hydrolysis. These may comprise: digestion of foreign material, engulfed by pinocytosis, athrocytosis or phagocytosis; physiological autolysis, as presumably occurs to some extent in all tissues, and particularly as part of the more specialized processes of involution, metamorphosis, holocrine secretion, etc.; pathological autolysis or necrosis.

The hypothesis may be qualified further by stating that the normal segregation of the lysosomal hydrolases within little impermeable bags may play an essential part in keeping the lytic processes localized and, therefore, in protecting the cell against generalized autolysis.

Intracellular Digestion and Engulfing Processes. In a previous publication (29), the hypothesis was put forward that lysosomes may be concerned with localized phenomena of acid digestion and attention was called to an old observation by Horning (52), who described the participation of mitochondria-like bodies in the formation of digestive vacuoles in amoebae. After the provisional morphological identification of lysosomes was presented (66), the suggestion was made by Bennett (11) that the particles may represent segregated phagocytosed or pinocytosed material and that the enzymes associated with the granules may have a role in breaking down some of the contents of the bodies. Referring to the 'residual bodies' of spleen macrophages, Palade (72) has expressed a similar opinion, assuming that they represent terminal apearances of phagocytic vacuoles and that the dense granular material they contain is a metal-organic compound (hemosiderin? ferritin?). The involvement in engulfing processes of fairly polymorphic bodies surrounded by a single membrane has been demonstrated by Odor (69), Felix and Dalton (33) and Harford, Hamlin and Parker (42).

The best evidence linking lysosomes with pinocytosis and related phenomena stems from the studies on kidney droplets. The relationship of these granules to 'athrocytosis'—a term which was actually invented to explain their origin—rests on a long line of morphological studies (see 37, 74, 70, 71), and these have been amply verified by the more recent biochemical investigations. Indications that the droplets contain the injected material have been obtained by Oliver, MacDowell, Moses and Lee (71) after the administration of proteins, and by Lee (61) and Kretchmer and Cherot (55) after the injection of amino acids. The segregation of egg white by the droplets was later demonstrated on purified fractions by Straus and Oliver (96) with the aid of a semiquantitative serological method. These results were, however, questioned by Mayersbach and Pearse (63), who were unable to confirm them by means of a histochemical technique employing fluorescent antibodies. The problem has recently been reinvestigated by Straus (95), who has devised an elegant method based on the intravenous injection of crystalline horse-radish peroxidase and the subsequent assay of the enzyme. A considerable concentration of the injected protein in the droplet fractions could be evidenced in this manner. According to Straus (personal communication), many tissues share this ability to take up circulating peroxidase. That the segregated protein may subsequently undergo hydrolysis within the droplets is suggested by the results obtained on kidney slices by Oliver, MacDowell and Lee (70).

In our laboratory Dr. Beaufay has examined the possibility that lysosomes may play a role in the segregation of substances which are specifically concentrated in bile. His results were negative with bromsulfalein and with an iodinated opacifying agent (biligraphin), which were recovered almost entirely in the final supernatant of liver homogenates from animals killed 10–30 minutes after the intravenous injection of these compounds. With neutral red, on the other hand, part of the dye was retained in the particulate fractions, the highest concentration being found in the fraction richest in lysosomes. This finding is in agreement with the statement by Brachet (16) that lysosomes may be identical with the vacuoles which can be demonstrated by staining cells *in vivo* with basic dyes (neutral red, toluidine blue). Whether the phenomenon is a specific one remains to be verified, since the control experiment of adding the dye to a homogenate was not performed. On the other hand, it is also possible that the negative results mentioned above may be due to an insufficient time lapse between injecting and killing the animals. In the case of kidney, it is stated by Oliver, MacDowell and Lee (70) that the injected proteins are first diffusely distributed within the cells and form droplets only after 2–3 hours.

These various results, especially the well documented observations on kidney droplets, suggest strongly a relationship between lysosomes and engulfing vacuoles, the functional link being presumably provided by the digestive processes taking place within these vacuoles. They do not, however, clarify the nature of this relationship. If, as appears to be the most reasonable assumption, the droplets or lysosomes actually contain material taken up by pinocytosis as well as the various enzymes which have been detected within them, we are then left with the problem as to how both types of components actually come to be segregated together.

It is generally agreed (e.g., 10), that pinocytosis vacuoles are formed from the cell membrane, which folds around a droplet of ambient fluid. Thus and almost by definition, the pinocytosed material may be said to be present within the vacuoles from the time at which they are first formed. That the droplets may become detectable in fixed tissue or in homogenates only at some later stage could be explained on the basis of the observations made by Holter and Marshall (51) and by Chapman-Andresen and Holter (19) in their elegant studies of pinocytosis in the amoeba *Chaos chaos*. According to these authors, the vacuoles are initially of low density; they become progressively denser owing to either loss of water, gain of matter, or both, and later show signs of loss of engulfed material, presumably due to digestion. It is possible that the vacuoles are very fragile in their early stages and are destroyed by fixation or homogenization.

The appearance of the lysosomal enzymes within the vacuoles presumably occurs after the latter have first been formed. This could happen either by a process of *de novo* synthesis within the vacuole, or by secretion from the outside. Rose (81) has recently published a study which appears to support the latter concept. This author has described in HeLa cultures a special cell variant called VP cell (variant pinocytic cell) and characterized by a lack of shrinking of the pinocytic vacuoles, which accumulate in the juxtanuclear zone as large spheres of 4–25 microns (VP granules). Associated with the latter are often seen smaller particles of 1–8 microns, to which Rose has given the name VP satellite. In addition both normal and VP cells contain minute particles 0.3 to 0.6 micron in diameter and termed microkinetospheres. These appear to be very active and to establish repeated contacts with pinocytic vacuoles, causing changes in the size, refractive index and staining properties of the latter. The VP satellites, on the other hand, seem to arise in VP cells from coalescing microkinetospheres. To explain these observations, Rose (81) has advanced the hypothesis that microkinetospheres secrete digestive enzymes into the vacuoles, and suggested that these granules as well as the VP satellites may be related to the liver lysosomes and the kindney droplets.

Other relevant information is provided in a recent paper by Straus (94), who has described some changes occurring in the kidneys of rats injected with egg-white 18 hours before killing. In comparison with untreated controls, these preparations showed a decrease in the number of small droplets, an increase in the number of large ones associated with a corresponding fall in the enzyme content per droplet, an increase in the proportion of the enzymic activities found in the final supernatant, and an absolute increase in total cathepsin and nucleases but not in acid phosphatase nor β-glucuronidase. These results were interpreted as an indication that after injection of egg-white the small droplets are transformed into large ones, with a concomitant release of part of their enzyme content into the surrounding cytoplasm. In conformity with previous remarks, the alternative possibility that the excess free activities may have originated not from the surrounding cytoplasm but from fragile pinocytic vacuoles, would deserve consideration. New synthesis was invoked to account for the net increase in catheptic and nucleolytic activities.

It is obvious that considerable additional work will be required before the relationship between lysosomes and pinocytosis can be clearly appreciated. At present, the evidence that such a relationship exists appears fairly convincing and it may be useful to keep in mind, pending further information, that the biochemical concept of lysosomes (fig. 1) may possibly cover several biologically and morphologically distinct entities, namely: *1*) zymogen-like granules containing newly synthesized enzymes; *2*) pinocytosis vacuoles at various stages of their evolution; *3*) residual bodies, containing only the remnants of the digested material.

The polymorphism of the dense bodies, the presence or absence of iron particles within their matrix, as well as the heterogeneity of lysosomes with respect to size, enzyme content and sensitivity to osmotic disruption, are perhaps related to this diversity.

The above considerations also inspire due caution with regard to the interpretation to be given to the free activities of lysosomal enzymes found in homogenates. As will be shown below, we have obtained evidence that high free activities may have a pathological significance and be associated with necrosis. The observations of Straus (94) discussed above could possibly also have such a significance, since the kidneys of animals treated with egg-white certainly show some degenerative changes, for instance of mitochondria (70). But the high free activities of lysosomal enzymes found in the homogenates of these kidneys could also reflect the enhancement of their pinocytic activity. A similar explanation could account for the high free activities of normal spleen homogenates and also for the relatively low content in lysosome-like particles of Kupffer cells (102). The distinction between pathological and physiological free enzymes would then depend on whether they are truly free in the cytoplasm or segregated within fragile digestive vacuoles.

Physiological Autolysis. Autolysis occurs as a physiological process in the life history of some organs (involution of the thymus at puberty, of the uterus after parturition, etc.); it plays a major role in the metamorphosis of insects and of some other zoological groups; it may also intervene in some secretory processes, in particular in those of the holocrine type. The possible involvement of lysosomes in any of these phenomena has so far not been studied, with the exception of a recent investigation by Weber (104, 105) bearing on the catheptic activity of the tail of *Xenopus* larvae. Weber finds that the specific activity of this enzyme decreases during the growth phase of the tail and increases during its subsequent resorption, reaching up to 22 times its initial level in the final stages of metamorphosis. He concludes that this enzyme plays no part in protein synthesis but is involved in proteolysis. Whether cathepsin is particle-bound in the investigated tissue is, however, not known.

In addition to these specialized processes, some degree of autolysis must be taking place in many if not all tissues, as is evidenced by the observed turnovers of their main constituents. So far, a great deal of work has been performed on the synthetic implications of protein or nucleic acid turnover, but their catabolic counterpart has hardly been considered. Investigations dealing with this problem are those of Reid and co-workers (76, 75, 91, 77, 78), who have attempted to correlate some enzymic and metabolic changes occurring in the liver and kidneys of hypophysectomized or adrenalectomized rats. Their results are very complex, and the original publications should be consulted for details. Most relevant to the subject of the present review were the increases observed by the authors in the acid ribonuclease and deoxyribonuclease activities of the supernatant fraction after adrenalectomy. In liver, the ribonucleic acid content of this fraction and its rate of labeling from C^{14} orotic acid were increased, whereas other fractions showed a decreased rate of synthesis of ribonucleic acid and of protein. It is difficult to assess the significance of these results, especially since the increased synthesis of ribonucleic acid in the supernatant fraction preceded the rise in unsedimentable ribonuclease activity. It should be noted that this rise was not accompanied by a similar increase in unsedimentable acid phosphatase (78). This is in contrast with all the results of a similar nature obtained in our laboratory.

As will be mentioned below, an increase in the unsedimentable activities of the lysosomal enzymes has been observed in the livers of starved rats. However, it is not known to what extent the loss of protein and ribonucleic acid which occurs in starvation is due to decreased synthesis or increased autolysis. According to Laird, Barton and Nygaard (60), the anabolic capacity of the liver is much depressed after 6 days' starvation.

Of interest in connection with these problems are the experiments of Simpson (88), who found that the release of radioactive amino acids which occurs in isolated liver slices from animals previously treated with these amino acids is inhibited by lack of oxygen, by cyanide and by 2,4-dinitrophenol. These results have been confirmed by Steinberg and Vaughan (90), who have observed that the inhibition is also produced by the amino acid analogues *o*-fluorophenylalanine and β-2-thienylalanine, but not by S-methylcysteine. They conclude that protein breakdown as it occurs under the conditions of these experiments is not the result of a simple proteolysis but is in some way energy-dependent and linked with protein synthesis. This phenomenon has been further investigated on isolated fractions by Korner and Tarver (54) who have found that dinitrophenol inhibits the release of amino acids in nuclear and mitochondrial fractions but actually increases it in microsomes, while ATP, especially when added with phosphocreatine or 3-phosphoglycerate, depresses this release in all fractions. The authors point out that the results are very difficult to interpret without separate knowledge of protein synthesis and breakdown, and of the specific activities of the amino acids in the fractions. It is obvious that these observations, while indicating that cathepsins may not be the sole agents of protein breakdown, do not demonstrate that these enzymes do not play a role in this process. From what is known of the pH optimum of the lysosomal cathepsin, this enzyme may be expected to become active only below pH 6; i.e., below the normal intracellular pH of liver (18). The peculiar type of release studied on liver slices (at pH 7.4) may thus apply to a process occurring at a relatively high pH, while catheptic proteolysis may become dominant in cells or cell regions exposed to acidification, as will be further stressed below. It has indeed been found by Korner and Tarver (54) that the release of amino acids from isolated fractions is much increased by a lowering of the pH.

Pathological Autolysis, Necrosis. Whatever may be the true physiological function of lysosomes, it is a fairly straightforward inference from the concept that we have of these particles that an excessive release of their enzymes within the cell may be associated with necrotic phenomena. As shown in figure 1, the lysosomal enzymes are capable of destroying the most important tissue constituents, and the principal defense of the cell against this attack may be assumed to lie in the integrity of the lysosomal membrane. In surveying the older literature on necrosis (see for instance the review by Bradley, 17), one is struck by the fact that enzymes such as cathepsin have long been suspected of playing a role in this phenomenon, but no satisfactory explanation has been provided for their inhibition in the healthy cell.

In our laboratory, the above hypothesis has been put to an experimental test in collaboration with Dr. Beaufay and with a group of workers from the Cancer Institute. In a first series of experiments, the results of which have so far been published only in abstract form (8), a ligature was put on the vascular pedicle of the left liver lobe of rats anesthetized with Nembutal. The animals were killed at times ranging between one-half hour and 48 hours after the operation; the ligated lobe and the healthy non-ligated part of the liver were taken out, homogenized by a carefully standardized procedure, and centrifuged at high-speed. Enzyme assays were performed on the whole homogenates, the sediments and the supernatants. Some free activities were also measured on the whole homogenates.

In figure 11 are shown the results relating to the cytochrome oxidase, glucose-6-phosphatase and total acid phosphatase activities of the ligated lobes, expressed in percentage of their activities in the non-ligated parts, which served as controls. The rapid inactivation of the first two enzymes contrasts with the relative stability of acid phosphatase. The other lysosomal enzymes showed a more complex behavior. The acid nucleases and cathepsin exhibited a progressive decrease to about half the control values during the first 6–8 hours and then remained approximately constant; β-glucuronidase was unchanged for 6 hours and subsequently increased slowly. Of considerable interest were the changes in non-sedimentable activities of lysosomal enzymes, which rapidly increased from an initial mean value of 7 per cent of the total activities to a plateau of about 40 per cent. This value was reached as early as 2–3 hours after ligation; thus at a time when,

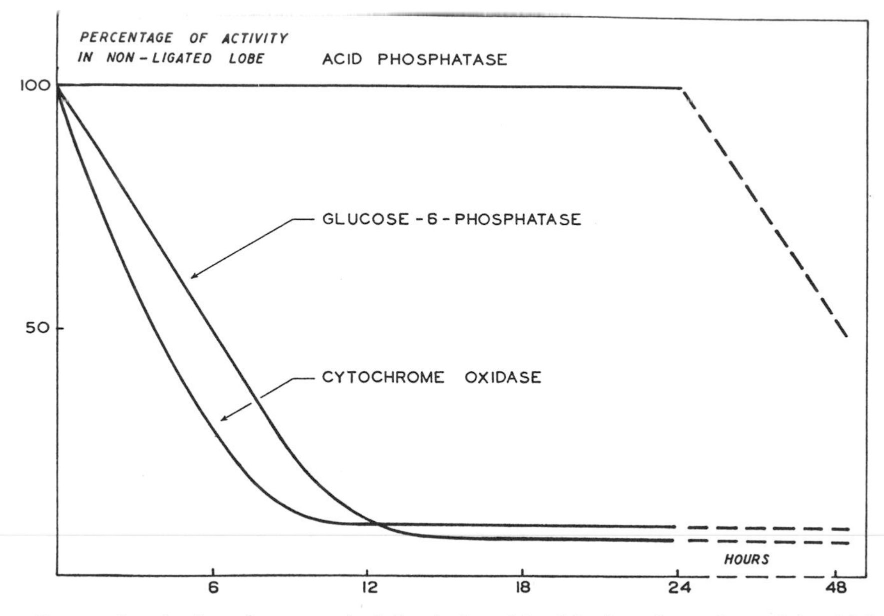

FIG. 11. Inactivation of enzymes in ischemic liver lobe. Ligation of vascular pedicle of left lobe as described in text.

according to Berenbom, Chang, Betz and Stowell (12), morphological and chemical changes are still very discrete. From the measurements of free activities it could be concluded that this plateau corresponded to a release of about 80 per cent of the lysosomal enzymes. These results are shown in figure 12. It will be noted that the unsedimentable activities of the control lobes also showed a transient increase, which appears to be related with the post-operative shock, since the values reverted to normal as the animals recovered from the anesthetic.

Similar measurements were performed on the liver of animals which had been *a*) subjected to prolonged fasting, *b*) given a deficient diet according to Himsworth and Glynn (46), or *c*) injected with carbon tetrachloride; also *d*) on one animal killed 8 days after ligation of the main bile duct. Striking changes were observed in the total activities of some of the lysosomal enzymes. Cathepsin was increased moderately in *group b* and two-fold in *groups c* and *d;* acid ribonuclease moderately in *group c* and two-fold in *group d;* acid deoxyribonuclease two-fold in *groups b* and *c* and more than three-fold in *group d.* In all groups, the unsedimentable activities of all five lysosomal enzymes were significantly raised above their normal levels. A number of animals were killed in a comatose state. In all these animals, the livers showed dramatic changes. The weight and nitrogen content of the organs were reduced to about half their normal values; their specific cytochrome oxidase activity to an even lower value. In contrast, the

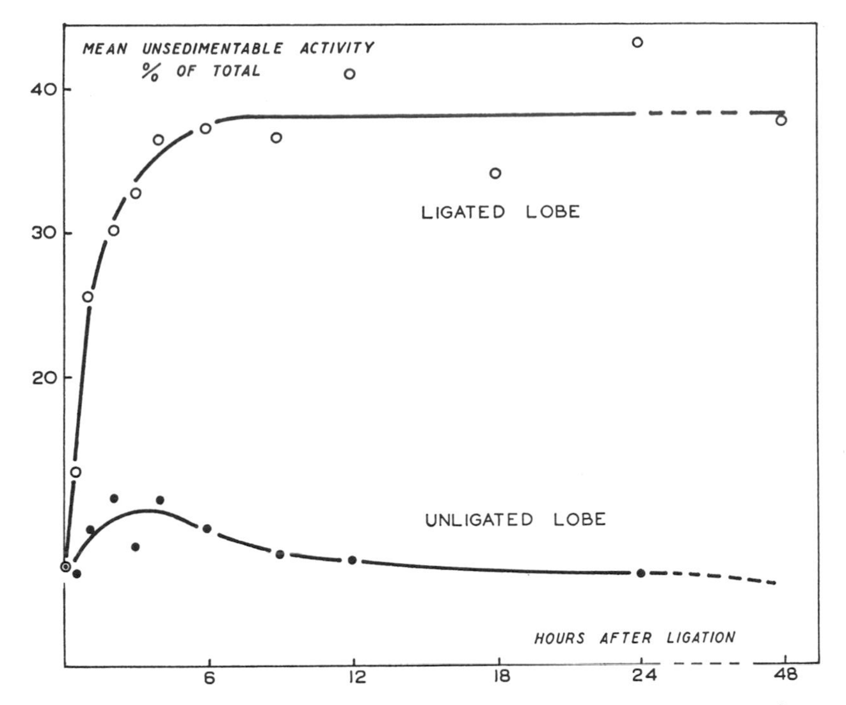

FIG. 12. Release of lysosomal enzymes in ischemic liver lobe. Same experiments as figure 11. Each point represents the mean for three animals of the averages of the unsedimentable activities of acid phosphatase, cathepsin and acid ribonuclease and deoxyribonuclease. The unsedimentable activity of β-glucuronidase follows the same course during the first 6 hours and then exhibits a second increase coincident with an unexplained increase in total activity.

specific activities of the lysosomal enzymes were notably increased, showing, therefore, that these enzymes had participated to only a small extent in the protein loss. Finally, the unsedimentable activities of these enzymes were increased almost as much as after ligation of the vascular pedicle and they could therefore be taken as being largely in free form. This biochemical picture, which is represented diagrammatically in figure 13, was exactly that which might be expected for an organ in the process of being digested by its own lysosomes.

The changes observed in the animals treated with carcinogenic dyes were very complex and have been described in detail (28, 20). The most significant ones were an increase in total cathepsin and acid nucleases and in the free or unsedimentable activities of all lysosomal enzymes in the precancerous livers and in the tumors.

The investigations summarized above have established a strong correlation between the intensity of necrotic phenomena and the proportion of lysosomal enzymes found in free or unsedimentable form in the homogenized tissue.

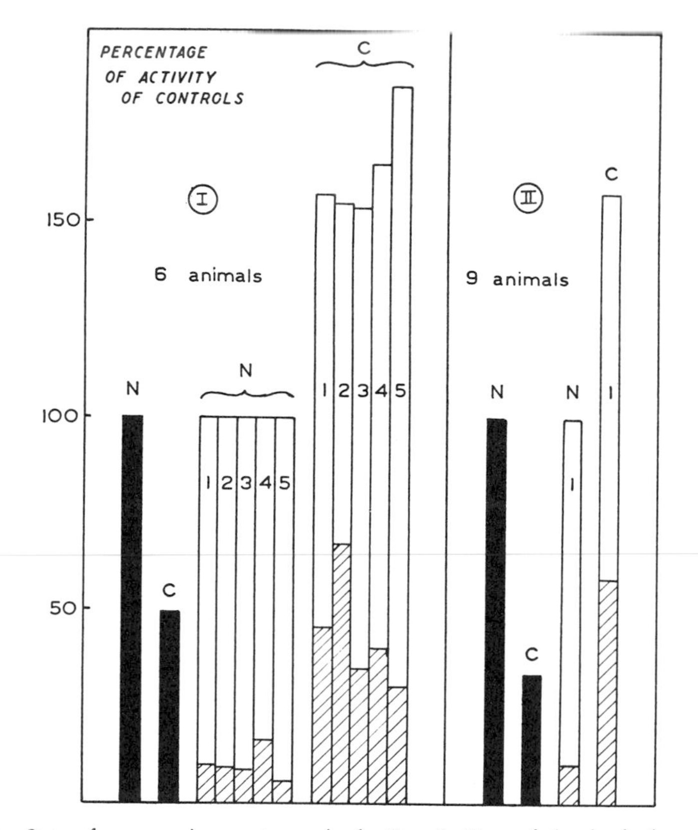

FIG. 13. State of enzymes in comatose animals. *Exp. I:* Mean of 6 animals (3 starved and 3 given deficient diet). Results expressed in U/mg N. *Exp. II:* Mean of 9 starved animals (5 untreated and 4 injected with CCl_4 before starvation). Results expressed in U/gm liver. *N*, controls (same treatment, but non-comatose). *C*, Comatose. *Full blocks*, cytochrome oxidase. (1), acid phosphatase; (2), β-glucuronidase; (3), cathepsin; (4), acid ribonuclease; (5), acid deoxyribonuclease. *Shaded blocks*, unsedimentable activities. Note that unsedimentable activities of controls are themselves higher than the normal values.

Whether the enzymes actually preexisted in free form in the intact cells cannot of course be known, but may be suspected from the evidence showing that increased autolysis was taking place. To this extent, the results obtained also indicate that the lysosomal enzymes are released together *in vivo* as they are *in vitro*. (See, however, ref. 78.) They do not, however, allow us to decide whether lysosomes may be considered as potential killers or 'suicide-bags,' since the observed breakdown of the particles could be a postmortal phenomenon. That they can act as scavengers and help to clear tissues of dead cells is at least clearly indicated.

The influence of total-body irradiation with a lethal dose of x-rays on the state of lysosomal enzymes has also been the object of some investigations.

According to Goutier-Pirotte (40), this treatment causes a labilization of the linkage betwen acid deoxyribonuclease and particles in rat spleen. No increase in the unsedimentable activities of hepatic lysosomal enzymes in liver nor of the acid phosphatase, or cathepsin of spleen has, however, been observed by Mrs. Deckers-Passau (unpublished observations) in rats killed 1 or 12 hours after having been subjected to a dose of 1000 r.

Mechanism of Lysosome Rupture in Intact Cells. Several of the phenomena discussed in the previous sections raise the problem of the nature of the mechanisms, either physiological or pathological, whereby lysosomes may become ruptured in living, dying or dead cells. Our only direct piece of information bearing on this point is provided by some experiments on liver slices showing that the rupture of lysosomes occurs more rapidly in the absence than in the presence of oxygen. Most of the observations described in the previous section could be related to partial or total anoxia, and the importance of this factor in the pathogenesis of necrosis has been repeatedly emphasized (see 17, 45).

As to how anoxia may affect the lysosomal membrane, one may consider several possibilities: *1*) the membrane is a dynamic structure which is continuously rebuilt with the help of oxidative energy; 2)the integrity of the membrane depends on the maintenance of some of its components in the oxidized state; *3*) anoxia releases one or more enzymes which break down the membrane.

With respect to the second possibility, we have not found any difference in the stability of isolated particles whether incubated aerobically or anaerobically. However, more complex phenomena may be involved and the results of Green and Mazur (41), who have described an anoxic release of ferritin apparently mediated by uric acid and other purines, deserve mentioning in view of the possible presence of ferritin and uricase in the lysosomal matrix. As to the third possibility, a particularly simple mechanism could be set up by the anoxic lowering of the intracellular pH, which might be sufficient to accelerate a catheptic rupture of the lysosomal membrane from within. The autolysis of the particles has indeed been shown to be strongly pH-dependent *in vitro* (2). It is interesting that other causes of acidosis, such as ketosis, could have a similar effect. In addition to anoxia, the possible involvement of rupturing agents, such as carbon tetrachloride or bile salts, should also be mentioned.

CONCLUSION

The principal aim of the preceding account has been to review and to delineate as clearly as possible the experimental facts which have led to the formulation of the lysosome concept. The possible relationship of the lysosome particles with mitochondria, although postulated by many authors on the basis of morphological observations, has not been discussed here; firstly, because the morphological identification of lysosomes has not yet been made with certainty; and, secondly, because such a relationship, if it exists, cannot alter the fact that lysosomes are different from mitochondria, as defined on the basis of functional and biochemical criteria.

In the third part of this paper, an attempt has been made to link lysosomes with the three natural processes of digestion, autolysis and necrosis, which could be accomplished by their particular enzymic equipment. A few suggestive data have been presented, but their number is still perilously small and great caution is required in their interpretation. One of the weaknesses of the hypotheses which have been examined is that no mention has been made of the neutral and alkaline hydrolases, which are present in other parts of the cell. Obviously, the part played by these enzymes in digestive and related processes, as well as the manner in which their activities are held in check and controlled within the cell, are matters of great interest about which, however, we know even less than we do concerning the lysosomes.

REFERENCES

1. Allard, C., G. de Lamirande and A. Cantero. *Biochim. et biophys. acta* 18: 578, 1955.
2. Appelmans, F. and C. de Duve. *Biochem. J.* 59: 426, 1955.
3. Appelmans, F., R. Wattiaux and C. de Duve. *Biochem. J.* 59: 438, 1955.
4. Axelrod, B. *J. Biol. Chem.* 172: 1, 1948.
5. Beaufay, H. *Arch. Internat. Physiol. Biochim.* 65: 155, 1957.
6. Beaufay, H. P. Baudhuin and D. S. Bendall. *IVth Internat. Congr. Biochem., Vienna,* 1958, p. 71.
7. Beaufay, H., A. M. Berleur and A. Doyen. *Biochem. J.* 66: 32, 1957.
8. Beaufay, H. and C. de Duve. *Arch. Internat. Physiol. Biochim.* 65: 156, 1957.
9. Bendall, D. S. *IVth Internat. Congr. Biochem., Vienna,* 1958, p. 57.
10. Bennett, H. S. *J. Biophys. Biochem. Cytol.* 2, Suppl.: 99, 1956.
11. Bennett, H. S. *J. Biophys. Biochem. Cytol.* 2, Suppl.: 185, 1956.
12. Berenbom, M., P. I. Chang, H. E. Betz and R. E. Stowell. *Cancer Res.* 15: 1, 1955.
13. Berthet, J., L. Berthet, F. Appelmans and C. de Duve. *Biochem. J.* 50: 182, 1951.
14. Berthet, J. and C. de Duve. *Biochem. J.* 50: 174, 1951.
15. Bessis, M. C. and J. Breton-Gorius. *J. Biophys. Biochem. Cytol.* 3: 503, 1957.
16. Brachet, J. In: *Biochemical Cytology.* New York: Acad. Press, 1957, p. 52.
17. Bradley, H. C. *Physiol. Rev.* 18: 173, 1938.
18. Caldwell, P. C. *Internat. Rev. Cytol.* 5: 229, 1956.
19. Chapman-Andresen, C. and H. Holter. *Exper. Cell Res.* 3: Suppl. 52, 1955.
20. Deckers-Passau, L., J. Maisin and C. de Duve. *Acta unio. internat. contra Cancrum* 13: 822, 1957.
21. de Duve, C. *Symp. Soc. Exper. Biol.* 10: 50, 1957.
22. de Duve, C., F. Appelmans and R. Wattiaux. *IIe Congr. internat. Biochim., Paris,* 1952, p. 278.
23. de Duve, C. and H. Beaufay. *Arch. Internat. Physiol. Biochim.* 65: 160, 1957.
24. de Duve, C. and J. Berthet. *Internat. Rev. Cytol.* 3: 225, 1954.
25. de Duve, C., J. Berthet and H. Beaufay. [illegible]
26. de Duve, C., J. Berthet, L. Berthet and F. Appelmans *Nature* 167: 389, 1951.
27. de Duve, C., R. Gianetto, F. Appelmans and R. Wattiaux. *Nature* 172: 1143, 1953.

28. DE DUVE, C., L. PASSAU AND J. MAISIN. *Acta unio. internat. contra Cancrum* 11: 638, 1955.
29. DE DUVE, C., B. C. PRESSMAN, R. GIANETTO, R. WATTIAUX AND F. APPELMANS. *Biochem. J.* 60: 604, 1955.
30. DODGSON, K. S., B. SPENCER AND J. THOMAS. *Biochem. J.* 59: 29, 1955.
31. DOYLE, W. L. *J. Biophys. Biochem. Cytol.* 1: 221, 1955.
32. FARRANT, J. L. *Biochim. et biophys. acta* 13: 569, 1954.
33. FELIX, M. D. AND A. J. DALTON. *J. Biophys. Biochem. Cytol.* 2: Suppl. 109, 1956.
34. FISHMAN, W. H. AND S. GREEN. *J. Biol. Chem.* 225: 435, 1957.
35. FRUTON, J. S., R. B. JOHNSTON AND M. FRIED. *J. Biol. Chem.* 190: 39, 1951.
36. GANSLER, H. AND C. ROUILLER. *Schweiz. Z. Pathol. u. Bakteriol.* 19: 217, 1956.
37. GERARD, P. AND R. CORDIER. *Biol. Rev.* 9: 110, 1934.
38. GIANETTO, R. AND C. DE DUVE. *Biochem. J.* 59: 433, 1955.
39. GIANETTO, R. AND R. VIALA. *Science* 121: 801, 1955.
40. GOUTIER-PIROTTE, M. *Biochim. et biophys. acta* 22: 396, 1956.
41. GREEN, S. AND A. MAZUR. *J. Biol. Chem.* 227: 653, 1957.
42. HARFORD, C. G., A. HAMLIN AND E. PARKER. *J. Biophys. Biochem. Cytol.* 3: 749, 1957.
43. HARFORD, C. G., A. HAMLIN, E. PARKER AND T. VAN RAVENSWAAY. *J. Biophys. Biochem. Cytol.* 2, suppl.: 347, 1956.
44. HERS, H. G., J. BERTHET, L. BERTHET AND C. DE DUVE. *Bull. Soc. Chim. Biol.* 33: 21, 1951.
45. HIMSWORTH, H. P. *The Liver and its Diseases.* Oxford: Blackwell, 1950, 2nd ed.
46. HIMSWORTH, H. P. AND L. E. GLYNN. *Clin. Sci.* 5: 93, 1944.
47. HOGEBOOM, G. H., E. L. KUFF AND W. C. SCHNEIDER. *Internat. Rev. Cytol.* 6: 425, 1957.
48. HOLT, S. J. *Proc. Roy. Soc., London, s. B* 142: 160, 1954.
49. HOLTER, H. *Proc. Roy. Soc., London, s. B* 142: 140, 1954.
50. HOLTER, H. In: *Fine Structure of Cells.* Groningen: Noordhoff, 1956, p. 71.
51. HOLTER, H. AND J. M. MARSHALL. *Compt. rend. Trav. Lab. Carlsberg* 29: 7, 1954.
52. HORNING, E. S. *Australian J. Exper. Biol. Med. Sci.* 3: 149, 1926.
53. HOWATSON, A. F. *J. Biophys. Biochem. Cytol.* 2: 363, 1956.
54. KORNER, A. AND H. TARVER. *J. Gen. Physiol.* 41: 219, 1957.
55. KRETCHMER, N. AND F. J. CHEROT. *J. Exper. Med.* 99: 637, 1954.
56. KRETCHMER, N. AND H. W. DICKERMAN. *J. Exper. Med.* 99: 629, 1954.
57. KUFF, E. L. AND A. J. DALTON. *J. Ultrastruct. Res.* 1: 62, 1957.
58. KUFF, E. L., G. H. HOGEBOOM AND A. J. DALTON. *J. Biophys. Biochem. Cytol.* 2: 33, 1956.
59. KUFF, E. L. AND W. C SCHNEIDER. *J. Biol. Chem.* 206: 677, 1954.
60. LAIRD, A. D., A. D. BARTON AND O. NYGAARD. *Exper. Cell Res.* 9: 523, 1955.
61. LEE, Y. C. *J. Exper. Med.* 99: 621, 1954.
62. MACFARLANE, M. G. AND N. DATTA. *Brit. J. Exper. Path.* 35: 191, 1954.
63. MAYERSBACH, H. AND A. G. E. PEARSE. *Brit. J. Exper. Path.* 37: 81, 1956.
64. MEYERHOF, O. AND H. GREEN. *J. Biol. Chem.* 178: 655, 1949.
65. NOVIKOFF, A. B. *Symp. Soc. Exper. Biol.* 10: 92, 1957.
66. NOVIKOFF, A. B., H. BEAUFAY AND C. DE DUVE. *J. Biophys. Biochem. Cytol.* 2: Suppl. 179, 1956.
67. NOVIKOFF, A. B., E. PODBER, J. RYAN AND E. NOE. *Fed. Proc.* 11: 265, 1952.
68. NOVIKOFF, A. B., E. PODBER, J. RYAN AND E. NOE. *J. Histochem. Cytochem.* 1: 27, 1953.
69. ODOR, D. L. *J. Biophys. Biochem. Cytol.* 2: Suppl. 105, 1956.
70. OLIVER, J., M. MACDOWELL AND Y. C. LEE. *J. Exper. Med.* 99: 589, 1954.
71. OLIVER, J., M. J. MOSES, M. C. MACDOWELL AND Y. C. LEE. *J. Exper. Med.* 99: 605, 1954.
72. PALADE, G. E. *J. Biophys. Biochem. Cytol.* 2: Suppl. 85, 1956.

73. PALADE, G. E. AND P. SIEKEVITZ. *J. Biophys. Biochem. Cytol.* 2: 671, 1956.
74. RATHER, L. J. *Medicine* 31: 357, 1952.
75. REID, E., M. A. O'NEAL AND I. LEWIN. *Biochem. J.* 64: 730, 1956.
76. REID, E., M. A. O'NEAL, B. M. STEVENS AND V. C. E. BURNOP. *Biochem. J.* 64: 33, 1956.
77. REID, E. AND B. M. STEVENS. *Biochem. J.* 67: 262, 1957.
78. REID, E. AND B. M. STEVENS. *Biochem. J.* 68: 367, 1958.
79. RHODIN, J. (Monogr.) Stockholm: Aktiebolaget Godvil, 1954.
80. RICHTER, G. W. *J. Biophys. Biochem. Cytol.* 4: 55, 1958.
81. ROSE, G. G. *J. Biophys. Biochem. Cytol.* 3: 697, 1957.
82. ROUILLER, C. *Compt. rend. soc. biol. Paris* 148: 2008, 1954.
83. ROUILLER, C. AND W. BERNHARD. *J. Biophys. Biochem. Cytol.* 2: Suppl. 355, 1956.
84. ROY, A. B. *Biochim. et biophys. acta* 14: 149, 1954.
85. ROY, A. B. *Biochem. J.* 68: 519, 1958.
86. SCHNEIDER, W. C. AND G. H. HOGEBOOM. *J. Nat. Cancer Inst.* 10: 969, 1950.
87. SCHULZ, H. *Exper. Cell Res.* 11: 651, 1956.
88. SIMPSON, M. V. *J. Biol. Chem.* 201: 143, 1953.
89. SJÖSTRAND, F. S. AND J. RHODIN. *Exper. Cell Res.* 4: 426, 1953.
90. STEINBERG, D. AND M. VAUGHAN. *Biochim. et biophys. acta* 19: 584, 1956.
91. STEVENS, B. M. AND E. REID. *Biochem. J.* 64: 735, 1956.
92. STRAUS, W. *J. Biol. Chem.* 207: 745, 1954.
93. STRAUS, W. *J. Biophys. Biochem. Cytol.* 2: 513, 1956.
94. STRAUS, W. *J. Biophys. Biochem. Cytol.* 3: 933, 1957.
95. STRAUS, W. *J. Biophys. Bochem. Cytol.* 3: 1037, 1957.
96. STRAUS, W. AND J. OLIVER. *J. Exper. Med.* 102: 1, 1955.
97. THOMSON, J. F. AND F. J. KLIPFEL. *Arch. Biochem. Biophys.* 70: 224, 1957.
98. THOMSON, J. F. AND E. T. MIKUTA. *Arch. Biochem. Biophys.* 51: 487, 1954.
99. THOMSON, J. F. AND E. M. MOSS. *Arch. Biochem. Biophys.* 61: 456, 1956.
100. UNDERHAY, E., S. J. HOLT, H. BEAUFAY AND C. DE DUVE. *J. Biophys. Biochem. Cytol.* 2: 635, 1956.
101. VIALA, R. AND R. GIANETTO. *Canad. J. Biochem. Physiol.* 33: 839, 1955.
102. WATTIAUX, R., P. BAUDHUIN, A. M. BERLEUR AND C. DE DUVE. *Biochem. J.* 63: 608, 1956.
103. WATTIAUX, R. AND C. DE DUVE. *Biochem. J.* 63: 606, 1956.
104. WEBER, R. *Experientia* 13: 153, 1957.
105. WEBER, R. *Rev. suisse zool.* 64: 326, 1957.
106. ZOLLINGER, H. U. *Am. J. Path.* 24: 569, 1948.

DISCUSSION

V. R. Potter, C. de Duve, M. L. Weiss, D. A. Marsland

DR. POTTER: What are the possible signals that set off the activation of the lysosomes in the cells; for example, is lactic acid production a factor?

DR. DE DUVE: One important factor is undoubtedly anoxia. See manuscript for possible mechanisms of anoxic rupture of lysosomes.

DR. WEISS: Coming back to the teleological point of view, would it not be possible that the lysosomal enzymes which might be released upon cell death digest cell constituents, making precursors available for regenerating cells, since where there is destruction there is also regeneration?

DR. DE DUVE: This is very true. Isotope studies have revealed the high turnover of many cell constituents. There are two aspects, one anabolic, the other catabolic, to turnover, and lysosomes might play a role in the latter. One could even consider a limited degree of destruction as essential to keep the enzyme forming systems in functional state.

DR. MARSLAND: Is it necessary to invoke necrosis and other pathological states in seeking a physiological role for the lysosomes? In perfectly normal cells could there not be a use for 'scavenger' activity to rid the cell of such things as inactivated enzymes and similar products resulting from the instability of normal cell components?

DR. DE DUVE: Indeed. Such activity might come under the heading of physiological autolysis.

NOTE ADDED IN PROOF

Additional information concerning the lysosomal enzymes has come from several sources. According to investigations by Rademaker and Soons (RADEMAKER, W. AND J. B. J. SOONS. *Biochim. et biophys. acta* 24: 451, 1957) and by Finkenstaedt (FINKENSTAEDT, J. T. *Proc. Soc. Exper. Biol. & Med.* 95: 302, 1957) the catheptic activity of the particles may be due to a mixture of cathepsins A, B and C. The localization of phosphoprotein phosphatase in the lysosomes has been established (PAIGEN, K. AND S. K. GRIFFITHS. *J. Biol. Chem.* 234: 299, 1959). In our laboratory it has been shown (SELLINGER, O. AND A. D. DOYEN. *Arch. Internat. Physiol. Biochem.* In press) that β-N-acetyl glucosaminidase is a lysosomal enzyme. With respect to the physiopathological significance of lysosomes, attention is called to an interesting study (STRAUS, W. *J. Biophys. Biochem. Cytol.* 4: 541, 1958) of the particles involved in the segregation of an injected protein (peroxidase) called by the author 'phagosomes.' Direct evidence that the release of lysosomal enzymes may play an important role in the involution of the Muller ducts in chick embryos has recently been provided (BRACHET, J., M. DECROLY-BRIERS AND J. HOYEZ. *Bull. Soc. Chim. Biol.* 40: 2039, 1958). The various unpublished observations from our laboratory referred to in the present review are described in detail in a series of papers which have been submitted for publication in the *Biochemical Journal.*

Intermediate Reactions in Protein Synthesis[1,2,3]

MARY L. STEPHENSON, LISELOTTE I. HECHT,
JOHN W. LITTLEFIELD, ROBERT B. LOFTFIELD
AND PAUL C. ZAMECNIK

Massachusetts General Hospital
Boston, Massachusetts

SINCE ACCEPTING THE PLEASANT INVITATION to participate in a symposium on subcellular particles we wondered what to present in the time allotted to us. Recently several reviews have covered the field of protein synthesis and the critical role of the ribonucleoprotein particle as the initial site of incorporation of amino acid into protein has been well established (32, 8, 20, 10). For these reasons we decided that a presentation of our current studies dealing primarily with the non-particulate enzymatic reactions preceding peptide bond formation would be timely and not out of place.

The present discussion of the problem is not on the whole a historical approach, but rather is designed to point out the essential factors and possible steps involved. Most of the experiments described herein have been carried out with mammalian cell systems and deal predominantly with the mechanism of the incorporation of amino acids into uncharacterized proteins rather than with the net synthesis of one or more specific proteins.

The initial site of the incorporation of amino acid into protein has been shown by several independent investigators to be in the microsome fraction (5, 25, 28, 30, 1, 36). In a representative experiment the amino acid was administered to the whole animal, after which, at various time intervals, the livers or other organs were removed, homogenized, and separated into fractions by differential centrifugation. The proteins in the microsomal fraction were the most rapidly labeled.

As is well known, the microsomal fraction refers to the pellet obtained after centrifugation of the 15,000 *g* supernatant of a homogenate for one or two hours at 15,000 *g*. The bulk of the cytoplasmic ribonucleic acid (RNA) is concentrated in this fraction (9, 7, 2). Two fractions can be obtained after treatment of microsomes with sodium deoxycholate (37). One is an insoluble fraction consisting of dense spherical particles with a diameter of about 150–250 Å, which contain

[1] This investigation was supported by grants-in-aid from the U. S. Atomic Energy Commission, the Public Health Service and the American Cancer Society.

[2] Publication no. [illegible] of the Harvard Cancer Commission.

[3] From the John Collins Warren Laboratories of the Collis P. Huntington Memorial Hospital of Harvard University at the Massachusetts General Hospital.

almost all of the RNA of the microsome and have been termed ribonucleoprotein particles; the other microsomal material, soluble in deoxycholate, probably represents the microsomal membranes with some associated soluble proteins (31, 33).

Littlefield *et al.* have shown that the ribonucleoprotein particles are the first part of the microsomes to incorporate amino acid into their protein (31). Following injection of a saturating dose of C^{14}-leucine the liver was homogenized and the microsome fraction was prepared and was separated further with sodium deoxycholate. The deoxycholate-insoluble ribonucleoprotein particles were the first to become labeled, as indicated in figure 1. Shortly thereafter, the labeled proteins were found in the remaining portion of the microsomes, and still later, in the proteins of the supernatant fraction of the cell.

The incorporation of amino acids into the ribonucleoprotein particles reached a steady state and remained constant while that into the other protein fractions proceeded at a linear rate. This suggests that the ribonucleoprotein particles are the site of the synthesis of the peptide linkage of the proteins and subsequently the proteins are released from these particles and appear in the deoxycholate-soluble and supernatant cell fraction.

Studies with cell-free homogenates have made it possible to define several enzymatic steps and specific cofactor requirements. The pioneer tissue slice experiments had indicated that some source of energy was required for formation of peptide bonds (14, 42), and the initial homogenate described by Siekevitz included the mitochondrial fraction (35). Later it was found that this fraction could be replaced by adenosinetriphosphate (ATP) plus an ATP-generating sys-

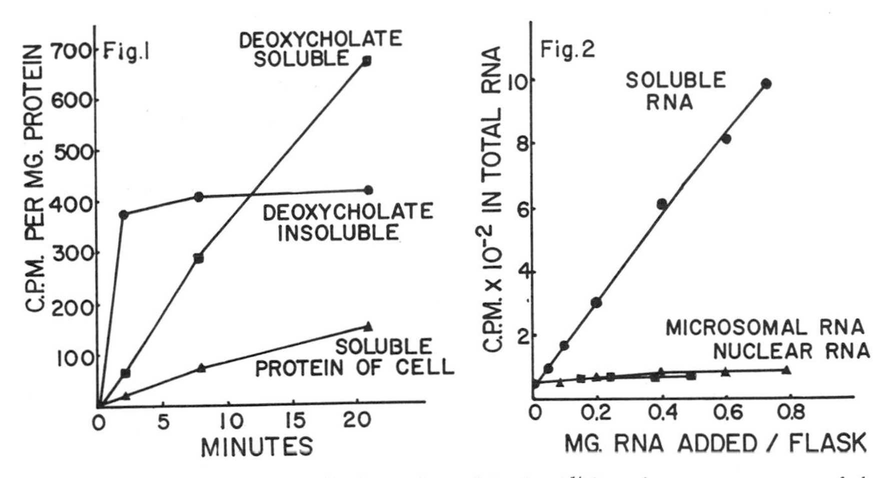

Fig. 1. Incorporation *in vivo* of a large dose of leucine-C^{14} into the two components of the microsomes and into the soluble proteins of the cell. [From (31).]

Fig. 2. Specificity of S-RNA as acceptor of the adenine nucleotide end group. [From (17).]

tem such as phosphopyruvate and pyruvate kinase (43). The amino acids were incorporated into the proteins of the microsome fraction, but some factors from the 15,000 *g* supernatant fraction were also necessary. These factors could be concentrated by bringing the 15,000 *g* supernatant fraction to pH 5.2 and redissolving the resulting precipitate in medium buffered at pH 7.4 (43). This crude enzyme fraction has been termed the 'pH 5 fraction.' With this system containing now the microsomes, pH 5 fraction and ATP, there was shown a requirement for small amounts of guanosine triphosphate (GTP) in addition to the rather high ATP requirement already demonstrated (29). The over-all incorporation into microsome protein was inhibited by ribonuclease (1, 43).

It should be pointed out that the incorporation of amino acids in the cell-free system proceeds for 15–20 minutes only. At the end of this *in vitro* incubation the distribution of labeled amino acids between the microsomal and supernatant protein fractions is similar to that found after a 3-minute *in vivo* experiment. Although net synthesis of protein has not been demonstrated, degradation studies and characterization of the labeled protein provide evidence that the amino acids are incorporated into a long polypeptide chain and, in one case, into the purified protein, ferritin. The 'protein' which is isolated in the usual experiment is a material which precipitates with trichloracetic acid (TCA) and has been thoroughly extracted with hot TCA and various lipid solvents. The incorporated amino acids cannot be removed from the protein fraction by dialysis; they do not react with ninhydrin; and they appear in small identifiable polypeptides on partial hydrolysis (30).

These early investigations have indicated that the ribonucleoprotein particles of the cell cytoplasm are the initial site of protein synthesis and that ATP, GTP and some soluble factors are necessary. More recent studies have described several enzymatic reactions which may be involved in the biosynthesis of protein. Although none of these steps is implicated with absolute certainty, enough evidence has been presented to enable one to speculate as to the possible role these isolated reactions may play in the over-all reaction.

The initial process appears to be the formation of an activated amino acid as indicated:

$$AA + ATP + E \rightleftharpoons [AA \sim AMP] - E + PP$$

The activating enzymes have received a great deal of attention (38, 19, 21, 12, 3, 11), and only a few of their properties will be discussed here. Briefly, an amino acid adenylate is formed enzymatically in the presence of L-amino acids and ATP with the elimination of pyrophosphate. This reaction is reversible and the activated amino acid appears to be tightly bound to the enzyme as it has not been isolated free in significant amounts from the incubation system. Activating enzymes have been found in a vast number of tissues, and for all of the natural amino acids. Some appear to be highly specific for an individual amino acid.

Although several of these have been isolated, the possibility of a separate activating enzyme for each amino acid remains to be confirmed. This reaction is not sensitive to ribonuclease, as is the over-all incorporation process. The ubiquity of the reaction makes it an attractive possibility that this activation of the carboxyl group of amino acids is an initial step in protein synthesis.

Another reaction possibly involved in the over-all incorporation of amino acid into protein was found quite unexpectedly. Because of the close association of RNA with the initial labeling of protein, we tried to correlate RNA and protein synthesis in this enzyme system. Labeled 8-C^{14}-ATP and labeled amino acid were incorporated separately in the cell-free liver system; then both the RNA and protein were isolated to see how much of the ATP label had appeared in the RNA, and how much amino acid was found in the protein. Surprisingly, the RNA incorporated not only the labeled nucleotide, but also leucine-C^{14}.

This binding of amino acid to RNA is being investigated by a number of workers (23, 22, 41, 4, 34, 39, 24). Further studies have shown that it is the RNA present in the soluble fraction of the cell (S-RNA) to which the amino acid becomes bound.

S-RNA, isolated by phenol extraction, retains its capacity to bind amino acid when added to the incubation system containing the supernatant fraction (22). Neither microsomal nor nuclear RNA is able to bind the amino acid to any great extent when added.

Studies of the binding of individual, and mixtures of, amino acids to the S-RNA indicated that there is no competition between the individual amino acids for sites on the S-RNA, since the binding of each amino acid is unaffected by the presence of other amino acids.

The soluble RNA (S-RNA) is conveniently concentrated in the pH 5 fraction mentioned above. The necessary enzymes for these incorporation reactions are also present in the pH 5 fraction, although not exclusively so.

A very specific requirement for ATP and cytosine triphosphate (CTP) has been demonstrated for the binding of the amino acid to this unique type of RNA (S-RNA). This requirement could not be demonstrated in the untreated pH 5 fraction, but following incubation of the pH 5 fraction for 20 minutes at 37°C in the absence of added nucleoside triphosphates and amino acids it became possible to demonstrate a dependence of the amino acid binding to S-RNA in the presence of CTP and ATP (15, 16). With untreated pH 5 fraction the binding of valine to S-RNA is not dependent upon the presence of CTP. However, when the pH 5 fraction is preincubated as described, the amino acid is not bound to S-RNA unless both CTP and ATP are present. Neither GTP nor uridine triphosphate (UTP) can replace CTP in this reaction and an absolute requirement for ATP is indicated (22). The CTP requirement has been observed for all 14 separate amino acids which have been tested.

The rôle played by CTP in binding amino acid to S-RNA has been elucidated by studies with labeled nucleotides. Our earlier attempt to correlate RNA synthesis with protein synthesis indicated that the same S-RNA which could bind amino acids also was able to incorporate C^{14}-labeled nucleotides. The nucleoside triphosphates were the precursors of the nucleotide incorporated into the S-RNA (45, 17, 6, 13, 18). ATP, CTP and to a lesser extent UTP were all precursors for the incorporation of nucleotides into S-RNA. GTP, however, was not utilized. The reaction mechanism appears to be as indicated:

$$ATP + RNA \rightleftharpoons AMP\text{-}RNA + PP$$

This incorporation is inhibited by pyrophosphate, and the reversibility has been demonstrated by an S-RNA dependent exchange of P^{32} into added CTP (17).

As with the binding of amino acids, the incorporation of the nucleotide was specific for S-RNA. Added nuclear and microsomal RNA were inert. This is shown in figure 2. A CTP requirement for the incorporation of the adenine nucleotide was demonstrated with the preincubated pH 5 fraction described previously (17).

Alkaline hydrolysis of the S-RNA isolated after incubation with C^{14}-ATP and C^{14}-CTP was used to indicate the positions of the nucleotide in the S-RNA chain. Mild alkaline hydrolysis of RNA degrades the molecule uniformly yielding 3′(or 2′) mononucleotides from the internal nucleotides of RNA, and nucleosides are liberated from one end of the chain. S-RNA isolated from the preincubated pH 5 fraction after incubation with C^{14}-ATP and/or C^{14}-CTP revealed a sequential incorporation of nucleotide into the S-RNA (17). As figure 3 indicates, the cytosine nucleotides and a terminal adenine nucleotide are added in sequence to 'apo-RNA.' The 'apo-RNA' is that isolated from the preincubated pH 5 fraction while the RNA isolated from the untreated supernatant fraction contains the terminal nucleotides and amino acids.

The CTP dependence of the binding of amino acid to the S-RNA indicates that the terminal groups on the end of the S-RNA chain play a role in the attachment of the amino acid to this type of RNA (16). Figure 4 indicates the available positions on this terminal end of the RNA. The existence of an ATP containing an amino acid on the 2′ (or 3′) hydroxyl of the ribose described by Weiss, Acs and Lipmann (40) provides some evidence that the same positions on the terminal ribose unit on S-RNA would be feasible in this type of molecule.[4]

Our evidence suggests that under certain experimental circumstances there are

[4] Note added in proof: Since the presentation of this paper more direct evidence has indicated that the amino acid is linked to the 2′ (or 3′) hydroxyl group of the terminal adenine nucleotide of S-RNA. (ZACHAU, H. G., G. ACS AND F. LIPMANN. *Proc. Nat. Acad. Sci.* 44: 885, 1958; HECHT, L. I., M. L. STEPHENSON AND P. C. ZAMECNIK. *Proc. Nat. Acad. Sci.* In press. PREISS, J., P. BERG, E. J. OFENGAND, F. H. BERGMANN AND M. DIECKMANN. *Proc. Nat. Acad. Sci.* In press.

1. CTP + RNA- ⇌ RNA-pCpC + PP
"Apo-RNA"

2. ATP + RNA-pCpC ⇌ RNA-pCpCpA + PP

FIG. 3. Schematic diagram indicating that when ATP is present, the terminal CMP residue of S-RNA is covered up.

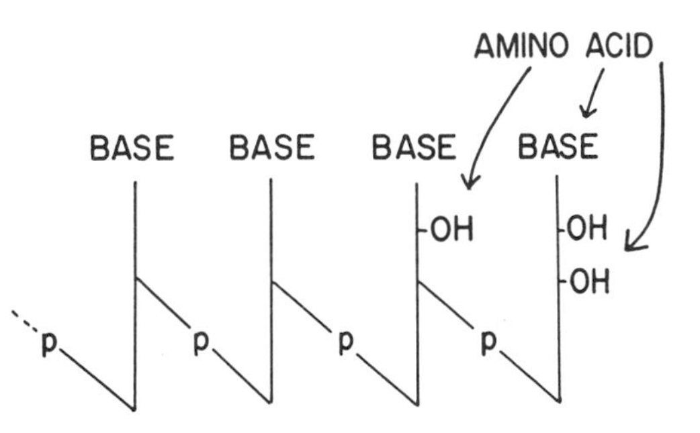

FIG. 4. Available sites for amino acid on S-RNA.

two separate steps involved in the binding of amino acid to S-RNA. These are indicated in figure 5. The first step would prepare the S-RNA with its specific nucleotide end groups, while the second enzymatic step would use this S-RNA containing the end groups as an acceptor for the amino acid. As evidence for a two-step process, we have never been able to demonstrate an amino acid effect on the addition of the nucleotide end groups to the S-RNA, and furthermore, in the ascites system the nucleotide labeling reaction is saturated at extremely low concentrations of ATP, i.e., 0.0005 M, whereas the ATP requirement to bind the amino acids to S-RNA is in the order of 50 times as much (17, 22).

What then is the significance of this highly specific S-RNA in the over-all incorporation of amino acids into protein, and where does it fit into the general scheme? GTP plays no role in the binding of amino acid to S-RNA, although it is essential to obtain incorporation into protein. An experiment using intact ascites cells gave us some clues as to the rates of incorporation of amino acid into the various RNA and protein fractions (22). The reactions were so rapid it was necessary to slow them down by carrying out the incubation at 20°C instead

ADDITION OF NUCLEOTIDE END GROUP

RNA- + ATP + CTP ⇌ RNA-pCpCpA + PP

NO AMINO ACID EFFECT

LOW ATP AND CTP REQUIREMENT

BINDING OF AMINO ACID

AMINO ACID + ATP + RNA-pCpCpA ⇌ RNA-pCpCpA-AMINO ACID

(AMINO ACID + ATP = activated amino acid)

HIGH ATP REQUIREMENT

FIG. 5. Postulated steps in binding of amino acid to S-RNA.

of 37°C. Ascites cells were incubated with C^{14}-leucine, and at various time intervals cells were lysed and fractionated by differential centrifugation. The S-RNA, RNA and protein of the ribonucleoprotein particles and the remaining soluble proteins were isolated. Figure 6 indicates that S-RNA was maximally labeled before the other fractions had reached their highest specific activity, thus indicating that this unique type of RNA might be an intermediate in the process.

Dr. Hoagland has added amino acid-labeled S-RNA to microsomes plus a small amount of supernatant enzyme, and has shown that 20 per cent of the amino acid appeared in the protein (22). This reaction was dependent upon GTP and ATP as well as a small amount of the supernatant fraction, whereas GTP was not necessary for amino acid activation or binding to S-RNA. Addition of C^{12}-amino acid to the reaction mixture did not change the amount of C^{14}-amino acid incorporated into protein. This indicated that the amino acids bound to the S-RNA do not equilibrate with free amino acids before they become incorporated into protein. Hultin and Beskow have also presented evidence for a bound amino acid intermediate which does not equilibrate with free amino acids (26, 27).

Figure 7 shows a time curve for the transfer of this type of S-RNA-bound amino acid to microsome protein (22). In this case, a liver pH 5 fraction was incubated with C^{14}-amino acid and ATP, and the free amino acids and ATP were removed by reprecipitation at pH 5.2 from dilute solution. This reprecipitated and redissolved pH 5 fraction contained C^{14}-amino acids presumably bound to the S-RNA therein. This labeled enzyme fraction was subsequently incubated with liver microsomes and GTP. The figure indicates the rapid loss of amino acid from this fraction with the concomitant incorporation of the amino acid into microsomal protein.

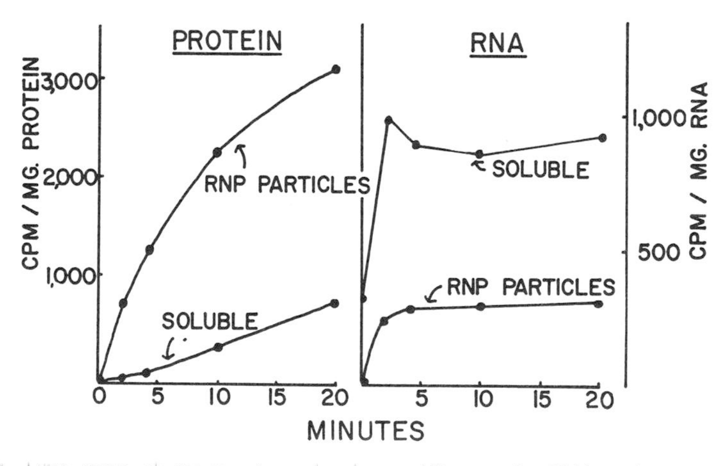

FIG. 6. Time curve of incorporation of L-leucine C^{14} into the RNA and protein of the ribonucleoprotein particles and the soluble fraction in intact ascites cells. [From (22).]

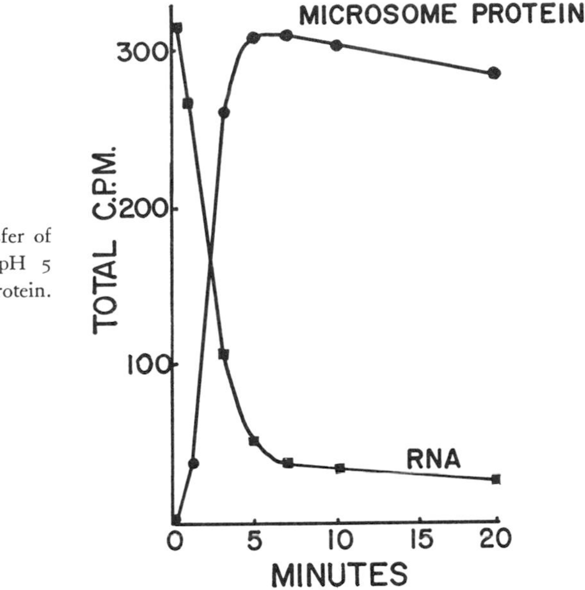

FIG. 7. Time curve of transfer of leucine-C^{14} from prelabeled pH 5 fraction to microsome protein. [From (22).]

It has been possible to demonstrate a partial requirement for S-RNA in the over-all incorporation of amino acid into protein by starting with a system containing very little S-RNA per se (44, 41). Addition of unlabeled S-RNA to ascites microsomes plus supernatant enzymes (S_4) resulted in an increased incorporation of C^{14}-leucine into the proteins. This is shown in table 1. This effect can be demonstrated only when there is little or no S-RNA already present in the incorporation system.

Less direct evidence for the participation of S-RNA in the over-all incorporation reaction is shown by the demonstration of a partial CTP dependence on the over-all incorporation of amino acid into protein. In order to do this it is necessary to remove all of the endogenous CTP. This is accomplished by centrifuging the microsomes from a very dilute 15,000 *g* supernatant and by using a preincubated pH 5 fraction plus a soluble fraction which had been treated with Dowex-1 in the chloride form to remove free nucleotides. The increase of incorporation in the presence of CTP is indicated in table 2.

TABLE 1. ENHANCEMENT OF INCORPORATION OF C^{14}-LEUCINE INTO PROTEIN BY ADDED S-RNA *

	TOTAL COUNTS	
	RNA	Protein
Control	136	134
Same plus 120γ S-RNA	927	357

* From (44).

TABLE 2. ENHANCEMENT BY CTP OF INCORPORATION OF C^{14}-VALINE INTO LIVER PROTEIN AND RNA

	CPM PER MG	
	Protein	RNA
ATP	8.6	983
ATP, GTP	20.0	992
ATP, GTP, CTP	63.3	1360

The incubation system contained microsomes centrifuged from a dilute 15,000 *g* liver supernatant fraction, soluble enzymes treated with Dowex-1-Cl to remove nucleotides, preincubated pH 5 fraction, 0.1mM valine-1-C^{14} containing 300,000 cpm/ml, 0.005 M ATP and a nucleoside triphosphate generating system. The indicated nucleotides were added at final concentration of 0.1 μM. The total volume was 1 ml. Incubation was for 15 min. at 37° C.

SUMMARY

The relationship of the isolated steps described herein is illustrated in table 3.

TABLE 3. POSTULATED STEPS IN INCORPORATION OF AMINO ACIDS INTO PROTEIN

1. Activation of amino acids:

$$\text{AMINO ACID} + \text{ATP} + \text{ENZYME} \rightleftharpoons [\text{AA}{\sim}\text{AMP}] - \text{ENZYME} + \text{PP}$$

2. Addition of nucleotide end groups to S-RNA:

$$\text{RNA} - \;+ \text{ATP} + \text{CTP} \rightleftharpoons \text{RNA} - \text{pCpCpA} + \text{PP}$$

3. Binding of amino acids to this S-RNA (enzymes may be identical with activating enzymes):

$$\text{AA} + \text{ATP} + \text{RNA} - \text{pCpCpA} \rightleftharpoons \text{RNA} - \text{pCpCpA} - \text{AA} + \text{PP}$$

4. Transfer of amino acids to ribonucleoprotein particles of microsomes, with binding to ribonucleoprotein RNA, followed by polymerization of amino acids:

$$\text{RNA} - \text{pCpCpA} - \text{AA} + \text{ATP} + \text{GTP} + \text{RNP} - \text{particles} + \text{soluble fraction} \longrightarrow \text{peptide chain}$$

5. Release of bound peptide chain and completion of protein by cross linking and secondary bonding

It should be stressed that much of the evidence is indirect, and some of the reactions described might be quite remote from the direct path of protein synthesis.

The first step, an activation of the amino acids, does not involve RNA. The reaction specifically requires ATP and cannot be replaced by CTP, UTP, or GTP. There are apparently many specific enzymes.

In another series of reactions, a unique type of soluble RNA (S-RNA) receives specific nucleotide end groupings. This reaction is independent of amino acids.

A third reaction binds amino acid to the S-RNA, which must contain the specific nucleotide end groups. There is no competition among the amino acids, indicating the presence of a specific binding site or a specific S-RNA molecule for each natural amino acid. This reaction may be carried out by the activating enzymes.

Evidence has been presented for a transfer of the S-RNA bound amino acid to both microsomal RNA and to microsomal protein. At this point we are on less stable ground. Whether the dependence upon GTP applies only to the binding of amino acid to microsomal RNA or also to the forming of proteins remains to be answered.

The ribonucleoprotein particles are, however, initially implicated in the formation of completed protein. We have been talking today for the most part about reactions which precede this polymerization and which require only the soluble elements of the cell.

REFERENCES

1. Allfrey, V., M. M. Daly and A. E. Mirsky *J. Gen. Physiol.* 37: 157, 1953.
2. Barnum, C. P. and R. A. Huseby. *Arch. Biochem.* 19: 17, 1948.
3. Berg, P. *J. Biol. Chem.* 222: 1025, 1956.
4. Berg, P. and E. J. Ofengand. *Proc. Nat. Acad. Sci.* 44: 78, 1958.
5. Borsook, H., C. L. Deasy, A. J. Haagen-Smit, G. Keighley and P. H. Lowy. *J. Biol. Chem.* 187: 839, 1950.
6. Canellakis, E. S. *Biochim. et biophys. acta* 25: 217, 1957.
7. Chantrenne, H. *Biochim. et biophys. acta* 1: 437, 1947.
8. Chantrenne, H. *Ann. Rev. Biochem.* 27: 35, 1958.
9. Claude, A. *Cold Spring Harbor Symp. Quant. Biol.* 9: 263, 1941.
10. Crick, F. H. C. *Soc. Exper. Biol. Symp., London,* 1958.
11. Davie, E. W., V. V. Koningsberger and F. Lipmann. *Arch. Biochem. Biophys.* 65: 21, 1956.
12. DeMoss, J. and G. D. Novelli. *Proc. Nat. Acad Sci.* 42: 325, 1956.
13. Edmonds, M. and R. Abrams. *Biochim. et biophys. acta* 26: 266, 1957.
14. Frantz, I. D., Jr., P. C. Zamecnik, J. W. Reese and M. L. Stephenson. *J. Biol. Chem.* 174: 773, 1948.
15. Hecht, L. I., M. L. Stephenson and P. C. Zamecnik. *Fed. Proc.* 17: 239, 1958.
16. Hecht, L. I., M. L. Stephenson and P. C. Zamecnik. *Biochim. et biophys. acta* 29: 460, 1958.
17. Hecht, L. I., P. C. Zamecnik, M. L. Stephenson and J. F. Scott. *J. Biol. Chem.* 233: 954, 1958.
18. Herbert, E. *J. Biol. Chem.* 231: 975, 1958.
19. Hoagland, M. B. *Biochim. et biophys. acta* 16: 288, 1955.
20. Hoagland, M. B. *IVth Internat. Congr. Biochem.,* Vienna, 1958.
21. Hoagland, M. B., E. B. Keller and P. C. Zamecnik. *J. Biol. Chem.* 218: 345, 1956.
22. Hoagland, M. B., M. L. Stephenson, J. F. Scott, L. I. Hecht and P. C. Zamecnik. *J. Biol. Chem.* 231: 241, 1958.
23. Hoagland, M. B., P. C. Zamecnik and M. L. Stephenson. *Biochim. et biophys. acta* 24: 215, 1957.
24. Holley, R. W. *Fed. Proc.* 17: 244, 1958.
25. Hultin, T. *Exper. Cell Res.* 1: 376, 1950.
26. Hultin, T. *Exper. Cell Res.* 11: 222, 1956.
27. Hultin, T. and G. Beskow. *Exper. Cell Res.* 11: 664, 1956.
28. Keller, E. B. *Fed. Proc.* 10: 206, 1951.
29. Keller, E. B. and P. C. Zamecnik. *J. Biol. Chem.* 221: 45, 1956.
30. Keller, E. B., P. C. Zamecnik and R. B. Loftfield. *J. Histochem. Cytochem.* 2: 378, 1954.

31. LITTLEFIELD, J. W., E. B. KELLER, J. GROSS AND P. C. ZAMECNIK. *J. Biol. Chem.* 217: 111, 1955.
32. LOFTFIELD, R. B. *Progr. in Biophys. Biophys. Chem.* 8: 347, 1957.
33. PALADE, G. E. AND P. SIEKEVITZ. *J. Biophys. Biochem. Cytol.* 2: 171, 1956.
34. SCHWEET, R. S., F. C. BOVARD, E. ALLEN AND E. GLASSMAN. *Proc. Nat. Acad. Sci.* 44: 173, 1958.
35. SIEKEVITZ, P. *J. Biol. Chem.* 195: 549, 1952.
36. SIMKIN, J. L. AND T. S. WORK. *Biochem. J.* 65: 307, 1957.
37. STRITTMATTER, C. F. AND E. G. BALL. *Proc. Nat. Acad. Sci.* 38: 19, 1952.
38. Symposium—Amino Acid Activation. *Proc. Nat. Acad. Sci.* 44: 67, 1958.
39. WEBSTER, G. C. *J. Biol. Chem.* 229, 535, 1957.
40. WEISS, S. B., G. ACS AND F. LIPMANN. *Fed. Proc.* 17: 333, 1958.
41. WEISS, S. B., G. ACS AND F. LIPMANN. *Proc. Nat. Acad. Sci.* 44: 189, 1958.
42. WINNICK, T., F. FRIEDBERG AND D. M. GREENBERG. *Arch. Biochem.* 15: 160, 1947.
43. ZAMECNIK, P. C. AND E. B. KELLER. *J. Biol. Chem.* 209: 337, 1954.
44. ZAMECNIK, P. C., M. L. STEPHENSON AND L. I. HECHT. *Proc. Nat. Acad. Sci.* 44: 73, 1958.
45. ZAMECNIK, P. C., M. L. STEPHENSON, J. F. SCOTT AND M. B. HOAGLAND. *Fed. Proc.* 16: 275, 1957.

DISCUSSION

E. L. Kuff, M. L. Stephenson, R. A. Lewin, J. Roth, R. E. Beyer, A. Marshak, R. Milkman

DR. KUFF: Is there any evidence for the incorporation of soluble RNA into the microsomal nucleoprotein concomitant with the incorporation of amino acid?

DR. STEPHENSON: Dr. Hoagland has labeled S-RNA *in vivo* using C^{14}-orotic acid. This pyrimidine-labeled S-RNA was isolated and was incubated with non-labeled microsomes, soluble enzymes and ATP. The microsomes were subsequently reisolated. Some radioactivity was found in the microsomal RNA and this labeling was enhanced by GTP. These findings are under study now. (STEPHENSON, M. L., P. C. ZAMECNIK AND M. B. HOAGLAND. *Fed. Proc.* 18: 331, 1959.)

DR. LEWIN: The observation that the incorporation of different amino acids is additive may be evidence for heterogeneity in the soluble RNA. Have attempts been made to separate RNA fractions which might be specific for different amino acids?

DR. STEPHENSON: No real attempts have been made to fractionate S-RNA in our laboratory. I understand that this is being done in other laboratories with preliminary indications that there are several specific RNA molecules.

DR. ROTH: Have you any evidence as to whether the labeled amino acids which are incorporated into the soluble RNA in the supernatant fraction are located at the ends of the chain or randomly along the chain? You know that the nucleotides are incorporated at the ends, for example.

DR. STEPHENSON: Because the binding of all amino acids to S-RNA and the incorporation of the terminal adenine residue into S-RNA are both dependent upon the presence of CTP, the amino acid is very likely attached to the end group of S-RNA. The [illegible] or [illegible] hydroxyl of the terminal ribose of S-RNA could be the binding site, especially since Dr. Lipmann and Dr. Weiss have reported finding an ATP-amino acid compound containing the amino acid in this position. The stability of this compound is not unlike that of amino acid-RNA. (See footnote 4 of text.)

DR. BEYER: Would you please discuss the recent findings of Drs. Moldave and Meister, and of Fruton concerning the nonenzymatic incorporation of activated amino acids into boiled proteins in connection with your findings of cofactors required for enzymic incorporation. Which do you think is the physiological pathway?

DR. STEPHENSON: The nonenzymatic incorporation of amino acid adenylates is obtained using relatively high concentrations of the adenylates. In the physiological system, the activated amino acids are apparently enzyme bound and the free amino acid adenylates are present in extremely low concentrations. Because of this and because of the various nucleotide cofactors, such as CTP and GTP, required for the incorporation of amino acid into RNA and protein, we assume that nonenzymatic reactions play a very small role in our incorporation system.

DR. MARSHAK: Your data indicate attachment of the amino acid on the 2′ or 3′ carbon of the ribose on the terminal adenylic or cytidylic acid group of the RNA. This site differs from that of Michelson's in his hypothesis for RNA and amino acid synthesis as alternate pathways by polymerization after initial attachment of amino acid in anhydride link to the 2′ or 3′ carbon of ribose of the nucleotide. Could you discuss these findings?

DR. STEPHENSON: At the moment I am uncertain of the details of Michelson's paper and cannot say how our data bear on this hypothesis. [The amino acid-RNA bond appears to be more stable than the 2′:3′ cyclic phosphate-amino acid anhydride bond suggested by Michelson. However, we have not ruled out this possibility. The stability of the AA-RNA is more like that of an amino acid ester which could conceivably be on the 2′ or 3′ hydroxyl of the ribose. Since our data suggest that each amino acid occupies a terminal position on an S-RNA chain, it would be difficult to see how polymerization of the amino acids could take place using this RNA as a template. Perhaps the microsomal RNA plays a role here.]

DR. MILKMAN: Are these techniques being applied to systems where ostensibly large amounts of one protein are being made; for example, immature red blood cells? Do you think the time is ripe for such applications of these techniques?

DR. STEPHENSON: Dr. Campbell has demonstrated the labeling of albumin in liver homogenates and the reticulocyte system is being studied by Drs. Rabinowitz and Dintzis, and by Dr. Loftfield in our laboratory. Recently Dr. Loftfield has obtained incorporation of C^{14}-valine into ferritin isolated after incubation of a cell-free liver system, using rats which had been stimulated to produce ferritin by *in vivo* injection of iron oxide. This has been our first real evidence that our cell-free incorporation was not just into large polypeptide or incomplete proteins which precipitated with trichloroacetic acid. You are right, the time is ripe for such studies.

In Situ Studies of Polynucleotide Synthesis in Nucleolus and Chromosomes[1]

J. HERBERT TAYLOR AND PHILIP S. WOODS

Columbia University and
Brookhaven National Laboratory
New York

IN SITU STUDIES AT THE INTRACELLULAR LEVEL by means of autoradiography have increased as higher resolution has been attained and appropriately labeled compounds have been prepared. In principle, the autoradiographic method is a simple one in which the wet emulsion is placed in contact with the specimen on a microscope slide, dried, exposed for an appropriate period, developed, fixed, washed and mounted for microscopic examination while still in contact with the specimen (see review by Talyor, ref. 11, for details). Significant improvement in resolution has resulted from the use of radiohydrogen (tritium) as a label. Since most of the beta particles emitted by tritium are stopped by the first micron of a photographic emulsion, the grains produced are very close to the object being exposed. Another improvement comes through advances in biochemistry which allow the selection of precursors which label a limited number of components of the cell. Likewise development of cytochemical techniques for differential extraction when only relatively nonselective labels are available makes possible similar studies *in situ*.

REPLICATION OF DNA

Although various types of cells may be capable of degrading thymidine, many of them utilize it almost exclusively for DNA (deoxyribonucleic acid) synthesis (8, 2). Thymidine was labeled with tritium and used as a selective label for chromosomes. Resolution was good enough to show labeled and unlabeled segments of single large chromosomes (18). When roots are grown in solutions containing tritium-labeled thymidine, the isotope is incorporated almost exclusively into nuclei. After 6–8 hours of growth, about one-third of the nondividing nuclei are labeled. The remainder of the cells in that period show no detectable amount of the isotope. Within 10 hours after the cells begin incor-

[1] The work of the senior author was supported in part by grants from the Atomic Energy Commission, Contract AT (30 1)1304, and the Higgins Fund, Columbia University. The technical assistance of Mrs. Toni Simon is gratefully acknowledged.

poration, labeled nuclei appear at division stages. The chromosomes in these first labeled cells which appear at division are sometimes nonuniformly labeled along their length; sometimes parts of chromosomes, and very rarely whole chromosomes may be unlabeled in an otherwise labeled group (12; Woods, unpublished). This observation suggests that duplication does not begin simultaneously at all points along a chromosome and, further, that variations may occur among individual chromosomes of a set. Cells appearing at divisions a few hours later have their chromosomes much more uniformly labeled. The first labeled cells to reach division have evidently completed part of DNA synthesis before coming in contact with the isotope, but after a few more hours only those which have been in contact with the isotope for the entire synthetic period are arriving at division stages. There appear to be variations among species in the degree and pattern of asynchrony. In *Crepis,* a plant with three pairs of relatively small chromosomes, the duplication appears to begin at both ends of a chromosome and progresses toward the centromere in a zipper fashion (12). In *Bellevalia,* a plant of the lily family with larger chromosomes, the amount of asynchrony is small. Nearly all chromosomes are labeled simultaneously. No exact measure of the time required for duplication is available, but in *Bellevalia* the period is a matter of from 4 to 8 hours at 25°C. This includes one-third or less of the interval between division stages.

At the first division after labeled thymidine has been incorporated, each of the two daughter chromosomes is similarly labeled and the amount of label in each can be shown to be equal within the limits of error of the method (13). Figure 1 shows a cell at the first division after treatment with colchicine to prevent spindle formation. The daughter pairs still lie close together but have separated in most instances. When the labeled thymidine is removed and the labeled chromosomes allowed to pass through a second duplication, they regularly yield one labeled and one non-labeled daughter chromosome (fig. 2). The pool of labeled precursors fortunately is small and is depleted before the second duplication.

The observed behavior is adequately explained if the original chromosomes are assumed to be composed of two units of DNA. When duplication occurs in labeled thymidine each daughter receives one original unit and one new labeled unit, and, therefore, both appear labeled. However, when these labeled chromosomes duplicate without the label, the two units separate and along each is built an unlabeled unit. Since only one unit of each chromosome is labeled they produce one labeled daughter and one unlabeled daughter. The apparent exceptions (fig. 2) are those in which exchange of segments occurs between daughter chromosomes (chromatids) before they appear at division. Since this is a rather frequent event, chromosomes usually appear labeled along part of their length and unlabeled along the remainder. However, when account of the exchanges

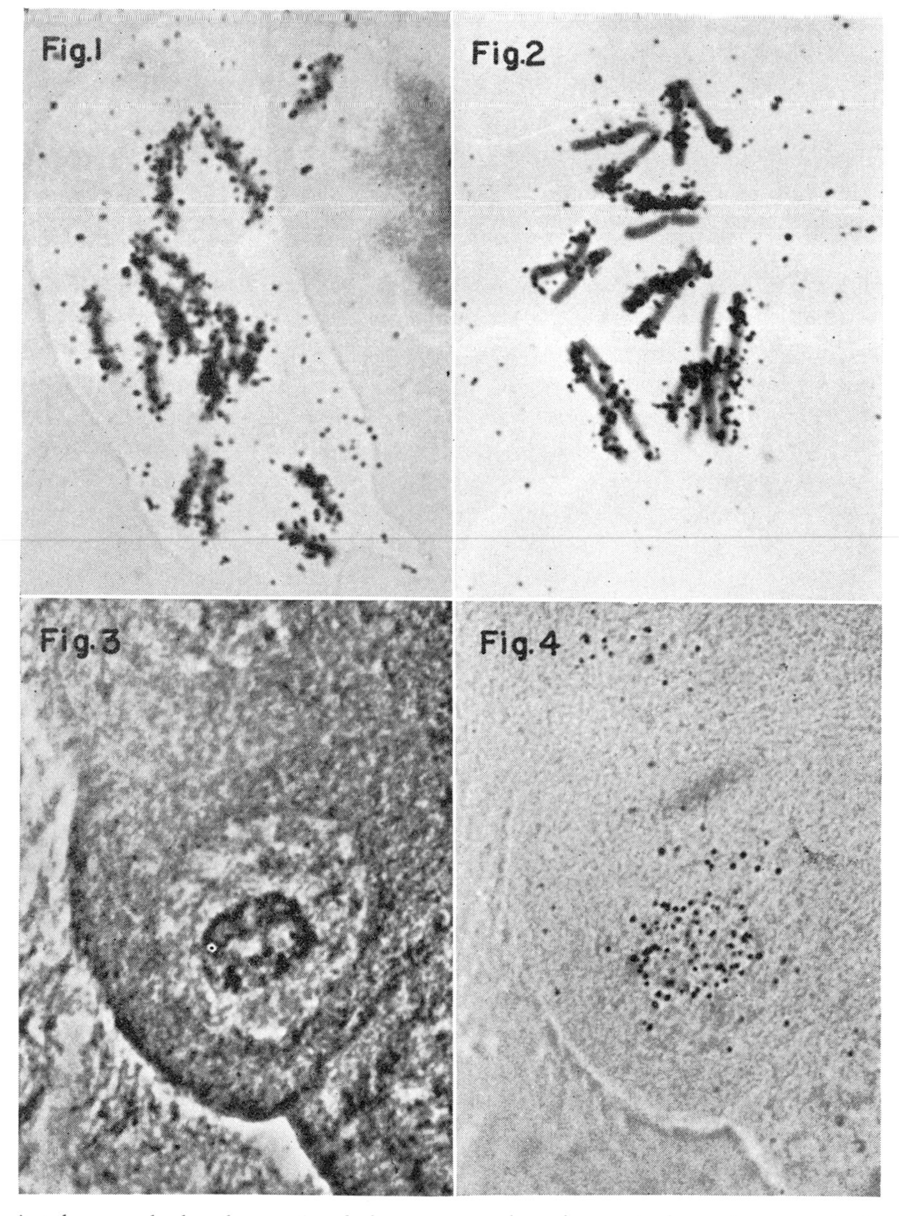

is taken, each daughter pair of chromosomes has the equivalent of a completely labeled chromosome and a completely unlabeled one.

These observations support the hypothesis that DNA replicates by a template mechanism such as that suggested by Watson and Crick (21). Additional support for the hypothesis has been obtained by an analysis of the frequency and pattern of the chromatid exchanges. The analysis indicates that the two units of DNA are structurally different, which supports the concept that they represent complementary units (13, 14).

Recently Meselson and Stahl (5) have obtained evidence that the first particles of DNA replicated in N^{15}-labeled *E. coli,* which have been transferred to a medium containing only N^{14}-labeled nutrients, are hybrid with respect to their content of N^{15} and N^{14}. At the next replication these hybrid particles, with a molecular weight of about seven million, produce one hybrid particle and one particle free of N^{15}. These results, which demonstrate the conservation and segregation of DNA at the molecular level similar to that indicated for the whole chromosome by the tritium experiments, make the concept of replication from a duplex type of template almost a certainty.

SYNTHESIS OF RNA

Since RNA (ribonucleic acid) is a similar type of molecule, the question arises concerning a template mechanism for its synthesis. The duplex nature of the molecule is not established and it has not been possible to build a precise model for its duplication. In the absence of large units which contain a permanent component of RNA, such as the chromosome provided for DNA, there does not appear to be a situation in which the hypothesis of replication can be tested by autoradiography. Chloroplasts provide a possible object for testing the idea, but so far a suitable biological material and a selective method of labeling have not been found. Another approach to the mechanism of synthesis is an indirect one, in which evidence concerning the site of synthesis or correlations in RNA and DNA synthesis within intracellular dimensions are determined. If RNA acts as a code for determining the sequence of amino acid in proteins, this information initially resides in the genetic material, which is most probably DNA. Therefore, many investigators have considered the idea that some of the RNA may be synthesized in the chromosomes on the DNA templates.

Is there a sequence in the synthesis of RNA and DNA? In other words, does one process stop when the other begins? If DNA were the template for both its duplication and RNA synthesis could the two processes proceed simultaneously

---

FIG. 1. Autoradiograph of chromosomes after one duplication in tritium-labeled thymidine. Root tip cell of *Bellevalia* following a short treatment in colchicine. [After (14).] × 1430.

FIG. 2. Autoradiograph of a similar cell after one duplication in tritium-labeled thymidine and one duplication in a medium free of labeled precursors. [After (13).] × 1430.

FIG. 3. Phase photograph of salivary gland cell of *Drosophila*. The dark object near the center of the nucleus (lighter region) is the nucleolus. × 1300.

FIG. 4. Autoradiograph of the cell in figure 3 fixed 30 minutes after the larva began eating tritium-labeled cytidine. Most of the grains are over the nucleolus, but a few are already over the chromosomes of the lower nucleus and also over the nucleus in the upper center of picture. The radioactivity is all removable with ribonuclease. × 1300.

in the same nucleus? Evidence cited above indicates that in some instances synthesis of DNA proceeds in a zipper-like manner along the chromosomes, but in others it apparently occurs nearly simultaneously in many parts of the chromosomes. In those in which asynchronous synthesis occurs in the various parts of chromosomes, DNA synthesis might be occurring on some molecules while others are acting as templates for RNA synthesis. However, if most or all of the molecules are replicating simultaneously, the template function for RNA synthesis might be temporarily interrupted. The information available on correlations of synthesis is still somewhat confusing. In several instances cells with DNA synthesis in progress show relatively little incorporation of label in RNA. For example, in the microspores of *Tulbaghia,* an onion-like plant, synthesis of DNA for the next division occurs immediately after meiosis is completed. During this period no synthesis of RNA in any part of the cell is indicated by incorporation of P^{32} (15). In addition, RNA synthesis is absent or at a low level during actual division stages and during the zygotene pairing stages when the chromosomes are perhaps in a non-metabolic condition. Sisken (9) also reports an inverse relationship between incorporation of orotic acid-C^{14} into RNA and DNA of root cells of *Tradescantia.* Cells with high incorporation in DNA show relatively little label in RNA. In premeiotic microsporocytes of lilies the incorporation of glycine-C^{14} into RNA of nucleus and cytoplasm appears to stop during DNA synthesis. However, when orotic acid-C^{14} is used as the precursor the two types of nucleic acid appear to be labeled simultaneously (16). In *Drosophila* salivary gland nuclei, RNA and DNA synthesis proceed at the same time.

In experiments carried out by one of us (Dr. Woods), tritium-labeled cytidine was used to follow RNA and DNA synthesis in root tip cells of *Vicia faba.* During interphase in these cells very little incorporation into RNA of chromosomes (chromatin) occurred. Incorporation did take place in the nucleolus and cytoplasm. Incorporation into the nucleolus occurred during all stages of interphase and during prophase. As soon as the nucleolus appeared in late telophase nuclei, some isotope was incorporated. Therefore, DNA synthesis did not interfere with RNA metabolism in the nucleolus of these cells. Not only was incorporation occurring at all of these stages, but at all stages the rate of incorporation into nucleolar RNA was much higher than in any other part of the cell. This observation shows that meristematic cells of plants are similar to salivary gland cells of *Drosophila* and several other types of cells in this respect.

SITE OF SYNTHESIS OF NUCLEOLAR RNA

What is the source of this nucleolar RNA? Is it derived from the chromosomes or is it synthesized in the nucleolus? The answer should help in deciding whether RNA can be synthesized without a DNA template, for typical nucleoli contain almost no DNA. The example used in this discussion will be the large cell of the salivary gland of *Drosophila*. In cells fixed in acid fixatives the nucleolus shrinks somewhat and separates from the chromosomes. In such material the only part of the chromosome attached to or included in the nucleolus is the small region around the nucleolus organizer which is very small in proportion to the total amount of chromatin in the nucleus. Therefore, the DNA associated with the nucleolus is insignificant compared to the total in the nucleus.

Plan of Experiment. Taylor *et al.* (17) and McMaster-Kaye and Taylor (4) have described the methods and plan of similar experiments using P^{32} as the label. Adenine-8-C^{14} was used in the experiment to be described, which was performed by one of us (Dr. Taylor). After extraction of cold acid-soluble nucleotides, nearly all of the remaining label from C^{14}-adenine is in RNA and DNA. Since there are periods in early third instar when very little incorporation into DNA occurs, the label is an excellent one for the study of RNA metabolism.

Drosophila repleta larvae moult two times during the first 8 days when grown at 20°C. After the second moult these third instar larvae grow during a period of about 5 days before forming pupae. During this period the salivary glands are presumably very active in secretion of proteins, and in addition the gland cells grow tremendously. The chromosomes are polytene giant structures at the beginning of third instar, but at one or more intervals during third instar they synthesize DNA, presumably duplicating, and eventually reach the large size typically studied by cytogeneticists.

The RNA concentration of the salivary gland cells is relatively high during the first half of third instar. Relative concentrations in the structures to be studied have been estimated by McMaster-Kaye and Taylor (4) by two quite different techniques which gave the same answer. The amounts of the basic dye, Azure B, bound by nucleolus and cytoplasm were compared by a mircophotometric technique. During the first half of third instar, while the cytoplasmic volume quadrupled, the ratio of RNA concentration in nucleolus and cytoplasm did not change appreciably.The ratio is very near 1 all during this period.

The other method is based on grain counts in autoradiographs. Larvae were fed continuously on a food containing P^{32}-labeled phosphate. Larvae were fixed at intervals until the label in RNA of all structures reached an equilibrium. At this time the number of grains over any area of the cell should reveal the concentration of RNA, since all RNA would be expected to have the same specific activity. Of course, all non-nucleic acid P^{32} was first removed from the cells and replicate slides were prepared with RNA removed from one by ribonuclease. The difference in number of grains over the cells on the two slides gave relative concentrations. The concentrations in nucleolus and cytoplasm were again shown to be equal (4). The chromosomes, i.e., the nuclear region without a nucleolus, had a little less than one-half the concentration of the nucleolus and cytoplasm.

With this information, grain counts from autoradiographs of cells in larvae fed isotope for different times can be presented as a curve representing changes in the relative specific activity of the RNA's of different structures. Table 2 and figure 5 show data obtained in this way when larvae were fed food containing adenine-8-C^{14}. In plotting the data for the nucleus the grain counts were multiplied by 2.37 to correct for difference in concentration; therefore, the curves represent relative changes in specific activity with time. For this experiment about 200 larvae hatched from eggs deposited during a 6-hour period were segregated when about one-half of the larvae in the culture had moulted the second time. By selecting only those in third instar a relatively uniform population was obtained. They were placed on food containing the isotope and a red colored material, carmin. Larvae were selected for the experiment only if they began eating immediately when placed on radioactive food. Likewise when the larvae were

TABLE 1. CHANGES IN CYTOPLASMIC, NUCLEAR AND NUCLEOLAR VOLUMES (CUBIC MICRONS) OF SALIVARY GLANDS IN EARLY THIRD INSTAR LARVAE OF DROSOPHILA REPLETA

TIME, HR.*	NO. LARVAE	NO. CELLS	CYTOPLASMIC VOL. ($\times 10^{-3}$)	NUCLEAR VOL. ($\times 10^{-3}$)	NUCLEOLAR VOL. ($\times 10^{-2}$)	RATIO, CYTOPLASM/ NUCLEUS	RATIO, CYTOPLASM/ NUCLEOLUS
1	4	20	12.80 ± 0.97	2.94 ± 0.25	4.70 ± 0.37	4.35:1	27.4:1
5	4	20	15.00 ± 1.96	3.56 ± 0.36	5.55 ± 0.45	4.10:1	27.0:1
10	4	20		6.30 ± 0.75	7.50 ± 0.53		
14	4	20	36.40 ± 0.92	7.00 ± 0.55	7.30 ± 0.52	5.20:1	49.8:1
24	4	20		8.40 ± 0.48	8.50 ± 0.66		

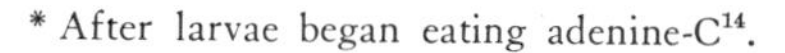

* After larvae began eating adenine-C^{14}.

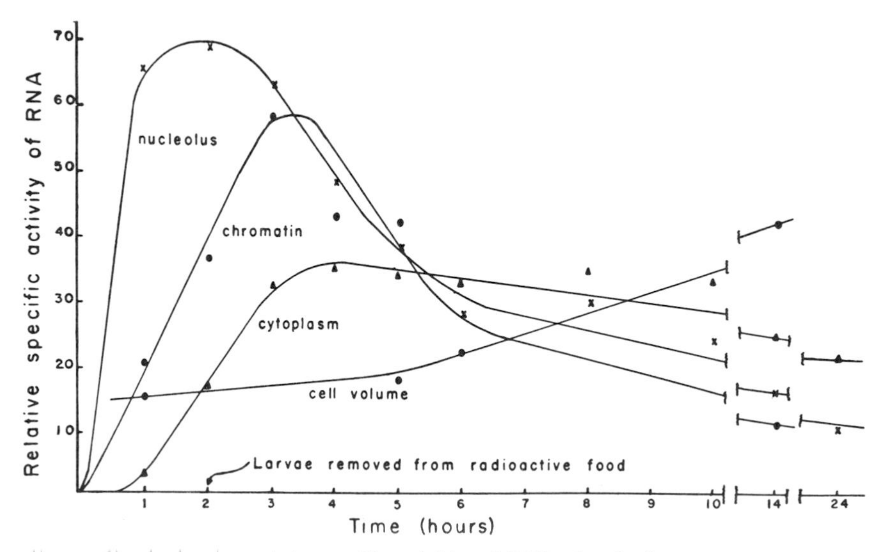

Fig. 5. Graph showing relative specific activities of RNA after feeding larvae of *Drosophila* for 2 hours on adenine-C^{14}. The points were calculated from grain counts in table 2.

transferred to non-radioactive food, only those which ate vigorously and passed all of the red colored food through the intestinal tract within 1 or 2 hours were used for fixation at the later times. At each time interval about 10 larvae were quickly frozen in isopentane, which had been cooled to near its freezing point with liquid nitrogen, and dehydrated in absolute ethanol at −45°C (22). They were then fixed by heating for 1 hour at 60° in 75 per cent ethanol in water. These larvae were then dehydrated, embedded, and in 5-micron sections prepared for autoradiography as previously described (17).

The cells of the salivary gland are growing rapidly during most of the third instar. In table 1 are shown data on the increase in volume for nucleolus, nuclei and cytoplasm for the cells of the group of larvae used for the experiment described here. Since nucleoli and nuclei are nearly spherical, their volumes were calculated from direct measurements of the diameters. However, the cells have very irregular shapes and their volumes had to be estimated by camera lucida drawings of serial sections. The successive tracings of each cell were cut out and weighed to get relative volumes. These were converted to absolute measurements by comparing with nuclear volumes which were determined directly from the measured diameters and by means of the tracings.

During the 24 hours of the experiment the nucleolus almost doubled its volume and RNA content, since the concentration remained constant. Nuclear volume increased by a factor of 3 during the same period. The cytoplasm increased by a factor of 3 in 14 hours. The nuclear-cytoplasmic ratio did not change appreciably during the first 14 hours of the experiment, but the cytoplasm probably grew faster in later stages. During the period of the experiment the whole cell probably was growing as fast as embryonic cells during exponential growth. The cell volume and its RNA content doubled in less than 10 hours.

Data and Interpretation. From the data in table 2 and figure 5, the fast rate of incorporation regularly seen in the nucleolar RNA is immediately apparent. The relatively more rapid rise in its specific activity compared to the experiments with P^{32} (4) indicates a smaller pool size for the adenine and derivatives as compared with phosphates. The smaller pool is a fortunate circumstance, for it allows quicker response to changes in food that reveal different metabolic types of RNA. Since water- and alcohol-soluble substances are always extracted from the tissues during preparation for autoradiography, direct determination of soluble precursors is not feasible.

When the larvae were removed from the radioactive food at the end of 2 hours the labeling of nucleolar RNA already showed evidence of an approach to an equilibrium while the label in both the cytoplasmic and chromosomal (chromatin or nuclear) RNA's, after an initial lag, was still increasing at approximately a linear rate. The change in specific activity of nucleolar RNA is rapid; it dropped in 3 hours to less than one-half its peak value. During this whole period of 5

TABLE 2. AUTORADIOGRAPHIC GRAIN COUNTS OVER CYTOPLASM, CHROMATIN AND NUCLEOLI OF SALIVARY GLAND CELLS OF DROSOPHILA REPLETA

TIME, HR.*	CYTOPLASM						CHROMATIN						NUCLEOLI					
	Cold TCA			Ribonuclease			Cold TCA			Ribonuclease			Cold TCA			Ribonuclease		
	No. larvae	No. cells	gr./unit area ± S.E.†	No. larvae	No. cells	gr./unit area ± S.E.†	No. larvae	No. cells	gr./unit area ± S.E.†	No. larvae	No. cells	gr./unit area ± S.E.†	No. larvae	No. cells	gr./unit area ± S.E.†	No. larvae	No. cells	gr./unit area ± S.E.†
1	4	20	5.3±0.9	4	20	1.7±0.3	4	20	11.6±0.4	4	20	2.8±0.5	4	20	68.5±3.1	4	20	3.0±0.6
2	4	20	19.7±1.0	4	20	2.6±0.3	4	20	19.0±0.6	4	20	3.5±0.5	7	35	74.3±1.4	4	20	5.2±1.1
3	4	20	35.1±1.9	3	15	2.0±0.4	4	19	28.7±0.4	3	15	4.0±0.7	4	20	66.8±2.9	3	15	3.6±1.0
4	4	19	37.9±1.8	4	20	3.1±0.3	6	30	23.1±0.9	4	20	4.7±0.8	4	20	52.9±3.8	4	20	3.9±0.8
5	4	20	36.7±1.6	4	20	2.7±0.3	4	19	22.2±1.2	4	20	4.3±0.5	4	20	41.4±2.0	4	20	2.7±0.3
6	6	29	37.9±1.2	7	40	4.7±0.8	4	20	21.9±1.2	4	25	12.4±1.7	3	14	38.8±1.6	7	40	10.6±1.6
8	7	35	37.9±1.2	4	20	3.1±0.4	3	15	21.2±1.2				7	35	35.1±1.1	4	20	5.1±1.1
10	4	20	34.0±1.6	4	20	1.3±0.3							4	20	27.6±1.1	4	20	3.4±0.5
14	4	20	26.5±0.8	4	20	1.8±0.3	4	20	17.9±0.9	1	5	6.8±0.2	4	20	21.4±0.8	4	20	5.4±0.8
24	4	20	23.1±0.5	4	20	1.8±0.3							4	20	16.1±1.1	4	20	5.0±0.7

* After larvae began eating adenine-C^{14}. † Circular area of 40 sq. μ. Background grain number of about 1.0 per unit area was not subtracted from these counts.

hours there is little net change in the amount of nucleolar RNA. Therefore, the change in specific activity has only two possible interpretations. Either the RNA is synthesized rapidly and then broken down at the same site, or it is being transported from the nucleolus to some other site in the cell.

About the fifth hour there is an abrupt change in the rate of loss of isotope from the nucleolus. After that time the decrease in specific activity can be accounted for by the increase in net amount of RNA. The result can be explained if the nucleolus contained two types of RNA with quite different metabolic properties. Vincent (19) has reported two such types in the nucleolus of starfish oocytes.

Two metabolic types are also indicated by the specific activity curves for the chromosomal RNA (fig. 5). As in the nucleolus, one fraction disappears in 2 or 3 hours while the other fraction changes specific activity at about the rate at which new RNA would dilute the labeled material during growth of the nucleus. The cytoplasm does not contain a detectable amount of the RNA with a fast turnover. The decreases in specific activity can be accounted for by net synthesis, as revealed by the increase in volume and RNA content. This increase is correlated with a proportional drop in specific activity of RNA (fig. 5).

An examination of the changes in specific activity indicates that neither cytoplasmic nor chromosomal RNA is likely to be the source of all of the rapidly labeled RNA which appears in the nucleolus. We reach the conclusion that part of it must be synthesized there. Therefore, we have an answer to the question originally posed. Some of the nuclear RNA is synthesized at a site where there are few if any DNA templates. However, we should point out that part of the RNA of the nucleolus, especially the fraction with a slow turnover, could come from the chromosomes. This could be the template RNA of the nucleolus, as suggested by Vincent (20), while the RNA with a fast turnover may be the product of these templates which is being transported to the cytoplasm.

Now let us consider the fraction with a high rate of turnover, which appears in the chromosomes or in that region of the nucleus occupied by chromosomes. It may not necessarily be attached to or associated with chromosomes. This RNA could be material from the nucleolus in route to the cytoplasm, perhaps in the form of relatively large particles; i.e., molecular aggregates which are below the resolving power of the light microscope. On the other hand, it could be a fraction produced in the chromosome for transport to the cytoplasm or even to the nucleolus. Autoradiographs made 30 minutes after the larvae begin to eat food containing cytidine-H^3 show label in both the nucleolus and among the chromosomes (figs. 3 and 4). Quantitative data are not yet available for the relative rates of incorporation. However, no label is yet detectable in the cytoplasm, even when the exposure is long enough to make the film above the nucleolus much blacker than in the photograph. The same result is obtained in root tip cells of the bean, *Vicia faba.* These observations favor the view that the differences between cytoplasm and nucleolus are not just differences in rates, but that a relatively long interval compared to diffusion rates of most molecules may be required for the labeled RNA to reach the cytoplasm. This would happen if the nucleus were the site of synthesis and the material moved out as large molecules or aggregations of molecules.

HYPOTHESIS AND CONCLUSIONS

If one makes the reasonable assumption that the chromosomes are composed of many different templates, the products of which may be required in greatly different quantities by the cell at certain periods in differentiation, an hypothesis may be formulated. For gene products required in greatest quantity, RNA master templates could be deposited in the nucleolus during periods of cellular differentiation. In this special environment, they either would be self-duplicating or would produce complementary molecules for transport to the cytoplasm. Other templates required in smaller amounts could be produced primarily or exclusively at the genetic locus, where extra RNA templates might also be temporarily deposited. Other types of RNA such as that in chloroplasts and viruses could be, under proper conditions, self-duplicating. The principal difficulty with such an hypothesis is that it will explain any result on turnover rates and base ratios which may be found, and no evidence for or against the hypothesis would appear to be obtainable by cytochemistry or biochemistry unless specific RNA's could be isolated. Since there might be thousands of these on this hypothesis, this would also appear to be an impossible task. For example, to try to find precursor relationships by examining base ratios of RNA's is probably hopeless. If one makes the assumption that both template and product are in the nucleus or nucleolus, and that different RNA's are duplicating at different rates in addition to their destruction in the cytoplasm at varying rates, any relationship found could be predicted. Certainly statements that nuclear RNA cannot be the precursor of cytoplasmic RNA based on such evidence is meaningless. Likewise, proof of the hypothesis with the evidence appears impossible. Nevertheless, additional circumstantial evidence is of value and a greater understanding of RNA metabolism can surely be gained by these various techniques.

Other clues concerning the mechanism of synthesis of RNA might be obtained by determining the sites of synthesis in various types of cells. The experiments of Goldstein and Plaut (3) indicate a transfer of labeled RNA from the amoeba nucleus when it is transferred into an unlabeled cell. However, the question of whether only a part or all of the RNA of this cell is made in the nucleus remains unclear. Prescott (7) reported no incorporation in anucleate pieces with C^{14}-uracil as precursor. On the other hand Plaut and Rustad (6) found uptake of adenine-C^{14} in amoeba fragments. Further experiments appear to be necessary, and if the rate of incorporation is low, one must distinguish between synthesis of new molecules and the addition of nucleotides to the end of RNA chains.

Brachet *et al.* (1) have shown that in anucleate pieces of the alga, *Acetabularia,* there is a net synthesis of RNA extending over a period of 30 days. This peculiar organism with a very large cytoplasmic to nuclear ratio may be a poor one from which to generalize, but it obviously does synthesize RNA in the absence of a nucleus. One wonders if this may result from the presence of chloroplasts which are increasing, or if this organism has certain specialized sites other than the nucleolus and chromosomes for the RNA master templates which enable it to get along with the peculiar nucleocytoplasmic ratio.

Evidence that can be cited in favor of the view that all or essentially all of the synthesis of RNA in cells without chloroplasts or viruses occurs in the nucleus is still rather limited. Four points are worth repeating. *1*) Some cells appear to have little synthesis of RNA, except perhaps in the nucleolus, during DNA synthesis. *2*) Synthesis of RNA stops during late stages of division when the chromosomes are condensed and the nucleolus is disappearing. *3*) There is a lag of 30 minutes or more, after the cell begins incorporation of an isotope, before label appears in cytoplasmic RNA. *4*) Specific activity time curves are compatible with the hypothesis that RNA of the nucleolus and chromosomes could be transported to the cytoplasm.

What turnover rates would be required for the nucleolus and nucleus if they were the sites of synthesis of all of the RNA in the salivary gland cell? From table 1 we see that the nucleolus has between one twenty-seventh and one-fiftieth the volume, and therefore the RNA content, of the cytoplasm. Assuming no appreciable turnover for cytoplasmic RNA, which doubles in amount in about 9–10 hours, we see that fewer than 50 nucleolar volumes of RNA would be required. If one-half of the RNA present in the nucleolus at any given moment were template RNA and one-half the material being transported out, this would mean that the template RNA would have to duplicate or produce a complementary particle 100 times in 10 hours, or 10 times an hour. This rate is perhaps too fast, but if we consider the chromatin also the rate is more reasonable. The volume of the nucleus is about one-fifth that of the cytoplasm. Correcting for concentration differences and assuming one-half is template RNA, the turnover rate would need to be only 1 per hour, not counting the nucleolus. Therefore if we consider both places sites of RNA synthesis for cytoplasm the required turnover rate becomes reasonable for cells with this nucleocytoplasmic ratio of RNA.

SUMMARY

Evidence for a duplex type of template for DNA synthesis has been obtained by autoradiography. All of the chromosomes of a cell appear labeled at the first division following a period of chromosome duplication (DNA synthesis) in a medium containing tritium-labeled thymidine. However, these chromosomes reveal their hybrid nature; i. e., their content of original unlabeled and new labeled

DNA, when they duplicate one more time in a medium free of labeled precursors. Each regularly produces one labeled and one unlabeled daughter chromosome.

Attempts are described to get circumstantial evidence for or against a template mechanism for RNA synthesis. Direct evidence is not available and there seems to be no feasible experiment by autoradiography to test the hypothesis directly, as was done for DNA. On the other hand circumstantial evidence for the idea can be cited. *1*) The synthesis of RNA and DNA, although not mutually exclusive of each other, are interrelated, as might be expected if DNA were the template for RNA synthesis as well as for its own duplication. In some types of cells RNA synthesis appears to stop during DNA synthesis and during the periods when the chromosomes are condensed in division stages. However, the nucleolus is active in RNA metabolism at all stages in the root-tip cells of *Vicia faba*. In these and other cells it incorporates labeled precursors of RNA much more rapidly than any other part of the cell. The conclusion is almost inescapable that synthesis occurs in the nucleolus where there is no DNA. Therefore, RNA may be self-duplicating. At least, in the nucleolus the possible templates available would appear to be limited to RNA, protein or a nucleoprotein. The time course studies of changes in specific activity of nucleolar, chromosomal and cytoplasmic RNA indicate that there are two metabolically different fractions in both the nucleolus and in the chromosomes. One fraction turns over very rapidly and could be the RNA transported to the cytoplasm and continually replaced by newly synthesized RNA. The fractions with slower turnover could be the master templates derived from the genetic loci. These would be able to duplicate or produce complementary molecules, which may be required in greater quantity than could be produced by a single site of genetic material.

REFERENCES

1. Brachet, J., H. Chantrenne and F. Vanderhaeghe. *Biochim. et biophys. acta* 18: 544, 1955.
2. Friedkin, M., D. Tilson and D. Roberts. *J. Biol. Chem.* 220: 627, 1956.
3. Goldstein, L. and W. Plaut. *Proc. Nat. Acad. Sci.* 41: 874, 1955.
4. McMaster-Kaye, R. D. and J. H. Taylor. *J. Biophys. Biochem. Cytol.* 4: 5, 1958.
5. Meselson, M. and F. N. Stahl. *Proc. Nat. Acad. Sci.* 44: 671, 1958.
6. Plaut, W. S. and R. C. Rustad. *Nature* 177: 89, 1956.
7. Prescott, D. M. *Exper. Cell Res.* 12: 196, 1957.
8. Reichard, P. and B. Estborn. *J. Biol. Chem.* 188: 839, 1951.
9. Sisken, J. E. Doctoral dissert., Columbia Univ., New York, 1958.
10. Taylor, J. H. *Science* 118: 555, 1953.
11. Taylor, J. H. In: *Physical Techniques in Biological Research,* edited by G. Oster and A. W. Pollister. Baltimore: Johns Hopkins, 1956, vol. III, p. 545.
12. Taylor, J. H. *Exper. Cell Res.* 15: 350, 1958.
13. Taylor, J. H. [illegible] 43: 515, 1958.
14. Taylor, J. H. *Trans. 1st Nat. Biophys. Conf.*, 1958.

15. TAYLOR, J. H. *Am. J. Bot.* 45: 123, 1958.
16. TAYLOR, J. H. *Am. J. Bot.* In press.
17. TAYLOR, J. H., R. D. MCMASTER AND M. F. CALUYA. *Exper. Cell Res.* 9: 460, 1955.
18. TAYLOR, J. H., P. S. WOODS AND W. L. HUGHES. *Proc. Nat. Acad. Sci.* 43: 122, 1957.
19. VINCENT, W. S. *Science* 126: 306, 1957.
20. VINCENT, W. S. In: *Beginnings of Embryonic Development,* edited by C. METZ, A. TYLER AND R. C. VON BORSTEL. Washington, D. C.: Am. A. Adv. Sci., 1957.
21. WATSON, J. D. AND F. H. C. CRICK. *Nature* 171: 964, 1953.
22. WOODS, P. S. AND A. W. POLLISTER. *Stain Tech.* 30: 123, 1955.

DISCUSSION

W. S. Vincent, J. H. Taylor

DR. VINCENT: In the starfish nucleolus soluble nucleotides appear to be produced in the nucleolus. Can you detect these, as a possible precursor of cytoplasmic RNA, by your procedures?

DR. TAYLOR: One of the limitations of the autoradiographic method is the difficulty of working with water-soluble substances. The film cannot be properly placed on the slides unless it is wet and, therefore, diffusion of water soluble substances occurs. There is also the original problem of retaining such substances *in situ* during the dehydration and fixation of the tissues. Methods for precipitation of nucleotides as salts of heavy metals have been utilized to some extent by others, but we have made no attempt to study the substances removed from the tissue by hot 70 per cent ethanol and cold trichloroacetic acid.

Biochemical Properties of the Isolated Nucleus

V. ALLFREY AND A. E. MIRSKY

The Rockefeller Institute
New York, N. Y.

THE EXPERIMENTS ABOUT TO BE DESCRIBED are concerned with synthetic reactions carried out by isolated cell nuclei—with particular emphasis on amino acid uptake into nuclear protein, the incorporation of purine and pyrimidine precursors in nuclear RNA, and nuclear ATP synthesis. Some of the experiments will emphasize the role of deoxyribonucleic acid in these nuclear activities, others will relate the state of the nucleus to methods of its isolation and its chemical environment.[1]

In earlier work in this laboratory we had been concerned with the chemical composition of cell nuclei isolated in different ways. Nuclei prepared in citric acid, sucrose or saline solutions were compared with those isolated in nonaqueous media by a modified Behrens' procedure (7, 8). The latter type of isolation was selected as a 'standard' because it prevents water-soluble materials from moving between nucleus and cytoplasm during the course of the isolation. Its success depends on rapid freezing followed by lyophilization to remove water from the tissue, which is then ground and fractionated in nonaqueous solvents such as cyclohexane and carbon tetrachloride. The nucleus has a characteristic density range which often permits its separation from other elements of the ground cell suspension by differential centrifugation. The separation of the nuclei is facilitated by selecting a medium of density lower than the nuclear specific gravity but higher than that of possible cytoplasmic contaminants. Centrifugation then yields a nuclear sediment which can often be shown by chemical, immunological and enzymatic tests to be essentially free of cytoplasmic contamination.

Nuclei isolated in nonaqueous media constitute a 'standard' against which nuclei prepared in aqueous media can be compared. For example, liver or kidney nuclei prepared in sucrose or citric acid solutions were shown to have lost much of their protein during isolation simply by comparing them with the corresponding Behrens type nuclei (8, 10).

However, when such comparisons were carried out in the case of calf thymus nuclei, it was found that thymus nuclei isolated in isotonic sucrose solutions were

[1] The following abbreviations are used throughout: RNA, ribonucleic acid; ATP, adenosinetriphosphate; DNA, deoxyribonucleic acid; AMP, adenosinemonophosphate; ADP, adenosinediphosphate; TCA, trichloroacetic acid.

the equivalent of the nonaqueous nuclei in many respects. The DNA analyses, protein composition and enzymatic constitution of the two preparations were strikingly in agreement (24). Once it had been established that thymus nuclei could be isolated in sucrose solutions without leaching out their water-soluble components, it was decided to test whether such nuclei had maintained their capacity for complex synthetic reactions.

The isolation procedure employed (6) is a modification of that introduced by R. M. Schneider and M. L. Petermann (22). The fresh tissue is minced with scissors and then homogenized in a low-speed blendor in 0.25 M sucrose–0.003 M $CaCl_2$ solution. The homogenate is filtered through gauze and through double-napped flannelette to remove clumps of tissue and fiber. The nuclei are separated by differential centrifugation and washed with sucrose-calcium chloride solution.

Under the light microscope, stained or unstained, such thymus nuclei seem remarkably clean. Contamination consists of a few whole cells, occasional red cells and some cytoplasm which adheres to some of the nuclei. The extent of cytoplasmic contamination can be estimated chemically (e.g. by nucleic acid analyses or tests for cytochrome *c* oxidase activity), and is found to be below 10 per cent. The number of whole cells cannot be estimated with accuracy in the light microscope because of the difficulty in distinguishing between free nuclei and very small thymocytes, but electron microscopy made it evident that whole cell contamination is also very small. For example, in two preparations examined we observed less than 50 cells per thousand nuclei. (We are indebted to Drs. M. Watson and G. Palade of the Rockefeller Institute for their cooperation in these tests.) In a recent paper, Ficq and Errera (11) report that nuclear fractions prepared by our procedure contain 3 per cent intact cells and that 8 per cent of the nuclei contain a small amount of adhering cytoplasm. In addition to these microscopic tests for purity of the nuclei there is other convincing evidence for the absence of appreciable whole cell contamination. This will be given below in connection with studies of deoxyribonuclease action on free nuclei.

AMINO ACID INCOPORATION INTO PROTEINS OF ISOLATED NUCLEI

When thymus nuclei are suspended in a buffered sucrose medium and incubated at 37°C in the presence of isotopically labeled amino acids, there is a rapid and considerable incorporation of the isotope into the proteins of the nucleus. Figure 1 shows the time course of incorporation of lysine, alanine and glycine. Curves similar to that shown for alanine or lysine are obtained with C^{14}-leucine, phenylalanine, tryptophan and valine. In these curves, and in most of the experiments to be described below, the uptake was followed by measuring the radioactivity of the total mixed proteins of the nucleus. The protein was prepared by first extensively washing the nuclei with trichloroacetic acid (TCA), removing the nucleic acids with hot TCA and finally removing the lipids with warm

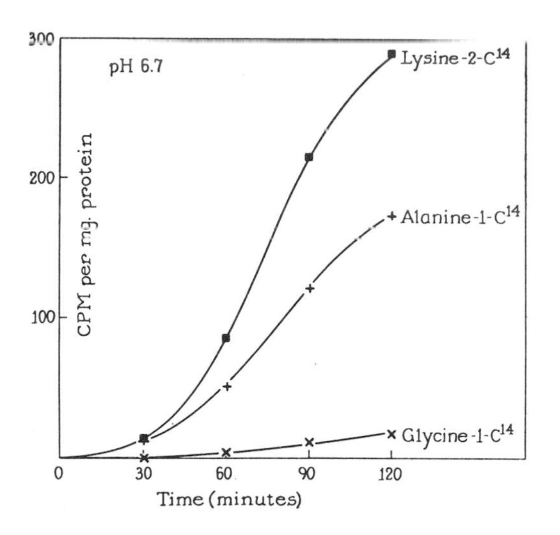

FIG. 1. Time course of incorporation of alanine-1-C^{14}, glycine-1-C^{14} and lysine-2-C^{14} into the proteins of isolated thymus nuclei. In this plot the data have been 'normalized' to show the relative uptakes for equivalent amounts of the different amino acids, when each has the same specific activity in millicuries per millimol.

ethanol, ethanol-ether-chloroform mixtures, ether and acetone. The protein residue was then homogenized in acetone, plated on filter paper planchets, and counted. Radioactivity measurements were made using a thin-window gas flow counter and scaling circuit, and the readings were subsequently corrected for self-absorption. Evidence that the uptake represents peptide bond formation and is not due to adsorption or ester linkage has been given previously (6).

The uptake curves obtained with several amino acids show a characteristic 'lag' phase of 5–15 minutes, followed by a rapid incorporation of label into the proteins of the nucleus. After about 90 minutes, the rate of uptake falls off as some of the nuclei begin to autolyze and lose DNA.

Although these results represent an average incorporation for all the nuclei (plus the few cells) in suspension, the uptake in single nuclei can be followed by radioautography; see (11) and (6).

The nature of the 'lag' in the uptake of amino acids into the proteins of the nucleus was investigated by experiments which are summarized in figure 2. Nuclei were preincubated at 37° for 10, 20, or 30 minutes before adding the alanine-1-C^{14}. The time course of C^{14} incorporation by such preincubated nuclei was compared with that of 'control' nuclei which had received the isotope at time zero. It is clear that preincubation diminishes the lag period without affecting the subsequent rate of C^{14} alanine uptake. These findings suggest that an activation of some sort occurs during preincubation. There is now evidence that this activation is synchronous with RNA synthesis in the nucleus (6).

There are a number of experiments which show that the uptake of amino acids is related to nuclear protein synthesis. It was found that only the L-amino acid isomers are taken up (6) and that an amino acid once incorporated into protein is not in rapid exchange with free amino acids in the medium (6).

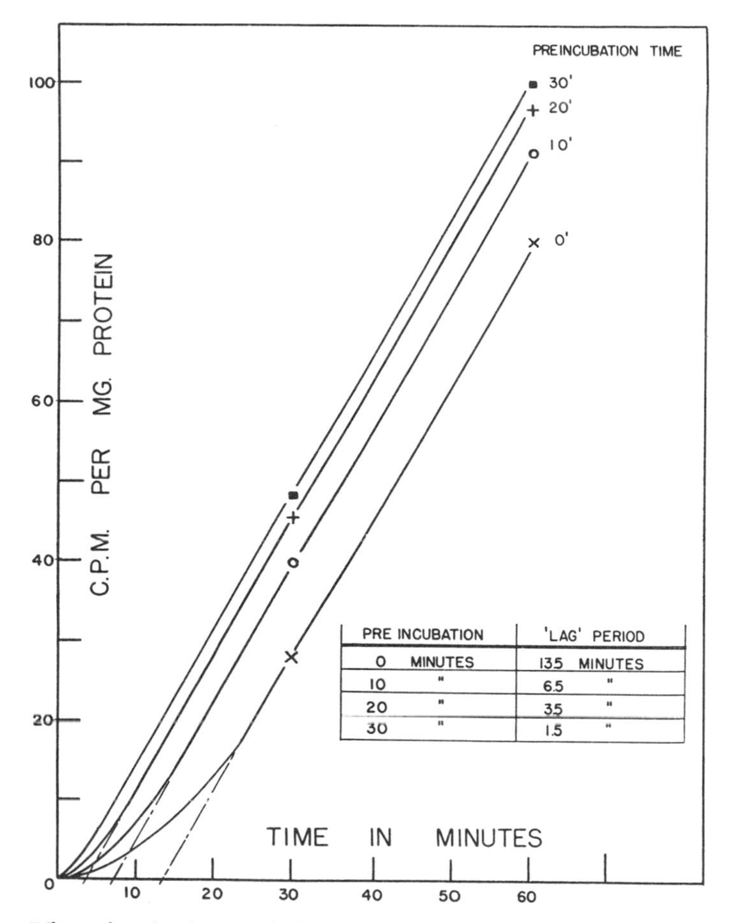

FIG. 2. Effect of preincubation of thymus nuclei upon the subsequent incorporation of alanine-1-C^{14}. The nuclear suspension was preincubated for 10, 20 or 30 minutes before adding the isotopic alanine. The time course of C^{14} incorporation by such preincubated nuclei is compared with that of control nuclei which received the isotope at time zero. Note that preincubation diminishes the lag period without affecting the subsequent rate of C^{14}-alanine incorporation.

Other evidence relating amino acid uptake to protein synthesis is obtained when one fractionates the proteins of the nucleus, following C^{14}-labeling experiments. Several classes of proteins of differing activities can be prepared. A flow sheet summarizing the fractionation is shown in figure 3. The distribution of isotope in these different fractions (table 1) is of some interest because it shows that the protein most closely associated with the deoxyribonucleic acid is more active than all other proteins of the nucleus (with the exception of a small fraction extractable in pH 7.1 buffer). A second point of interest is the fact that the level of isotope

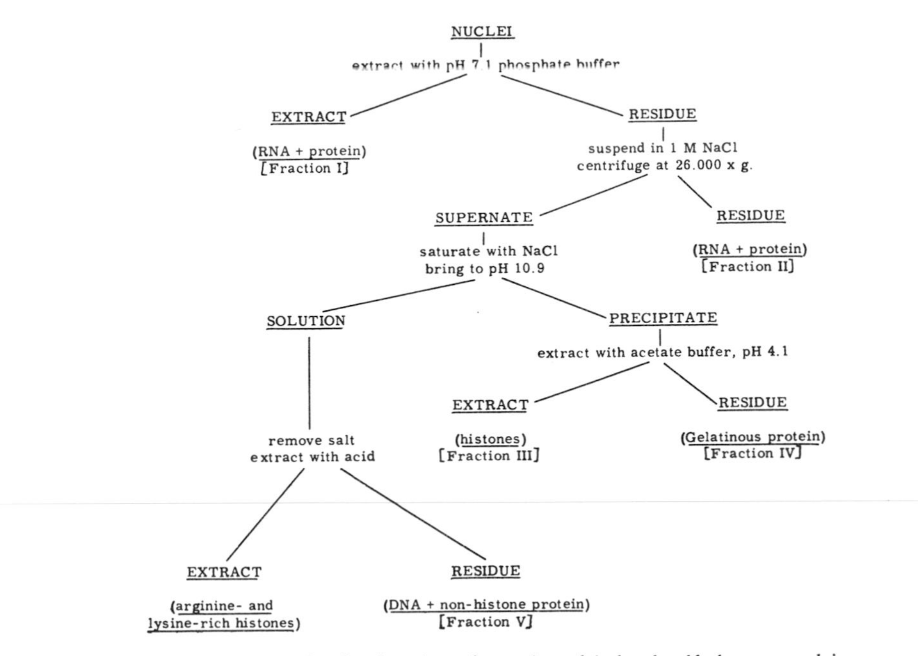

FIG. 3. Flow-sheet for fractionation of proteins of isolated calf thymus nuclei.

TABLE 1. ALANINE-1-C^{14} INCORPORATION INTO DIFFERENT PROTEIN FRACTIONS OF THYMUS NUCLEI

PROTEIN FRACTION	INCUBATION TIME, MIN.	S. A., CPM/MG
1. Total nuclear protein	90	107
Fraction I (protein-soluble in pH 7.1 buffer)	90	179
Fraction II (residue after extraction in 1 M NaCl)	90	117
Fraction III (histones)	90	36
Fraction IV (gelatinous protein)	90	157
Fraction V (non-histone protein associated with DNA)	90	243
2. Protein released to medium during incubation	30	5
	60	8
	90	16
Fraction I	30	10
	60	66
	90	105
Arginine-rich histones	30	2.3
	60	4.5
	90	6.7
Lysine-rich histones	30	
	[illegible]	[illegible]
	90	6.9

incorporation into such well defined proteins as the arginine- and lysine-rich histones is progressive with time. The relatively low uptakes into histone obtained in these *in vitro* experiments agrees with earlier results obtained *in vivo,* in which it was noted that the uptake of N^{15}-glycine into the histones of liver, pancreas and kidney is much lower than the uptake into the residual proteins of the chromosome. The agreement between *in vivo* and *in vitro* studies is further support for the belief that amino acid uptake in isolated nuclei is an indication of protein synthesis.

ROLE OF DEOXYRIBONUCLEIC ACID IN PROTEIN SYNTHESIS

The notion originally suggested by Brachet and Caspersson, that ribonucleic acids play a role in protein synthesis, is now widely accepted as demonstrated. Thus it has been shown that, in bacterial cell residues (13) and in liver microsomes (1, 19) ribonuclease acts to suppress amino acid incorporation.

The isolated cell nucleus affords a unique opportunity to test the role of the deoxyribonucleic acids in the process of protein synthesis and in other synthetic systems, and the results have a special interest because they ultimately bear on the function and mode of action of the gene, and on the chemical relationships between the nucleus and the cytoplasm.

A number of experiments relating DNA to protein synthesis in the nucleus have been described (5, 6). These experiments deal with the effects of treating nuclei with crystalline pancreatic deoxyribonuclease (DNAase) on the nuclear capacity for amino acid uptake. Briefly, when isolated nuclei are treated with DNAase before adding C^{14} amino acids, the incorporation of the latter is markedly impaired. The degree of impairment becomes greater as more and more of the DNA is depolymerized and removed from the nucleus. Experiments showing the relationship between loss of DNA and inhibition of alanine-1-C^{14} and lysine-2-C^{14} uptakes are summarized in figure 4. It is clear that removal of much of the DNA seriously damages the capacity of the nucleus for subsequent protein synthesis. It should also be pointed out that the sensitivity of the nucleus to treatment with deoxyribonuclease is further evidence for the absence of appreciable whole cell contamination, because intact cells are not sensitive to treatment with this enzyme. Thymus tissue slices or minces, for example, show only a slight inhibition of alanine-C^{14} uptake following treatment with DNAase, and the decrease observed could easily be attributed to enzyme attack on cells which had been damaged mechanically.

The amino acid incorporating ability of nuclei is not irreversibly destroyed by treatment with deoxyribonuclease. It was found that the addition of a DNA supplement to nuclei depleted of their DNA would restore much of their capacity for C^{14} uptake (5).

The most striking point about such 'restoration' experiments is the lack of

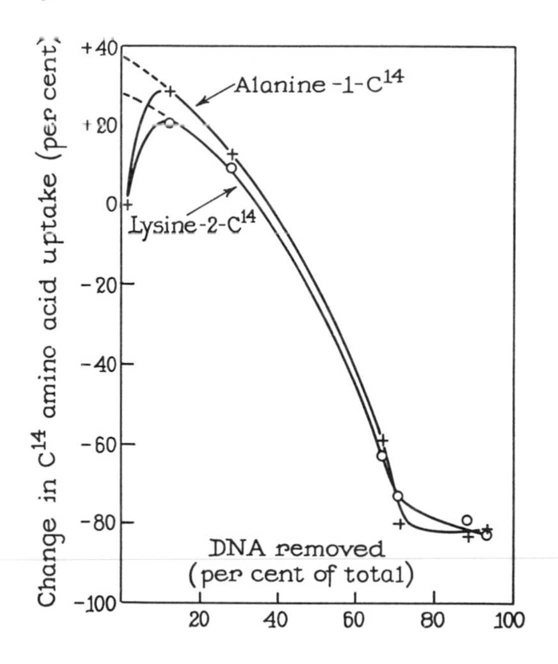

Fig. 4. Effect of removing DNA from thymus nuclei upon the subsequent incorporation of alanine-1-C^{14} and lysine-2-C^{14}. Nuclei were pretreated with DNAase to remove increasing amounts of their DNA. They were subsequently incubated for 60 minutes in the presence of the isotopic amino acid. The decrease in specific activity of the nuclear protein in treated nuclei, relative to that observed in untreated nuclei, is plotted against the percent removal of the DNA.

specificity which they demonstrate. It is not necessary to add the homologous DNA. Many DNA preparations from widely diverse sources promote amino acid uptake just as well as the DNA of calf thymus (table 2). Furthermore, the DNA molecule need not be intact, for alkali-denatured DNA and the larger split products obtained by DNAase digestion can be just as effective as the original DNA preparation. Even ribonucleic acids will substitute for the DNA of the thymus in restoring amino acid incorporation into nuclear proteins (table 3). The lack of a specificity requirement is shown quite conclusively by experiments in which both C^{14}-alanine and C^{14}-leucine uptakes were restored in DNAase-treated nuclei by the addition of polyadenylic acid. (Other experiments, which are referred to in the DISCUSSION of this paper, concern the restoration of synthetic function by other polyelectrolytes, including non-nucleotide structures.)

Although the spectrum of suitable DNA substitutes is very broad, it does not include a number of other related, and perhaps equally likely compounds. For example, amino acid uptake cannot be restored to DNAase-treated nuclei by the free purine and pyrimidine bases, or by mixtures of nucleosides. It was also observed that although ribonucleic acid will substitute for DNA, an alkaline digest of RNA (to yield the component nucleotides) has no effect. By the same token, a mixture of the nucleoside 2′- and 3′-phosphates does not restore the capacity for amino acid incorporation (table 4). Mixtures of the ribonucleoside-5′-phosphates, AMP, ADP, ATP, and a number of dinucleotides were also tested and all were inactive. (We are grateful to Dr. R. B. Merrifield of the Rockefeller Institute for

TABLE 2. EFFECT OF SUPPLEMENTARY DNA'S IN RESTORING C^{14}-ALANINE UPTAKE IN DNAase-TREATED NUCLEI

SUPPLEMENT TESTED	SPECIFIC ACTIVITY OF NUCLEAR PROTEIN			Recovery of Lost Activity, %
	'Controls', cpm/mg	DNAase-treated cpm/mg	Treated + Supplement, cpm/mg	
1. Calf thymus	91	25	70	68
Calf kidney	91	25	70	68
Chicken erythrocyte	91	25	60	53
Paracentrotus sperm	91	25	72	71
2. Calf thymus	135	21	93	63
Trout sperm	135	21	89	60
3. Calf thymus	145	69	101	42
Trout sperm	145	69	101	42
Wheat germ	145	69	86	22
4. Thymus	99	33	101	103
Thymus, alkali-denatured	99	33	104	108
5. Thymus	38	7:5	28	67
Thymus, 'core' after DNAase-digestion	38	7.5	24.5	56
Thymus, dialyzable products of DNAase digestion	38	7.5	29	70

the gift of these dinucleotides.) Among the dinucleotides tested was adenylic-adenylic dinucleotide, chromatographically purified after rapid acid hydrolysis of yeast RNA; this compound failed to promote alanine uptake in DNAase-treated nuclei. This observation takes on added interest when it is compared with the previous finding that polyadenylic acid will restore alanine (and leucine) uptakes. Thus the polynucleotide is effective when the corresponding dinucleotide is not,

TABLE 3. EFFECT OF RNA AND POLYADENYLIC ACID SUPPLEMENTS ON AMINO ACID INCORPORATION BY DNAase-TREATED NUCLEI

SUPPLEMENT TESTED	AMINO ACID	SPECIFIC ACTIVITY OF NUCLEAR PROTEIN			Recovery of Lost Activity, %
		'Controls', cpm/mg	DNAase-treated, cpm/mg	Treated + Supplement, cpm/mg	
1. Calf liver RNA	alanine-1-C^{14}	92	54	80	68
Calf thymus DNA	alanine-1-C^{14}	92	54	81	71
2. Yeast RNA	alanine-1-C^{14}	68	23	58	78
Thymus DNA	alanine-1-C^{14}	68	23	54	69
3. Polyadenylic acid	alanine-1-C^{14}	450	167	263	34
Yeast RNA	alanine-1-C^{14}	450	167	302	48
Thymus DNA	alanine-1-C^{14}	450	167	273	38
4. Polyadenylic acid	leucine-2-C^{14}	257	87	151	38
Yeast RNA	leucine-2-C^{14}	257	87	152	38
Thymus DNA	leucine-2-C^{14}	257	87	144	34

TABLE 4. EFFECT OF RIBONUCLEOSIDES, NUCLEOTIDES AND DINUCLEOTIDES ON C^{14}-ALANINE UPTAKE BY DNAase-TREATED NUCLEI

SUPPLEMENT TESTED	SPECIFIC ACTIVITY OF NUCLEAR PROTEIN			Recovery of Lost Activity, %
	'Controls', cpm/mg	DNAase-treated, cpm/mg	Treated + Supplement, cpm/mg	
1. Yeast RNA	450	167	302	48
A,G,C,U, nucleoside mixture	450	167	106	0
2. Yeast RNA	68	23	58	78
Yeast RNA, hydrolyzed in 0.3 N NaOH	68	23	23	0
A,G,C,U, nucleotide mixture *	68	23	23	0
3. Yeast RNA	243	84	165	51
Polyadenylic acid	243	84	140	35
A,G,C,U, mononucleotide mixture †	243	84	84	0
4. Yeast RNA	83	14	45	45
Adenylic-adenylic dinucleotide	83	14	18	6
Adenylic-guanylic dinucleotide	83	14	18	6
Adenylic-uridylic dinucleotide	83	14	18	6
Guanylic-cytidylic dinucleotide	83	14	18	6

* Nucleoside 2′ and 3′ phosphates. † Nucleoside 5′ phosphates.

and molecular size emerges as one of the factors which determines whether a compound will substitute for DNA in restoring amino acid uptake to DNA-depleted nuclei.

Among other factors which determine the capacity of a polyelectrolyte to substitute for DNA is its electrical charge. Polycations, such as polylysine or protamine, which carry a net positive charge at neutral pH values, cannot restore function. On the contrary, the addition of polylysine to 'control' nuclei which still retain their original DNA content, markedly inhibits amino acid incorporation into nuclear protein. The findings suggest that there is a correlation between negative charge and the biochemical activity of the nucleus. Further tests of this hypothesis are now in progress. If it is sustained, it may be possible to demonstrate that one role of the basic proteins (histones and protamines) in the organization of the chromosome is to reduce or control chromosome function by masking the negative charges of the DNA.

It may be mentioned in passing that 'neutral' proteins, such as serum albumin, serum globulin or mixed plasma proteins, have no effect on amino acid uptake by DNAase-treated nuclei.

NUCLEAR ATP SYNTHESIS AND ITS RELATION TO PROTEIN SYNTHESIS

Isolated nuclei prepared from calf thymus have been shown to be capable of phosphorylating the AMP which they contain to form ADP and ATP (3, 20). This process differs in several important respects from the type of oxidative phosphorylation usually observed in mitochondrial suspensions. A few of the resemblances and some of the most striking differences can be briefly summarized.

In the isolated nucleus, the synthesis of ATP requires oxygen and it is inhibited by anaerobiosis, by 2, 4-dinitrophenol, sodium azide, sodium cyanide, antimycin A, and Amytal. In all these respects it resembles ATP synthesis by mitochondria. On the other hand, several inhibitors of mitochondral oxidative phosphorylation, including carbon monoxide, calcium ions, Janus green B, methylene blue and dicumarol, have little or no effect on ATP synthesis by the nucleus (20).

It is a matter of some interest to compare the effects of these different compounds on ATP synthesis with their effects on nuclear amino acid incorporation. Such a comparison is given in table 5. It is clear that agents which block ATP synthesis in the nucleus also block amino acid uptake into its proteins.

The evidence relating amino acid incorporation to ATP synthesis is not limited to the inhibition studies summarized in the table. A more direct test of linkage became possible when it was discovered that acetate ions at pH values below 5.9 remove nuclear ATP (20). A study of C^{14}-alanine uptake then showed that nuclei exposed to acetate buffers over the pH range 4.4–5.9 were far less active than 'control' nuclei maintained at comparable pH values in other buffers which did not extract nuclear ATP. The extent of C^{14}-alanine incorporation was measured by subsequent incubation of the 'control' and acetate-extracted nuclei in a neutral medium (20). For example, it was found that nuclei which had lost 77 per cent of their ATP had also lost over 90 per cent of their capacity to incorporate alanine-1-C^{14}.

The ATP requirement for protein synthesis by the nucleus is, of course, reminiscent of observations on cytoplasmic systems. The resourceful and stimulating experiments of Hoagland, Keller, Zamecnik and Stephenson have shown that the activation of L-amino acids prior to their incorporation into microsomal proteins involves the formation of amino acyl-adenylate compounds. These compounds appear in reactions requiring specific enzymes and adenosine triphosphate (16, 15).

TABLE 5. EFFECTS OF METABOLIC INHIBITORS ON PHOSPHORYLATION OF NUCLEOTIDES AND INCORPORATION OF AMINO ACIDS IN ISOLATED THYMUS NUCLEI

INHIBITOR	CONCENTRATION	CHANGE IN PHOSPHORYLATION DUE TO ADDED INHIBITOR, %	CHANGE IN ALANINE-1-C^{14} UPTAKE DUE TO ADDED INHIBITOR, %
Sodium cyanide	1×10^{-3} M	−100	−76
2, 4-dinitrophenol	2×10^{-4} M	−100	−84
Sodium azide	1×10^{-3} M	−100	−91
Antimycin A	1 μg/ml	−61	−89
Methylene blue	2×10^{-5} M	+30	+3
Methylene blue	2.5×10^{-4} M	+21	−18
Calcium ions	2×10^{-3} M	0	0
Calcium ions	3×10^{-3} M	0	0
Calcium ions	4×10^{-3} M	0	

A search for similar activating enzymes in isolated nuclei is now under way, and preliminary experiments indicate that activated amino acids can be isolated from nuclei as the hydroxamates (17).

ROLE OF POLYNUCLEOTIDES IN NUCLEAR ATP SYNTHESIS

The experiments now to be described relate the DNA of the nucleus directly to the synthesis of adenosinetriphosphate. The first of these is the demonstration that nuclei pretreated with deoxyribonuclease lose their ability to synthesize ATP (fig. 5).

In this experiment nuclear suspensions were incubated for 30 minutes at 38° in the buffered sucrose-NaCl medium used in amino acid incorporation experiments (2). Crystalline pancreatic deoxyribonuclease was added to half of the flasks; nuclei in the other flasks served as 'controls.' After incubation the nuclei were centrifuged down and the supernates removed for analysis (to measure the extent of DNA depolymerization and loss). The supernates obtained from DNAase-treated nuclei indicated a loss of more than 55 per cent of their DNA. Parallel analyses showed that more than 70 per cent of the DNA in the treated nuclei had been depolymerized and made soluble in cold 2 per cent $HClO_4$. To test their capacity for ATP synthesis, the nuclear residues were resuspended in buffered sucrose containing citrate (to inhibit further DNAase action) and were shaken in air for 30 minutes at 38°. Following this second incubation, the nuclei were collected by centrifugation. They were extracted with cold 2 per cent $HClO_4$ (to remove ATP and other acid-soluble nucleotides) and the extracts were neutralized with KOH. The filtered extracts were then placed on Dowex-1 (formate) columns and the nucleotides were chromatographically separated and analyzed, following the procedure of Hurlbert *et al.* (18). The results are summarized in figure 5*A* and *B* and in table 6. Nuclei treated with DNAase in this way contain less than 30 per cent of the ATP found in untreated 'controls.' To test the possibility that DNAase-treated nuclei can synthesize ATP but cannot retain it, the supernates obtained by centrifuging the nuclei after incubation were examined chromatographically; only traces of ATP were found. Since the ATP is not in the nuclei and not in the supernate, it follows that removal of the DNA from the nucleus impairs its capacity for ATP synthesis.

A second type of experiment shows that the capacity for ATP synthesis is restored to DNAase-treated nuclei if they are given a DNA supplement. The procedure used was similar to that described above. Nuclei were pretreated with DNAase and centrifuged down, discarding the supernates. Some of the nuclei were then resuspended in sucrose-citrate solutions containing thymus DNA; other nuclei received no DNA supplement. The suspensions were incubated as before and the nuclei were collected by centrifugation. The acid-soluble nucleotides were extracted in cold 2 per cent $HClO_4$ and separated chromatographically. The

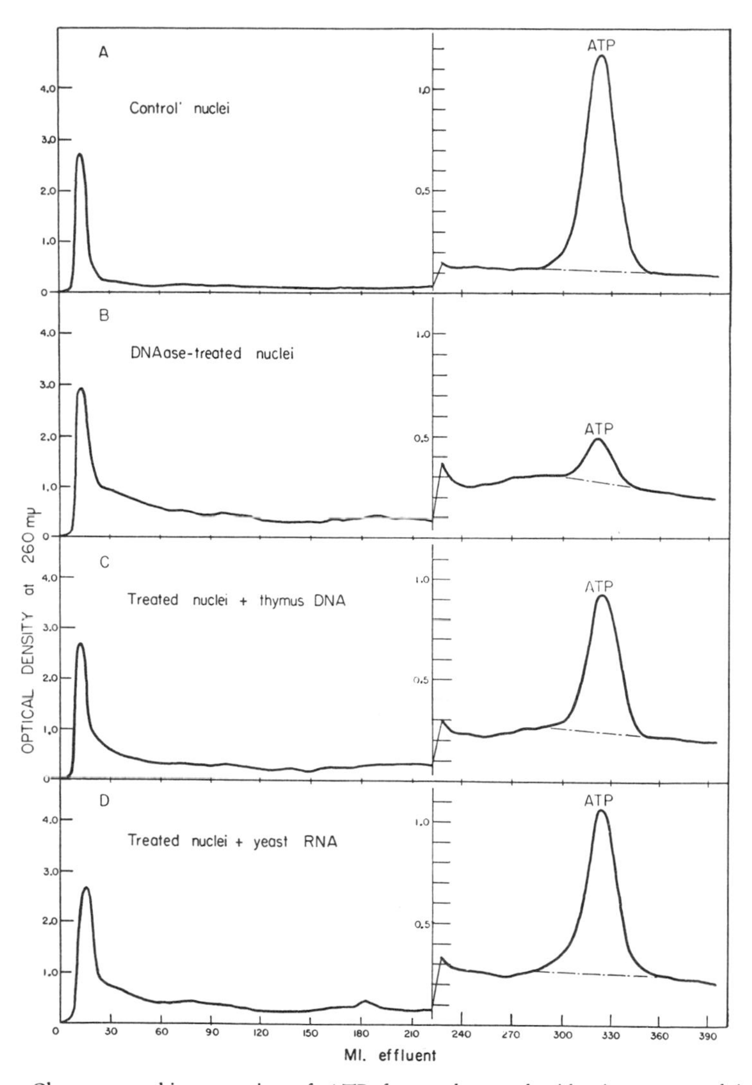

FIG. 5. Chromatographic separation of ATP from other nucleotides in extracts of isolated cell nuclei. The optical density of the effluent, E_{260}, is plotted against the volume of solution passing through a column of Dowex-1 (formate). *Curve A* shows the pattern obtained from an acid extract of untreated thymus nuclei. *Curve B* shows the corresponding pattern obtained from nuclei pretreated with deoxyribonuclease. Note the decrease in the ATP peak. *Curves C* and *D* show the result of adding supplements of thymus DNA and yeast RNA to the DNAase-treated nuclei. The magnitude of the increase in ATP synthesis under these conditions is given in table 6.

TABLE 6. EFFECT OF POLYNUCLEOTIDES ON ATP SYNTHESIS BY DNAase-TREATED NUCLEI

CONDITIONS OF EXPERIMENT	ATP CONTENT OF NUCLEI		ATP CONTENT RELATIVE TO 'CONTROLS', %
	Total E_{260}	μg	
1. 'Control'	16.2	562	100
DNAase-treated	4.86	169	30
2. 'Controls'	14.27	495	100
DNAase-treated	3.96	137	28
DNAase-treated + thymus DNA	10.28	357	72
3. 'Controls'	26.14	907	100
DNAase-treated	4.75	165	18
DNAase-treated + thymus DNA	16.95	588	65
DNAase-treated + yeast RNA	21.33	740	82
4. 'Controls'	13.18	457	100
DNAase-treated	3.85	134	29
DNAase-treated + thymus DNA, in air	9.39	326	71
DNAase-treated + thymus DNA, in nitrogen	5.23	181	40

results are summarized in figure 5*C* and in table 6. It is evident that a DNA supplement restores much of the nuclear capacity for ATP synthesis.

It is of interest that mononucleotides are not extracted from the nucleus when the DNA is removed. This retention of mononucleotides is in accord with previous observations which show that neither the histone nor the ribonucleic acid contents of the nucleus are appreciably diminished by DNAase treatment (6).

Subsequent tests of ATP synthesis in DNA-depleted nuclei showed that the ability to phosphorylate AMP can be restored to nuclei by polynucleotides other than DNA. Figure 5*D* shows the results obtained when one adds a supplement of yeast RNA. (In other experiments, mentioned below in the DISCUSSION, it has been found that other polyanions of non-nucleotide nature will also restore this synthetic ability.)

The question now arises as to how DNA and other polynucleotides play a role in nuclear ATP synthesis. A number of possible mechanisms might be suggested which utilize the relatively high energy of the internucleotide linkage. For example, the reversibility of the ADP$\rightleftharpoons$polyadenylic acid reaction (catalyzed by polynucleotide phosphorylase (14)) suggests one way in which such energy could be utilized. Experiments which will not be described in detail here have made such phosphorylysis mechanisms very improbable, and also make it rather unlikely that ATP synthesis involves the formation of an intermediate complex with nuclear DNA. Any consideration of the mechanism of ATP synthesis in isolated nuclei should begin with the observation that it is essentially coupled to oxidative processes. This is shown most directly by the results of the following experiment (1).

Thymus nuclei were treated with DNAase, centrifuged, and resuspended in the presence of thymus DNA. Half of the nuclei were placed in a nitrogen atmosphere; the other half remained in air. After 30 minutes of incubation at 38° the nucleotides were extracted and analyzed. The results are presented in table 6. It is clear that oxygen must be present if DNA is to restore ATP synthesis, and that a DNA supplement under anaerobic conditions has a very small effect indeed.

The evidence so far presented indicates that in the intact nucleus deoxyribonucleic acid plays a definite role in both amino acid incorporation and ATP synthesis. Other synthetic reactions of the nucleus which are DNA-dependent will now be considered.

INCORPORATION OF OROTIC ACID-6-C^{14} AND ADENOSINE-8-C^{14} INTO NUCLEAR RNA'S

It has been shown previously that isolated cell nuclei will incorporate orotic acid-6-C^{14} into RNA pyrimidines, and that both C^{14}-glycine and adenosine-8-C^{14} will enter into RNA purines (5, 6). Treatment of the nuclei with deoxyribonuclease impairs its capacity for both orotic acid (6) and adenosine uptake (4). As in the case of amino acid incorporation or ATP synthesis, the addition of polynucleotides will restore adenosine-C^{14} uptake in DNA-depleted nuclei.

It has also been found that DNA synthesis is inhibited by removal of the deoxyribonucleic acid. This was first observed by Friedkin and Wood (12), who showed that C^{14}-thymidine uptake was impaired when thymus nuclei were treated with DNAase. More recent experiments by Sekiguchi and Sibatani have extended these observations to include P^{32} uptake in both DNA and RNA (23). In their experiments the addition of a DNA supplement also restored P^{32} incorporation in DNA-depleted nuclei.

Studies of RNA synthesis in the isolated nucleus, as measured by the incorporation of both C^{14}-orotic acid and C^{14}-adenosine, have indicated a marked heterogeneity of the nuclear ribonucleic acids (3). These experiments will not be described here, but it is of interest that the RNA of the nucleolus is far more active than the soluble and readily extractable RNA of the nucleus. The high metabolic activity of nucleolar RNA in isolated thymus nuclei is thus in accord with the autoradiographic work just described by Dr. Taylor and also with observations by Dr. Vincent of RNA synthesis in nucleoli isolated from starfish oocytes (25).

DNA SUBSTITUTION

From the experiments which have been described testing the synthetic capacities of isolated nuclei, it is clear that DNA plays a central role in the biochemical activity of the nucleus. Its presence is essential for amino acid incorporation into protein, for adenosine and orotic acid uptake into RNA, and for nuclear ATP production. Protein and RNA synthesis are, of course, dependent upon the nuclear capacity for ATP synthesis, but the fact remains that all these functions in the living nucleus are DNA-dependent. The question which now arises concerns the significance and interpretation of DNA substitution experiments.

It has been seen that it is possible to remove the greater part (up to 76%) of the DNA of isolated thymus nuclei and to substitute other negatively charged molecules (such as polyadenylic acid) for the missing nucleic acid. This substitution, if properly carried out, yields a nucleus which again shows a capacity for ATP synthesis, amino acid incorporation into protein, and adenosine uptake into RNA. In tests of amino acid or adenosine uptake the substitution of the DNA by other polyelectrolytes is effective only in the case of polyanions. Added polycations, such as polylysine and protamine, do not restore function to nuclei depleted of their DNA. On the contrary, a polylysine supplement will actually inhibit amino acid uptake in nuclei which retain their DNA. Much of this uptake represents incorporation into the proteins of the chromosome (6), and the dependence of uptake on charge suggests that electrical charge is one of the main variables involved in chromosome activity. In line with Dr. McLaren's suggestions, it may be that a zone of decreasing pH, associated with negative surface charge, plays a role in regulating the biochemical activity of the chromosome.

One aspect of the DNA substitution experiments which is important to their interpretation concerns the role of the residual DNA which remains in the nuclei even after prolonged DNAase treatment. Much of this residue has been depolymerized and is soluble in acid, but 5–15 per cent of the original DNA may remain insoluble in acid. Because this polynucleotide residue remains one cannot conclude, on the basis of substitution experiments, that any polynucleotide is as effective as DNA in stabilizing the structure of the chromosome or in mediating chromosome function. Yet it is surprising that, given an organized nucleus, more than 75 per cent of the DNA can be replaced by comparatively simple molecules such as polyadenylic acid, and that 'hybrid' nuclei, so constituted, are still capable of carrying out at least three fundamental nuclear activities.

DEPENDENCE OF ACTIVITY OF ISOLATED NUCLEUS ON ITS CHEMICAL ENVIRONMENT

In addition to its value in studying the function and synthesis of the nucleic acids, the isolated thymus nucleus has considerable utility as a test system for studying the effects of a changing chemical environment on nuclear function. Apart from testing the effects of inhibitors of protein or nucleic acid synthesis, (which will not be discussed here), the nuclear response to changes in the suspension medium indicates some interesting requirements for its biochemical activity.

One of the most important variables in controlling nuclear syntheses is the osmotic concentration of the medium. It was soon found that nuclei exposed to high sucrose concentrations lost their ability to incorporate amino acids into protein. A more detailed picture of this dependence of uptake upon sucrose concentration is presented in figure 6. There is a fairly sharp optimum at a sucrose concentration near isotonic (i. e. at 0.20 M in a medium which also contains sodium phosphate buffer (0.025 M), glucose (0.02 M) and NaCl (0.03 M)). Although the effects described bear some resemblance to the osmotic behavior of semipermeable membranes, it should be pointed out that *isolated* thymus nuclei are not enveloped by an intact, semipermeable membrane and that they are freely permeable to large molecules such as ribonuclease (mol. wt. 15000), deoxyribonuclease (mol. wt. 60000), nucleic acids, histones, protamines, polylysine and basic dyes. It is a surprising aspect of nuclear organization that it is freely permeable to molecules of this size yet is able to retain its mononucleotides (such at ATP) and its histones even when the DNA is removed (6).

The marked effects of sucrose concentration on nuclear activity suggest that the fine structure necessary for nuclear syntheses is in osmotic balance with its environment and that nuclear function can vary with that balance. This conclusion finds support in parallel observations that the sucrose optimum for orotic acid-6-C^{14} incorporation into RNA (0.13 M) is far below the concentration optimum for protein synthesis in the same nuclei (0.20 M).

One of the most striking effects on nuclear amino acid incorporation is that produced by sodium ions. Nuclei isolated in sucrose by the procedure described, need a sodium supplement in order to incorporate amino acids actively. Figure 7 shows the effect of varied sodium concentration on the level of glycine-1-C^{14} uptake. The sodium requirement has been found to exist for the uptake of other

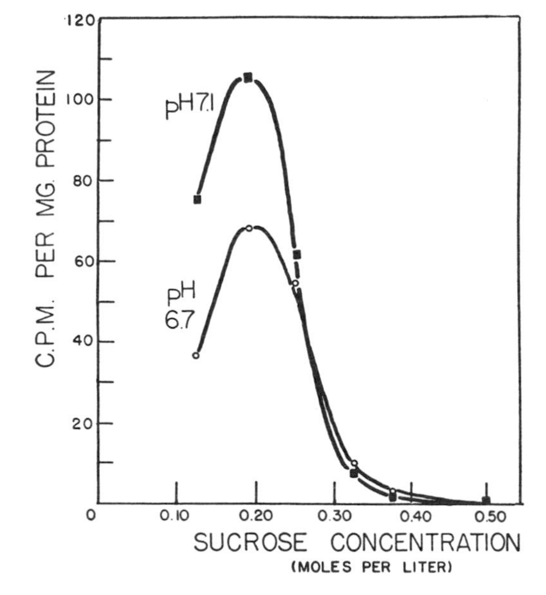

FIG. 6. Effect of varying the sucrose concentration of the medium upon the ability of thymus nuclei to incorporate alanine-1-C^{14}. The specific activity of the nuclear protein after 60 minutes' incubation is plotted against the sucrose concentration of the incubation medium.

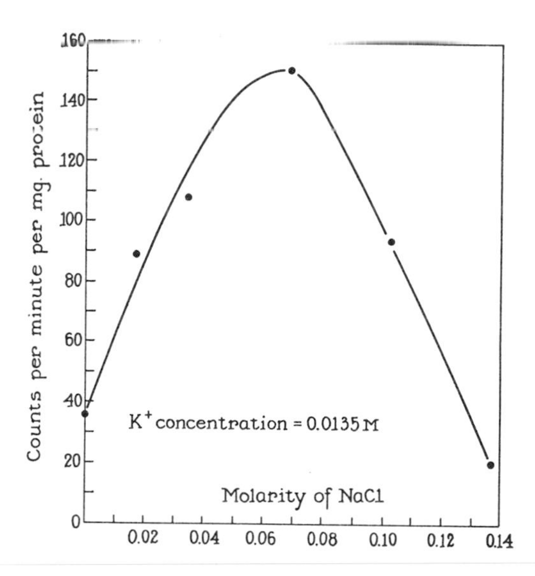

FIG. 7. Effect of varying the sodium ion concentration of the incubation medium on the ability of thymus to incorporate glycine-1-C^{14}. The specific activity of the nuclear protein after 60 minutes' incubation of the nuclei in the presence of glycine-C^{14} is plotted against the sodium concentration of the medium.

amino acids as well, including alanine, leucine, lysine, phenylalanine and tryptophan. The sodium ion requirement seems to be specific.

Figure 8 summarizes the results of experiments in which an attempt was made to substitute all or part of the sodium in the medium with an equivalent amount of potassium. Only the ratio NaCl/KCl was varied; the total salt concentration was kept constant. When all the sodium is replaced by potassium the uptake falls to 15 per cent of the optimal value. Increasing the sodium to potassium ratio gives a corresponding increase in the amount of amino acid taken up. When the sodium concentration is optimal, the addition of small amounts of potassium (chloride) does not influence the uptake. (Similar experiments show that lithium can partially replace sodium in nuclear function.)

It has already been pointed out that osmotic balance is important to nuclear activity. Yet this is only a part of the over-all requirement for maintaining nuclear function. Nuclei removed from sucrose to isotonic salt solutions lose their ability to incorporate amino acids. Nuclei washed with neutral 0.1 M phosphate buffer prior to incubation in a sucrose medium are also inactive. The presence of the sucrose seemed to be essential in maintaining nuclear structure.

To test whether this requirement was specific, or whether other sugars could replace sucrose, nuclei were isolated in a wide variety of media and then tested for their capacity to incorporate radioactive amino acids. Without presenting the details of such isolations, the main conclusions can be briefly summarized. It was found that the nature of the sugar made little difference to the synthetic capacity of the isolated nucleus. Other disaccharides (maltose, lactose) in 0.25 M solutions permitted the isolation of nuclei which were just as active as those prepared in sucrose; the monosaccharides tested (fructose, glucose) also gave preparations

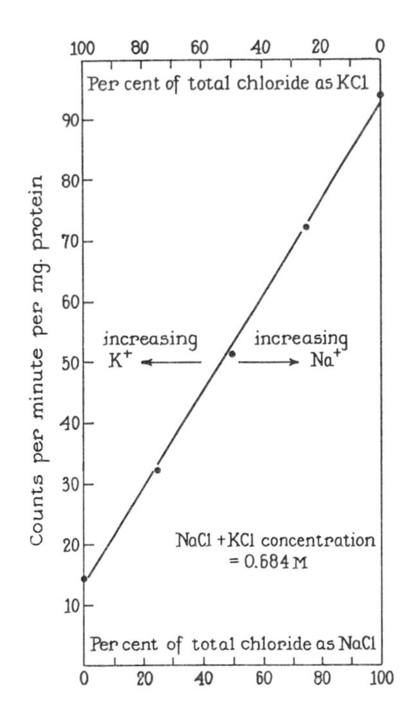

FIG. 8. Effect of varying sodium/potassium ratio on glycine-1-C^{14} incorporation by isolated thymus nuclei. The specific activity of the nuclear protein after 60 minutes' incubation is plotted against the ratio of sodium to potassium ions in the medium, the total salt concentration being held constant.

which were the equivalent of sucrose nuclei in this respect. However, neither glycerol nor ethylene glycol at isotonic concentrations could preserve the synthetic capacity of the nuclei.

These experiments illustrate another useful role of the isolated thymus nucleus. The presence or absence of function can be used as a test for the suitability of an isolation method. Many of the nuclear isolation procedures which now exist employ hypertonic solutions of sucrose, glycerol or ethylene glycol. These procedures have advantages in many tissues because the density of the medium permits the sedimentation of nuclei, while cells and cytoplasmic debris remain in suspension. The methods of Philpot and Stanier (21) and of Chauveau *et al.* (9) are especially satisfying in producing optically homogeneous nuclei in a high state of purity. It is unfortunate that thymus nuclei cannot withstand such isolations and fail to retain their biochemical activity after exposure to the hypertonic media employed. Yet the value of the thymus nucleus in testing these and other methods of nuclear isolation is considerable, and it should serve as a useful guide to the development of newer procedures for the preparation of pure and synthetically active free nuclei.

SUMMARY AND CONCLUSION

The results which have been described are only the first inklings of the chemical nature and potential synthetic capacities of the nucleus. It is now clear that, in the intact nucleus, the presence of deoxyribonucleic acid mediates amino acid incorporation into protein, ATP synthesis, and the uptake of purines and pyrimidines into nuclear ribonucleic acids. The role of DNA in these activities is not yet clear, but from the DNA-substitution experiments which have been carried out with isolated nuclei, one can conclude that the polyanionic nature of the DNA plays a large part in its activity. The need for large negatively charged molecules as DNA substitutes, and the inhibitory action of polycationic compounds such as polylysine, suggest a correlation between negative electrical charge and the biochemical activity of the nucleus.

REFERENCES

1. Allfrey, V. G., M. M. Daly and A. E. Mirsky *J. Gen. Physiol.* 37: 157, 1953.
2. Allfrey, V. G. and A. E. Mirsky. *Proc. Nat. Acad. Sci.* 43: 589, 1957.
3. Allfrey, V. G. and A. E. Mirsky. *Proc. Nat. Acad. Sci.* 43: 821, 1957.
4. Allfrey, V. G. and A. E. Mirsky. *Proc. Nat. Acad. Sci.* 44: 981, 1958.
5. Allfrey, V. G., S. Osawa and A. E. Mirsky. *Nature* 176: 1042, 1955.
6. Allfrey, V. G., S. Osawa and A. E. Mirsky. *J. Gen. Physiol.* 40: 451, 1957.
7. Allfrey, V. G., H. Stern, A. E. Mirsky and H. Saetren. *J. Gen. Physiol.* 35: 529, 1952.
8. Behrens, M. In: *Handbuch der biologischen Arbeitsmethoden,* edited by E. Abderhalden. Berlin and Vienna: Urban and Schwartzenberg, 1938, vol. x, p. 1363.
9. Chauveau, J., Y. Moulé and C. Rouiller. *Exper. Cell Res.* 11: 317, 1956.
10. Dounce, A. L., G. H. Tischkoff, S. R. Barnett and R. M. Freer. *J. Gen. Physiol.* 33: 629, 1949.
11. Ficq, A. and M. Errera. *Exper. Cell Res.* 14: 182, 1958.
12. Friedkin, M. and H. Wood. *J. Biol. Chem.* 220: 639, 1956.
13. Gale, E. F. and J. P. Folkes. *Biochem. J.* 55: xi, 1953.
14. Grunberg-Manago, M., P. J. Ortiz and S. Ochoa. *Science* 122: 907, 1955.
15. Hoagland, M. B., E. B. Keller and P. C. Zamecnik. *J. Biol. Chem.* 218: 345, 1956.
16. Hoagland, M. B., P. C. Zamecnik and M. L. Stephenson. *Biochim. et biophys. acta* 24: 215, 1957.
17. Hopkins, J., V. G. Allfrey and A. E. Mirsky. Unpublished experiments.
18. Hurlbert, R. B., H. Schmitz, A. F. Brumm and V. R. Potter. *J. Biol. Chem.* 209: 23, 1954.
19. Keller, E. B. and P. C. Zamecnik. *J. Biol. Chem.* 221: 45, 1956.
20. Osawa, S., V. G. Allfrey and A. E. Mirsky. *J. Gen. Physiol.* 40: 491, 1957.
21. Philpot, J. St. L. and J. E. Stanier. *Biochem. J.* 63: 214, 1956.
22. Schneider, R. M. and M. L. Peterman. *Cancer Res.* 10: 751, 1950.
23. Sekiguchi, M. and A. Sibatani. *Biochim. et biophys. acta* 28: 455, 1958.
24. Stern, H. and A. E. Mirsky. *J. Gen. Physiol.* 37: 177, 1953.
25. Vincent, W. S. *Science* 126: 306, 1957.

DISCUSSION

J. W. Green, V. Allfrey, R. E. Beyer, L. Ernster, D. A. Marsland, E. L. Kuff, J. W. Littlefield, A. Marshak, W. S. Vincent

DR. GREEN: Do you have any information on the specific role sodium plays in the nucleus?

DR. ALLFREY: At present no specific chemical role is known for sodium ions in nuclear metabolism. It is unlikely that it is involved only in amino acid incorporation, because the uptake of adenosine-8-C^{14} into nuclear RNA has also been found to be sodium-dependent. It might be added that the thymus nucleus is not the only instance of a nucleus displaying a sodium requirement. Several years ago Abelson and Duryee (P. H. ABELSON AND W. R. DURYEE, *Biol. Bull.* 96: 205, 1949) showed by radioautographic techniques that the nucleus in intact frog oocytes rapidly takes up $Na^{24}Cl$ from the medium.

DR. BEYER: In view of the synthesis of DPN by the nucleus, I wonder if you have tried to add DPNH or other electron donors as well as AMP or ADP to see if you can measure a greater synthesis of ATP?

DR. ALLFREY: In synthesizing ATP the nucleus will phosphorylate only the AMP which it contains, and added AMP or ADP is not acted upon. We have not tried the combination you suggest to see if DPNH will alter the rate of ATP synthesis.

DR. ERNSTER: Have you tried to measure oxygen consumption, or also to replace oxygen by an artificial hydrogen acceptor, e.g. ferricyanide, reduction of which may be easier to measure than is oxygen consumption?

DR. ALLFREY: We have measured oxygen consumption in the isolated nuclei: it is definite, but quite low, and we have not tried to calculate P/O ratios for this system. The suggestion to use ferricyanide as an acceptor is a good one and should be tried, but we are more interested at present in trying to unravel some of the problems of nuclear protein and RNA synthesis.

DR. MARSLAND: After you remove the ATP by acidification and adding acetate, can you restore it in active form?

DR. ALLFREY: The addition of acetate (0.02 M) at pH 5.1 removes 85–90 per cent of the nucleotides from the nucleus, including both AMP and ATP. It should be mentioned that, at these lower pHs, the nucleoside triphosphates and diphosphates are largely converted to the monophosphate form, and that when they are removed, potassium is released at the same time. Attempts to restore nucleotides to nuclei treated in this way have not been carried out.

DR. KUFF: Is any incorporation actively demonstrable in preparations of nuclei that have been disrupted by mechanical or other means?

DR. ALLFREY: Nuclei which are broken by high speed stirring in a blender are completely inactive as tested by amino acid incorporation. The same result is observed in nuclei disrupted by freezing and thawing. But Drs. Breitman and Webster (T. R. BREITMAN AND G. C. WEBSTER, *Fed. Proc.* 17: 194, 1958) have recently reported that sonic disintegration, if carefully carried out, gives nuclear fragments which can incorporate radioactive adenine and AMP into nucleic acids.

DR. LITTLEFIELD: Two quick questions: First, is there any way, perhaps by differential centrifugation in gradients, of lowering the whole cell concentration below 3 per cent? Second, have you perhaps looked in nuclei for ribonucleoprotein particles similar to those in the cytoplasm?

DR. ALLFREY: The few whole cells which are present in preparations of thymus nuclei do not constitute a problem in the experiments we have carried out so far. It is possible to separate and remove these cells by centrifuging in 2.2 M sucrose solutions. In such dense media, the nuclei will sediment and the cells go to the top of the tube. Unfortunately, once the nuclei are exposed to such hypertonic media they lose ability to incorporate radioactive amino acids or radioactive orotic acid.

We do not know whether the nucleus isolated in sucrose-$CaCl_2$ has in it ribonucleoprotein particles similar to those seen in the cytoplasm. Electron microscopy of nuclei isolated in calcium-containing media is disappointing from a morphological point of view, because there seems to be a general precipitation or clumping of intranuclear structures.

DR. MARSHAK: Would you discuss further the degree of contamination in your preparations and its significance in the results you report. It seems to me that the criterion of the effect of added DNA is one which may be so indirect as in possible interpretations to be not reliable. In this connection I recall that the figure given for contamination in published data is 10 per cent by volume. Could not this mean more than 10 per cent in terms of cRNA contamination? Also, Osawa's data on turnover of nuclei prepared by this method show specific activities in this Nuclear #1 nRNA fraction intermediate between Nuclear #2 nRNA and the cRNA. Also the composition of nRNA #1 is intermediate between #2 and cRNA.

DR. ALLFREY: The estimates of nuclear contamination are based on DNA and RNA analyses and on tests for cytochrome *c* oxidase activity (and using thymus nuclei prepared in nonaqueous solvents as a standard). These tests led to an upper limit of 10 per cent as the possible extent of contamination. It is true that some of the RNA in these nuclear fractions may be cytoplasmic in origin, but there is a simple functional test which, I believe, settles whether a component in this system is nuclear or not. One can test for the effect of DNAase treatment on the labeling or synthesis of the compound. If the uptake of radioactive precursors into the compound is impaired when one removes the DNA from the nucleus, then it can be concluded that in all probability such DNA dependence indicates nuclear localization. This is true for the protein and ribonucleic acid fractions we have considered. Dr. Osawa's experiments on nuclear RNA fractionation follow some of the fractionation procedures we have employed, but he has also substantially modified them, for example, by introducing a streptomycin precipitation step. I am not familiar with the relative specific activities of the RNA fractions he has prepared, but I think it can be shown that fractions he has considered to be derived from the nucleus are indeed sensitive to DNAase treatment.

DR. VINCENT: Will other polyanions than polynucleotides replace in ATP synthesis in the nucleus?

DR. ALLFREY: Attempts to substitute other polyelectrolytes for DNA have led to some very interesting and surprising results. After finding that polyadenylic acid would restore amino acid uptake to nuclei depleted of their DNA, we tried to extend the observations to include polyanions which were *not polynucleotides*. Among the compounds tested were three molecular sizes of polyethylene sulfonate, heparin and chondroitin sulfate. All these compounds could restore some of the capacity for amino acid incorporation into protein, or adenosine uptake into RNA. On the premise that the removal of the DNA followed by a continued and prolonged incubation would lead to instability and irreversible changes in the state of the chromosomes, attempts were made to stabilize nuclear structure by substituting these polyanions for DNA at the time of its removal. If this is done properly, it is possible to remove 76 per cent of the DNA and replace it with polyethylene sulfonate (mol. wt. 12,900) without apparent change in nuclear ability to take up amino acids into protein or adenosine into RNA. Nor did we observe any impairment in nuclear ATP synthesis if DNA substitution by polyethylene sulfonate was carried out rapidly.

INDEX